Rescue from the Skies

Badge of the Goldfish Club – the maritime equivalent of the Caterpiller Club (Goldfish Club)

Rescue from the Skies

THE STORY OF THE AIRBORNE LIFEBOATS

Stephen Brewster Daniels

London: HMSO

ISBN 0 11 772761X

Stephen Brewster Daniels has asserted his right under the Copyright,
Designs and Patents Act, 1988, to be identified as Author of this work

British Library Cataloguing in Publication Data
A CIP catalogue record for this book is available from the British
Library

Frontispiece illustration taken from a painting
by Terence Cuneo

Cover illustration taken from a painting
by Stan Gleed. (Collection of the author)

Dedicated to the men who flew the Air/Sea Rescue planes, especially those who carried the Airborne Lifeboats; to the crews of the rescue boats; to the Royal Air Force, Royal Navy and 'Red Duster' men – not forgetting their back-up teams from the WAAF and WRNS; to those who brought the Lifeboats from thought to reality, not forgetting the girls who 'clinked' those thousands of nails etc.; and to the 'Erks' and sailors of the ground and shore crews.

Contents

Acknowledgements

It is over three years since a rough draft of this book was sent to His Royal Highness The Prince Philip, Duke of Edinburgh and his kindness in promising a Foreword was tremendous encouragement to complete a work which had already been several years in the making.

Any author conducting research into recent history has to rely on the information and views of many people outside the normal circle of association, and for a work like this comes into contact with correspondents all over the world who submit material from their personal records or memory. Various authorities and firms also supply technical data etc. and to all these people a debt of gratitude is owed. To name them all would be impossible but a few who are worthy of especial mention are listed below.

At times a judgement has to be made regarding apparently conflicting reports and if I have misinterpreted or erred in my decisions I apologise, whilst explaining that all views expressed are mine personally and fault should not be laid at any other threshold. It has been my policy to avoid distractions by not including reference notes, but all factual information has been garnered from impeccable sources such as the Public Record Office and various official bodies, and I am grateful to them for the assistance they have rendered.

Mr 'Tim' Board, Isle of Wight
Mr Chaz Bowyer, Norwich
Mr J. Chartres, Altrincham
Air Marshal Sir E. Chilton,
    Henley on Thames
Mr Sam Cooke, Caister on Sea
Mr H. Davey, Oulton Broad
Mr R. Day, Johannesburg
Mr M. Dixon and
    Mr T. Dixon, Cowes
Mr R. V. Edwards MBE, Prenton,
    The Wirral
Mr H. S. Fitchett, London
Mr Sid Harvey of Wrentham,
    Suffolk, who contributed so much
    of the American information
Mr K. M. Hunter, RAF Museum
Mr P. E. Irving, Warrendyte,
Australia
Mr P. Jude, Oulton Broad
Mr A. J. La Marco, New York
Staff Sgt. K. Latimer (née Daniels)
    RAAF
Mr R. Malster, Ipswich
Mr J. W. Mitchley, Lowestoft
Mr John Nichol, Lairds of
    Beaumaris
Mr B. Piper, Canberra
Lt. Cdr. S. G. Sheppard, Stafford
Mr C. Shutt, Stratton Strawless
Lt. Gen. J. P. J. Smit, Pretoria
Mr R. C. Sturtivant, St Albans
Air Vice Marshal Ian Sutherland,
    Melbourne
Mr J. Turner, Hickling, Norfolk
Mrs E. Veitch, Pretoria

Mr Stan Williams, Cowes
Air Force Department (MOD)
Air Sea Rescue/Marine Craft
    Sections Club
Austin Rover
Australian War Memorial Museum
Boulton & Paul Ltd
Brooke Yachts Ltd
The Edo Corporation
Fairey Holdings Ltd
Fleet Air Arm Museum
Uffa Fox Ltd
The Goldfish Club
GQ Parachutes Ltd

Imperial War Museum
Lairds of Anglesey
Lockheed Aircraft Corporation
McDonnell Douglas Aircraft
    Corporation
RFD Ltd, Godalming
Royal Air Force Association
Royal Air Force Museum
Schermuly Ltd
South African Air Force
United States Army Air Force
United States Navy Department
Westland Helicopters
Herbert Woods Ltd

Foreword

The North Sea and the Channel provided a wonderful defence against invasion during the Second World War, but they were also serious hazards for aircrew returning from operations against the enemy over Europe. Structural damage or shortage of fuel frequently entailed the unpleasant and dangerous business of 'ditching' in the cold waters of our first line of defence. The problem was how to rescue the airmen who found themselves unable to bring their aircraft home.

One of the more imaginative answers was the Airborne Lifeboat. It sounds simple enough, but it was a novel idea at the time and it was just the sort of challenge to stimulate the genius of that brilliant yacht designer and helmsman, Uffa Fox. Many other people contributed to the development of the project, including those who built the boats and those who flew the Search and Rescue aircraft, but there can be little doubt that Uffa Fox's persistence, enthusiasm, experience and unorthodox methods were crucial to the final success of this life-saving device.

All sorts of strange things were invented during the war, some, like the 'bouncing bomb' devised by Barnes Wallis, became famous, others either failed or dropped into obscurity. Stephen Daniels has done a great service in recounting the story of the Airborne Lifeboat. This book shows how difficult it is to get an original idea accepted and how even more difficult it is to get it to work properly.

Preface

The majority of wartime fliers never encountered an Airborne Lifeboat during their whole Service career, and most would deem that fortunate; indeed, many were hardly aware they existed, for these boats were a very minor section of a vast organisation which had branches all over the world embracing trades encompassing a range of skills unequalled in the other Services. Even today, half a century since the War finished, there have been very few literary mentions of these boats despite the many books written about the RAF. Thus this compilation which endeavours to sketch the need for and development of these wonderful craft, so that the stages in conception, design, construction, equipment and operation can be followed.

This book is the culmination of more than nine years of research at places as diverse as the Public Record Office, the Royal Air Force Museum, Air Historical Branch, the Imperial War Museum, the National Newspaper Library, the Australian War Museum Library and sundry others, augmented by letters from interested people all over the world, personal interviews with designers, boatbuilders and ex-Servicemen, not to mention assistance by many firms and concerns which were involved. Research so long after the events poses many problems; firstly the Thirty Year Rule which prevented access to the majority of official papers until the late 1970s; also some compilers of records seemed to have felt a need to 'keep their end up' where their own organisation was concerned; then the deaths of so many of those who were concerned with all stages of the project; but the greatest frustration has been caused by the effect of the 'weeding out process' on official papers and records before acceptance into the Public Record Office. This was a very necessary procedure, for if all papers and documents of the RAF and RN had been filed the Office would need to be ten times its present superb vastness. Selection seems to have been carried out very sympathetically to leave a thorough overall general record, but the researcher of a specialist subject inevitably encounters gaps which leave loose ends, so that the eventual outcome of some matters is left unresolved. In some operations the records of different bodies concerned do not always tally in details, even to the position of a ditching or the number of survivors: where this has occurred the author has attempted to present a reliable overall picture of events and craves indulgence if his interpretation differs from any personal memories.

STEPHEN BREWSTER DANIELS
Isle of Eday, Orkney and Great Yarmouth, Norfolk
February 1993

Index of Illustrations

1 The Air/Sea Rescue Background

If, in 1937, I'd have said to the rest of the crew, as we stood yarning in the Lifeboat Shed, that within a few years a twin-engined wooden boat; half as long as the 48-foot clencher-built Norfolk & Suffolk type lifeboat secured on its slipway rollers behind us, would be carried under the belly of a plane, then dropped by parachutes to men in the sea, they'd all have replied 'Rubbish'; and if the hypothetical statement had gone on to say that the boat would have automatically inflating turtlebacked buoyancy chambers at bow and stern to make it self-righting and virtually unsinkable, and have electrically operated rockets to throw out a sea anchor and project buoyant 'grab' lines out to port and starboard; they'd have thought this to be the fantasy world of a modern H. G. Wells. But within six years their words would have to be eaten, for by then such a craft was coming into service with the Royal Air Force, and it had other sophisticated equipment beyond our wildest dreams and aspirations; for in 1937 we'd only just had electric lighting installed aboard the lifeboat in place of the colza oil navigation lights and looked forward hopefully to the day when we might also have a radio.

The War brought many changes, not least in scattering our crew over the face of the globe, some never to return; for despite the twelve months' grace given by the Munich Agreement the British people and Services were very unprepared in some sectors of thought and equipment. Not least among these was the problem of rescuing airmen forced down at sea. Admittedly the RAF had a few launches for this purpose, mainly attached to bases from which flying boats operated, for they, and the Fleet Air Arm, were almost the only planes which made regular maritime flights, apart from the cross-Channel planes to France, and if one of them came 'down in the drink' the coastal lifeboats and the plethora of merchant and fishing vessels in the area could reasonably be reckoned to cope with the emergency. So no overall Air/Sea Rescue organisation existed. During the subsequent twelve months an expansion of the RAF's Marine Section was commenced and embryo local rescue plans brought into being with the co-operation of the Royal Navy, the Coastguard, the Lifeboat Service, the Royal Observer Corps etc. and many airmen were saved, although flights far out over the sea were still relatively few. Dunkirk was the turning point, when the realisation came that the War would have to be fought in the skies over Britain and the further out the battle could be joined the lower would be the chances of enemy penetration; coupled with the growing urge for bombing of German industrial and shipping capacity.

Germany, on the other hand, had been preparing for a war against Britain

1 *Command structure and areas of Air Sea Rescue*

for many years and had an established Sea Rescue Branch within the Luftwaffe, consisting chiefly of float planes with marine craft support. This was not unobserved by the RAF but not copied in principle; partly because float planes cannot operate efficiently in other than reasonably smooth waters – and the North Sea and English Channel are not often very calm. High Speed Launch (HSL) No. 100 had been handed over to the control of RAF Manston in 1936 and in view of its potential 15 more had been ordered for the bases such as Malta, Aden, Basra, Ceylon, Hong Kong and Penang, so that each area could set up its own local rescue service. In 1939 a further 13 HSLs were ordered, mostly with the southern North Sea in view; over which it was considered most of our aerial activity would be concentrated. All boats originally destined for overseas stations were now reserved for British waters with emphasis on new bases to be opened at Great Yarmouth, Blyth, Newhaven and Grimsby. Alas, plans were all very well, but implementing them proved much more difficult. Suddenly, as the war effort gathered momentum there was an urgent call on craftsmen and materials, so the new building programme fell sadly into arrears; as the new boats and bases gradually came into operation the gaps narrowed, but resources were still woefully stretched. A partial breakthrough was achieved in August 1940 when it was decided to pool the resources of Coastal Command Rescue Boats and the rescue facilities of the Naval Auxiliary Patrol, both to be under the command of the local Naval Authority with the RAF responsible for air searches and feeding information. In addition 12 Lysander planes were borrowed from the Army Co-operation Command and placed under Fighter Command control with the duty of covering a search area up to 20 miles from the coast, an unenviable duty especially in and near the straits of Dover.

In the last three weeks of July 1940, during the Battle of Britain, 220 airmen were missing or killed over the southern North Sea and the eastern Channel; this was a loss rate which could not be tolerated in human terms nor strategically sustained. How many of these men could have been saved by an efficient and fully equipped rescue organisation can never be known but the realisation was brought home that every possible flyer must be rescued – and cost was secondary.

One of the essentials of successful rescue was speed, speed in locating as well as in 'pick-up', for the waters around our coasts are not kind, even in midsummer; hypothermia quickly sets in with loss of limb movement and power aggravating mental inertia and a lowering of determination. At RAF Thornaby an attempt to prolong survival was made by introducing in 1940 the 'Thornaby Bag'. This was an ordinary parachute container padded with kapok to keep it afloat and stuffed with tins of self-heating soup, drinking water, cigarettes and other comforts. Not having its own parachute it had a tendency to burst on impact with the sea, spilling the contents, and even if intact, was very hard to see and recover unless dropped very close to survivors. So RAF Bircham Newton went one better with the 'Bircham Barrel' by utilising the cardboard containers in which the tail fins of 250 lb bombs were delivered. After internal strengthening a canvas bag was fitted inside which was packed with distress signals, water, First Aid materials, self-heating soup etc. It was

2   Mk II under sailing trials on the River Thurne (Sam Cooke)

then sealed watertight ready for dropping from the bomb rack of a search aircraft. Being strong and very buoyant it was not liable to burst on impact and floated high enough in the water to be seen from a considerable distance. Not to be outdone Gp. Capt. Waring at RAF Lindholme, with the assistance of the Armaments Officer, came up with a new life support apparatus to be known as the 'Lindholme Gear'. Again it utilised empty fin containers; in the first, of 500 lb bomb size, was packed an eight-man rubber dinghy which self-inflated on being withdrawn from its packing, and in the other four, of 250 lb size each, were packed various stores, food, clothing, medicines and signalling equipment. The train of five were fastened to each other with a fair length of brightly coloured buoyant line, making the whole 212 lb apparatus easier to see as well as recover, for the containers were dropped in sequence so that with the connecting lines a considerable string was offered for paddling to or drifting onto.

Collectively these measures made an impact on the casualty figures, but possibly more important was the boost to aircrew morale. Whilst this was always exceptionally high it tended to suffer dents when comrades went missing, known to be 'in the drink' but beyond finding or helping; it was good, too, for the searchers in the sky, who having been previously only able to observe and report could now drop positive help, and by that help sustain the spirits as well as the survival time of the downed men. Flyers now knew and appreciated that every effort would be made to find and save them. In July 1940 it was estimated (and it had to be an estimate, for no official figures were compiled) that only 20%, at most, of aircrew who came down in the sea were saved. By the early months of 1941 firm figures show that 35% were being saved, and this over the worst weather months of the year. Further perusal reveals that in 46% of 'ditchings' some aircrew were rescued. This recovery rate was not regarded as satisfactory when the increasing air offensive indicated that there was a real possibility that more and more planes, with larger crews, would be forced down at sea for one reason or another.

At a meeting on 24 January 1941, Gp. Capt. L. G. Le B. Croke, Commanding Officer at RAF St Eval, was appointed the first Director of Sea Rescue, and his immediate decision was to change the name to Air/Sea Rescue Services, from then on A/SR, with the new body based at Coastal Command Headquarters. A simple chain of command was established with an A/SR Officer at each Area Coastal Command HQ; with power to call on all RAF Stations within that area to contribute machines and men so far as they were able. The east, south and west coasts, from the Wash round to Lands End, and thence northwards to Milford Haven were designated a Special Search Area with regular Lysander patrols. A/SR took itself very seriously and interpreted its brief to include investigating improvements to aircraft dinghies, lifejackets, pyrotechnics, aircraft flotation, survival clothing, liferaft and dinghy rations and equipment; in fact all aspects which could possibly assist in the life and health of men in the sea or afloat on a flimsy rubber dinghy. A vast field opened up in the improvement of aircraft so they could survive the impact of 'ditching' without breaking up or sinking rapidly, thus improving survival chances at the pre-dinghy stage. This slowly led to many modifications to RAF training and aircraft so that later in the War some had a very enviable record amongst Allied airmen for staying afloat, one Lancaster even remaining on the surface for 33 hours until an attempt was made to take it in tow with a rope round the rudder, whereupon the tail came off, and it went down like a stone. In a different incident a ditched Lancaster had to be depth-charged after repeated shelling failed to sink it.

Another innovation was to interview as many survivors of ditchings as possible, so that the best impact positions could be devised to allow maximum crew survival as well as prompt evacuation into the dinghies. By June 1941 special air diagrams were being circulated which illustrated these and other points and procedures for each type of aeroplane. Flying and Operational Training Units especially came in for extra attention on this score, with ditching and evacuation techniques as part of the courses.

Two important features make little appearance in books on wartime flying; these were firstly the immense effort made by the General Post Office and its staff to expand and extend its telephone network and services to cope with the new airfields and depots mushrooming all over the country, each with its phenomenal traffic load by day and night, embracing even out of the way Observer Corps posts and isolated gun, searchlight and barrage balloon positions. The other concerned neutral Eire, where the RNLI continued mainly (as it does today) to be responsible for the coastal Lifeboat Service; an extra lifeboat was permitted on the Killibegs station primarily for aircraft and shipping survivors, with back-up from a trawler operated by an Irish civilian company on behalf of the British Admiralty. Whenever possible survivors were landed in Northern Ireland so as not to be interned in Eire. The General Post Office radio stations at Valentia and Malin Head were also allowed to operate for distress over and on the Atlantic Ocean.

By August 1941 A/SR had managed to 'extract' a few Walrus flying boats from the Navy and these joined the 'Kipper' patrols along the coast, together with more Lysanders. At this time, too, were formed the first specific A/SR Squadrons, Nos 275, 276, 277 and 278, using Spitfires at Valley, Colerne, Stapleford Tawney and Coltishall respectively. Their primary duty when they became operational would be patrolling further from the shore than the 20-mile Lysander and Walrus zone, although their role could be little more than search and report, dropping of survival equipment and homing of surface craft. But their heyday was to come. Meanwhile production of HSLs was still very slow; most of the materials had to be brought into the country by a hard-pressed Merchant Navy, the Services were calling up skilled men, air raids were destroying resources, communications and production facilities, and above all the Fighting Services had higher priorities on everything. A/SR made up some of the deficiencies by cajoling a few boats from the Navy, some were transferred from flying boat bases and even private motor yachts were pressed into service where they could be usefully employed; almost any tactics were used so that the maximum number of aircrew could be saved.

No. 279 Squadron became operational from RAF Bircham Newton in March 1942 and during May and June proved their worth in 'deep' search by locating six crews totalling 35 men, all of whom had carried out correct ditching procedure. Five of these crews were picked up in the last hour or so of daylight

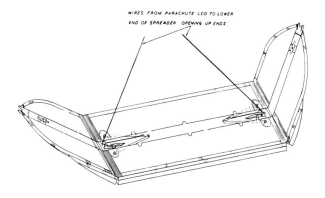

WIRES FROM PARACHUTE LED TO LOWER
END OF SPREADER OPENING UP ENDS

FOLDING AIRBORNE LIFEBOAT

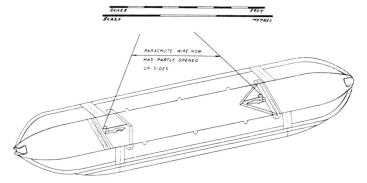

PARACHUTE WIRE NOW
HAS PARTLY OPENED
UP SIDES

3   The Uffa Fox projected Folding Airborne Lifeboat (Uffa Fox Ltd)

4   Uffa Fox at his desk (Murray Dixon)

on the day they ditched, the sixth was found in darkness within 65 minutes of going down. Nineteen other airmen were also located and rescued. Many of these survivors were Polish and it is interesting to note from the records that they were much more concerned with correct signals and ditching drill than their British counterparts. No. 280 Squadron also became operational in June and quickly chalked up results.

In the early part of the War there had been a high degree of tolerance by the Luftwaffe for the activities of the rescue boats but this slowly faded, leading to some armament being reluctantly provided, later augmented to a formidable extent; it was possibly the sinking of various rescue boats in the English Channel in the latter part of 1941 which triggered off the thought of an Airborne Lifeboat. It was in September that Gp. Capt. Waring (of Lindholme) first disclosed his plan, produced with the assistance of Lt. Robb RNVR, for a 20-foot dinghy for up to seven men which could be carried by an aircraft and dropped by parachute, complete with motor, sails, oars and supplies if the ditched aircrew were close to an enemy coast, or in a mined area; anywhere normal surface craft could not safely operate. He submitted his proposals and plans to the Air Ministry where they appeared to drop into limbo amidst the welter of urgent, conflicting and imperious demands of other branches of the RAF. For quite a while this precarious scheme remained submerged until an outside catalyst, apparently by chance, finally brought fruition.

2 How the Lifeboats Evolved

It's not too hard for any amateur with basic knowledge and skills to design and build a boat to suit his own needs; but to design and build one to a number of exacting demands and diverse requirements calls for an ability almost amounting to genius; and it would not be an exaggeration to describe Mr Uffa Fox as approaching that. During his lifetime he designed many of the fastest sailing boats of his day; in 1928 his Avenger, at the end of her first season, sported Prize Flags for every race started; 52 firsts, 2 seconds and 3 thirds. It could be that the outstanding hydro and aero dynamics of this yacht played a significant part in the ultimate hull shapes of the Mark I and II lifeboats.

Whilst the initial 1941 idea of Gp. Capt. Waring, assisted by Lt. Robb RNVR, for an Airborne Lifeboat, negotiated various official desks, probably with dozens of other ideas, good, bad and indifferent which the overtaxed staff were trying to assess, evaluate and bring into production, the required 'catalyst' appeared on the scene in the unlikely form of Uffa Fox. Apparently Lt. Robb was attending a yachting function when he came into conversation with the great yacht designer himself and took the opportunity to pose a couple of technical questions, which Uffa was only too happy to answer, but which whetted his appetite to the extent of enquiring what sort of boat the questions related to. Lt. Robb told him all about the Group Captain's innovative idea and Uffa Fox was 'hooked'. In one of his books he states how he eagerly embraced the concept which Lt. Robb had mentioned to him, and threw himself wholeheartedly into the project with all the boundless enthusiasm he possessed and was renowned for, but on a different line of approach to Waring's. He further narrates how he initially experimented with folding cardboard models held together with strawberry jam and dropped on handkerchief parachutes from the top of a building. Once this spell of experimenting had passed he describes how he designed a 20-foot long boat, to be built of plywood which would unfold by the pull of the parachute cords after being released from the bomb-bay of a plane; tubular alloy struts would then automatically lock the sections into position and *hey presto* there was a boat which could be rowed, sailed or motored. Having worked this out he went straight to the top by gaining the ear of Lord Brabazon, then Minister of Aircraft Production, and convinced him personally of the value of the idea (although one of Waring's letters quoted later seems to refute this). With the 'go ahead' for a trial boat he went back to Cowes and got down to serious work; scrapping the folding system and apparently partially adopting the design of Waring and Robb. The later appointment of Waring to be Deputy Director

A/SR (DDASR) probably made progress considerably easier.

The criteria for the design and construction of the boat, although diverse, were relatively easy to define:

- It had to be light enough to be carried by the aeroplanes of the day.
- Strong enough to withstand the stresses and pressures of being airborne and then dropped by parachute.
- It must not unduly detract from the safety and performance of its carrier plane.
- It must have the ability to withstand the colossal impact of landing on the sea at up to 25 mph in vertical drop.
- It had to be self-righting and virtually unsinkable.
- Have engines which could be easily started by hand, by men without experience of marine power units, probably not at the peak of fitness after the ordeal of ditching and spending considerable time in an aircraft dinghy or Mae West.
- Its range would need to be up to 500 miles, as economically and swiftly as practicable, though refuelling might be possible.
- It would need sails and rigging, for in a small boat engines and salt water have a high degree of incompatibility, or there could be conditions where the fuel was exhausted and replacement not possible.
- The sails and rigging would need to be very simple for handling by men who would probably be complete novices on water.
- It would need to be very seaworthy, for ditching aircraft cannot wait upon fine weather, and the North Sea and Channel (where the greatest usage would be expected) can be very very unfriendly at times.
- Finally, it had to be constructed quickly and efficiently within the dictates of a shortage of skilled labour and supplies of basic materials, most of which would need to be imported in merchant ships already being called upon to brave the perils of the oceans and the enemy to an unprecedented degree, and whose freight capacity was already in overwhelming demand.

These simple definitions were very easy to set out but to weld their many diversities into a suitable craft needed a mind which could embrace all the conventional skills of boat design and construction – and more, for one of the greatest problems was how to allow the boat to splashdown without damage to itself or its equipment. To this there was a very simple though unorthodox solution of which more later, and long experience with racing yachts convinced Uffa Fox that the answer to all the other demands must rely mainly on the theory that a good seagoing racing hull, suitably adapted and strengthened would be best for the job. His first experimental set of designs do not appear to have been ideal for, or acceptable to, the A/SR authorities. A letter, dated 16 January 1942, from S. W. Townsend, RDS3, for the Director of Technical Development, to Uffa Fox is quoted herewith:

Sir,

1   I am directed to refer to the discussion this morning between yourself and Major Nixon and Sq. Ldr. Levy and the undersigned and to confirm that action will be taken to place with you a contract, for an airborne

Rescue Boat on the lines of your suggestion.

2   The matter has since been discussed with the Deputy Director of Air/Sea Rescue Services who has certain criticisms to make and it is felt that further discussions of these points will be necessary before construction can proceed; it is therefore proposed that the Deputy Director, Group Captain Waring, and the undersigned should visit you on the 22nd. instant.

3   For your advanced information some of the points criticised were as follows:

(i)   The engine drive shaft should be shortened considerably as proposed in Lt. Robb's design in order to permit the engine weight to be lowered.

(ii)   Owing to the limited ground clearance permitted by your design some means of retracting the propeller will also be necessary, but it is desired to minimise the physical effort required by the crew who may be in a state of complete exhaustion.

(iii)   Similarly, it is desirable that all ancillary equipment, such as rudder, rowlocks, mast etc. should be permanently in position when stowed, to be brought into use by some simple mechanical movement.

(iv)   It was generally agreed that the release mechanism from the aircraft should be from a single suspension. I am enquiring as to the most suitable position for this and will inform you as soon as possible.

(v)   Stowage for pyrotechnics, food, water, wireless sets will also be required.

(vi)   An auxiliary petrol tank will also be necessary to provide a range of at least 100 sea miles.

(vii)   Weather protection for the crew will be required.

(viii)   DDASR wishes you to consider the introduction of bulkheading so as to minimise the risk of total flooding of the boat. In view of your semi-rigid method of construction, presumably you will wish to provide such bulkheads with some degree of flexibility.

(ix)   Provision will also be required for mounting two rockets, arranged to fire automatically on impact with the sea, each rocket carrying about 200 feet of buoyant line at angles of 45 degrees forward from the centre line of the boat.

4   With regards to possible effects of the boat on longitudinal control of the aircraft, it is proposed to construct a mock-up of the boat and mount it beneath an Hudson aircraft for confirmation by full scale flight tests. The risk of any adverse effects can be minimised by making step by step additions to the full profile which you require. For the purpose of these tests DDASR hopes to arrange for an Hudson to be flown to the Isle of Wight, probably Bembridge, in order to facilitate your part of this work, though it is, at the moment, uncertain as to whether the actual flight tests can be done from the Island.

5   The above advance information will enable you to proceed some way further with your design, prior to the conference on the 22nd. at which it is hoped to give you a final indication of our requirements.

In the absence of original sketches, blueprints or trial reports on the proto-type boat (not the folding one), all information on it is from examination of 'loose minutes' and a series of 17 photographs which give a good idea of its size and shape and from these its characteristics may be deduced. The Air Ministry had indicated that a Hudson aircraft would be an available machine for carrying the lifeboat and Cunliffe Owen of Bournemouth were instructed to assist by allowing access to one of the planes they were adapting for RAF duties. It was a twin-engined, fairly large aircraft by the standards of the time, but had rather low ground clearance. The first boat produced seems to have been a properly built hull, about 20 feet long with a beam equal to the width of the flat underside of the Hudson's fuselage, mounted with the stem abreast of the plane's propellers and the stern abaft the trailing edge of the wing. The sheerline appears completely straight and with the plane on the tarmac there is less than the diameter of the plane's wheels in ground clearance, and this decreases towards the stern. It would appear that the 'semi-rigid' method of construction mentioned in paragraph 3 (viii) in the letter above had been completely abandoned.

Seen afloat the boat has a wide, shallow transom and low freeboard, very much on the racing dinghy style. Three more pictures show it being dropped from a crane on 'splashdown' impact tests, whilst a further three show the side rockets firing and it is evident that the distance between the deck and the top of the gunwale is less than the length of the rowlock also in the picture. Capsizing tests are also shown in one photograph in which a man is sitting on the fore end of the upturned hull. Roughly amidships rectangular holes each side of the keel suggest that the propellers of two outboard motors were to be passed through the planking, presumably in trunks extending up to and through the deck. An accompanying rather poor print shows the boat ashore with a man alongside holding what could be a Marston Seagull twin-cylinder longshaft outboard, which could be indicative of the propulsion system.

Photographs taken on the trials show the boat with a single triangular mainsail set on a short sturdy mast, stepped just over a quarter of the boat's length from the bow. Forward of this, and extending aft a little at both sides is a turtlebacked inflated buoyancy chamber, fixed right down onto the gunwale all round the bows. Across the aftermost one fifth of the boat is another inflated chamber, arched in shape, fastened to the gunwales at each quarter, but open through fore and aft, where a steering oar or trailing rudder enters the water. A stern on view whilst the boat is under both motor and sail shows a considerable wake from an apparently good turn of speed. Four men are aboard and the stern sits very low.

In a 'loose minute' an eye-witness to these trials described the craft as a disaster, and went on to say that Uffa Fox was very annoyed at the critical reports.

A summary of extracts from the minutes of the conference held on 22 April 1942 at the works of the RFD Company at Godalming can be quoted. Present were S. W. Townsend, Gp. Capt. Waring, Uffa Fox, Mr Quilter (head of the GQ Parachute Company), Mr Dagnall of RFD and several others. It is briefly stated that work is proceeding on the trial boat; as agreed, modifications to the aircraft are taking place; the boat is to be fitted with buoyancy chambers fore and aft to increase stability and freeboard and to produce a self-righting effect in the event of the boat overturning on alighting, chambers to be in the form of inflatable tubes, construction of which, subject to the requirements, was to be left in the hands of the RFD Company, etc. So it would appear that even though Gp. Capt. Waring's original design was not entirely adopted many of his basic features were brought forward onto the Uffa Fox design.

One can feel very sorry that Lt. Robb completely dropped out of the proceedings. It would seem that the Royal Navy refused to release him for this special duty. Gp. Capt. Waring wrote to Admiral Sir Lionel Preston on 10 January 1942:

Dear Admiral,
May I ask you for your assistance in developing a scheme for rescuing airmen who have been forced to land at sea. Quite briefly, the idea is carry a lifeboat by air to the scene of the forced landing and to drop it by parachute. I had given the matter much thought and when one, day I met one of your Officers, Lt. Robb RNVR, I discussed some of the problems involved with him. He showed great interest in the scheme and undertook to make a sketch drawing of a suitable type of boat. He soon did so, but I should like to explain that all this was done unofficially. I have now succeeded in having the scheme taken up officially but I want to avoid the usual slow and cumbersome method of development. I feel the best way of doing this would be to get Robb to supervise the construction of his boat and am therefore asking if you would be good enough to allow him to do so. One or two days a week would suffice.

The reply was brief:

Dear Waring,
Whilst fully appreciating the value of such an invention I'm quite unable now to spare Lt. Robb. The demand for small craft in the Far East is such that he and similar Officers are fully employed.

It would appear from 'loose minute S 72453' of 18 January 1942 that Gp. Capt. Waring had previously made soundings on this matter for he writes to RDS3, in part:

(1) Admiral Preston stated that any work Robb was able to do for us must be on his own initiative and in such time as he could find without interfering with his proper duties. (2) As regards to your paragraph commencing with the words 'no one seems to have considered etc', Robb is:- (a) a serving Officer. (b) The idea is not his but mine. (c) The detail drawings are Robb's but even then many of the points incorporated in the design are mine. This does not detract from the value of Robb's work. (d) Lt. Robb was introduced to me by a friend with whom I had discussed the scheme. Robb became interested therein and voluntarily

undertook to draw up a design. It was fully explained to him that there was nothing official about it at the time. (e) For the reasons given your offer of remuneration seems to me to be likely to lead us into difficulties, as you have rather implied that the whole scheme from beginning to end is entirely due to the inventive ability, imagination, initiative and resourcefulness of that officer.

The fair thing to do would be to reimburse him for his out of pocket expenses, but even then care must be taken not to get into trouble with the Admiralty by doing so through the wrong channels.

From these interchanges it would seem that there were ruffles on the waters of inter-Service relations, and that Lt. Robb stayed with the Small Vessels Pool, even though a letter to Lt. Robb from RDS3 on 16 January discussed the prospect of a contract being placed with a firm at Twickenham which he had recommended, and that his Admiral was willing for his assistance to be utilised.

Very little about the Uffa Fox prototype appears in the records though one letter strongly condemns the steering oar idea and the open transom, so its production was apparently not carried through; who actually gave it the 'thumbs down' is not stated but one would think that an experienced sailor like Uffa Fox would have quickly realised its inherently dubious features in anything like the choppy, even rough, or cross seas which would be expected under operational conditions. All subsequent pictures and drawings depict a very different hull form, buoyancy chambers and engine installations. An obvious case of 'Back to the drawing board'.

It should not be thought that the considerable expenditure of time and materials would have been completely wasted for basic facts about length, beam and depth would have been delineated, and the freeboard and stern shape brought very much into question; the former to be increased to give a safer hull and the shape of the stern redesigned to make it more seaworthy; also the 'narrow-guttedness' of the hull could only indicate a very 'tender' boat almost impossible for any but an experienced small boat sailor to handle safely – and it could not be expected that there would be even one in every ditched crew. The Hudson's lack of ground clearance also exacerbated the problem, especially when it was realised that on 'touchdown' the undercarriage was designed to absorb part of the shock by the legs telescoping by as much as a foot. So there was little scope for deepening the hull right aft.

To an old hand like Uffa Fox the answer would immediately be obvious; use the type of stern which he had found so suitable for his racing canoes. By extending the overall length to 23 feet, but only increasing the waterline by a foot, the same, or greater beam, could be maintained at the 20-foot mark and brought aft to a rounded stern at deck level going down in a full, very buoyant, flattened curve to the keel. This coupled with a total turtleback buoyancy chamber attached all round the stern would eliminate most of the danger of the boat being pooped by a following sea. The only snag was that increasing the length without proportionately adding to the beam would make the boat even more tender and possibly unseaworthy. On small sailing boats the beam to length ratio is frequently between 27% and 32% according to the purpose of the design. The 20-foot (approximate) prototype with a beam of say 4′ 3″ would have a ratio of 20–21%, very low indeed considering the purpose of the boat. A Norfolk Racing Punt, designed for sailing speeds of up to 17 knots, has a ratio of around 22%, and they're terribly tender; thus an increase of beam was an absolute necessity. The problem was how to achieve it when the underside of the Hudson was so narrow. A study of a sectional drawing of the plane presented a solution. Above its flat base the fuselage widened in substantial curves before becoming the vertical sides, so by increasing the boat's beam at deck level and the height amidships the gunwales could climb up these curves and then be allowed to 'tumblehome', which would also present a slight angle on the top of the gunwales to allow better seating onto the curves of the fuselage. This would give the lifeboat a section through the centre of the hull reminiscent of the old 'Wooden Walls of England' whose rising gun decks were each set inboard from the one below. It was a very satisfactory answer for it brought the beam to waterline length ratio of the Mark I to around 29% when the boat was unladen.

Translated to the drawing board the final overall length was brought in at 23′ 2″ and the maximum beam at 5′ 5″, both sizes to absolute exteriors. Introducing the 'canoe' stern produced a more streamlined hull aerodynamically and a better sea boat when taken in conjuction with the increased beam; but viewing the drawing from the side the boat presented a most unusual form in that the height of the gunwales amidships was slightly greater than at the stem and much more that at the stern – what today could be called 'reverse sheer'. In actuality this fitted in admirably with the overall design, for by making the fore and aft self-righting chambers bulbous at the gunwales the operational sheer was brought up to a conventional and very seaworthy level. Using the reverse sheer in conjuction with inflated turtlebacks at bow and stern is a direct throwback to the old style self-righting, coastal lifeboats, except that their self-righting chambers at bow and stern were of wood, leaving the central, rowing, space lower, and to a degree sheltered. By turning to modern methods and materials developed by the RFD Company (makers of the inflatable buoyancy chambers) it was possible to obtain the best profile both in the air and on the sea by having the self-righting chambers deflated during flight, but fully inflated when on the water.

It goes without saying that a firm airtight seal was vitally necessary between the fuselage of the plane and the gunwales of the boat, for ingress of air at 200 mph would be fatal for the boat, and probably for the carrier plane too, so a canvas-covered two-inch thick cushion of soft rubber was designed to fit to the top of the gunwales; this also increased the freeboard.

In fairness to the great yacht designer it must be stated that there has been no access to Uffa Fox's personal notes or papers, so one can only perceive the problems as he may have done and with the benefit of hindsight, plus the evidence of achievement, assume how the problems were met, tackled and overcome; although there has been considerable assistance in this by long conversations with such men as Stan Williams, draughtsman, and 'Tim' Board, boatbuilder, both with almost a lifetime working with Uffa Fox.

So the length, breadth and sheer of the Airborne Lifeboat Mark I could have been determined but the actual hull shape still had to be resolved within the earlier definitions, but incorporating a canoe stern and tumblehome topsides. One of the greatest dangers in a small boat is 'broaching to' in a following sea; that is, allowing the stern to come round in an attempt to catch up with the bow, causing the boat to lie broadside on to the waves and thus be in danger of capsize or swamping – or both. In conditions when this could occur the only recourse for the crew is eternal vigilance and a strong arm on the tiller. Unless a wave is actually breaking the canoe stern with its flat 'floor' aft would lift if the boat could be held on a straight course, however intimidating the wall of water coming up astern might appear. Speed is no saviour, you cannot outrun a following sea. But design can make broaching less likely by introducing a 'firm' forefoot and this is what the Mark I plans show – an almost square juncture where the stempost meets the keel. This would give the bow maximum grip on the water, thus lessening the chance of it slewing sideways. Amidships it would be essential to give the hull as much depth as possible to accommodate the power unit, and to give maximum buoyant storage space below the deck; also to give the craft adequate weight-carrying ability without too much loss of freeboard the bilges would need to be full rounded from only a slight rise of floor (angle) from the keel. From these cardinal facts and premises the rest of the hull shape could evolve once the vital matter of powered propulsion was settled.

This must have caused some headaches. A conventional marine engine would have many disadvantages; too heavy; too high, both physically and in centre of gravity; with too much vulnerable installation work in the fuel supply and the cooling system as well as provision for the engine bearers, the propeller shaft log and skeg – realising too that a normal shaft would be liable to buckle in the stress in the parachute descent and that a protruding propeller aft would reduce ground clearance on the plane as well as provoke air drag in flight. So a self-contained engine, or engines, seemed the obvious answer, but how to fit them without going beyond the specification limits? One solution might be to adopt the 'tunnel' system, using a low centre of gravity, light-weight, horizontally opposed diesel engine coupled to a short shaft driving a propeller in a tunnel built upwards into the hull (the system later adopted for the Mark II). In the circumstances of the time, and with a real appreciation of the overall weight problem for the carrier plane, another installation was decided upon – an 'inboard outboard'.

Some years previously the British Motor Boat Company had produced an engine which they called 'Middy'; maybe in an analogy with that overworked and downtrodden race of seafarers better known as midshipmen, or possibly because it was midway between both types of marine engines. In this motor the power unit was that of a conventional self-contained outboard but instead of driving its propulsion unit via a shaft projecting overboard from the hull it terminated in a circular base-plate which could be bolted down inside the planking, through which a small hole could be cut to allow the drive unit, similarly bolted from the outside of the hull, to be mated. This outer unit comprised a short vertical shaft driving a propeller through right-angled gearing; the propeller itself forcing water up through the connecting spigot to cool the cylinder block before passing overside with the exhaust fumes. These engines were very low in height and being mostly of an aluminium alloy also in weight. They needed no long engine beds to spread their weight, no shaft log and skeg so there was no fear of a buckled shaft, no elaborate fuel or cooling systems, not even the large holes in the hull as with the prototype and its outboard/s.

But there were two snags. Firstly the Middy was only rated at 4 hp and the designer reckoned that one of these motors would only drive the 23-foot boat at 3–4 knots; and more speed than that was desirable and necessary if way was to be maintained against adverse conditions. Secondly there were none currently available. The first snag was happily overcome by using two engines, mounting one on each side of the keel, thus obviating any cutting and weakening of that vital central strength member and making installation and operation even simpler. The second obstacle could perhaps be overcome by appealing to the boating population of the country to surrender the engines they had so carefully stored away until peace returned. Admittedly the two propellers would protrude below the hull, but being well forward they would not affect ground clearance, and being of much smaller diameters than would be needed for one mounted aft the drag factor would not be significant. Their smaller size was due to a higher pitch and faster speed which could be countenanced because they were running in 'clear' water – that is, not screened by a skeg or keel through or over which their grip water would have to pass.

To some people a mast and sails would be auxiliary to the motors, but I'm convinced that in the mind of Uffa Fox they would be ancillary so he would have put an equal amount of thought into this part of the subject. Once again the criteria were simple to define:

- The mast had to lie within the topsides of the boat during flight.
- It had to be easily erected with the minimum of rigging.
- The sail(s) had to be simple to hoist and control.
- They had to be of sufficient area to keep the boat forging ahead, but not of such size as to make capsizing liable by an inexperienced crew.

The answers were just as direct. A short, sturdy mast less than 21 feet long, in use stepped into a socket in the deck and supported by a forestay and two shrouds, covered the first two points. The type and shape of the sails left no room for argument, for only a loose footed Bermuda rig can be operated without any spars. In this the triangular mainsail is hoisted at its head to the top of the mast by a halyard, is secured near the base of the mast by the tack, and allowed to run in or outboard at its after end (clew) by the mainsheet. Two very simple rope systems only are involved. The foresail would be of the same style, raised by a single halyard, secured to the boat at its fore-end and controlled by the foresheet, which would be fastened at its centre to the clew with the two tails leading aft for trimming. The question of area left more room for debate and a moderate square footage was decided upon with a simple reefing arrangement so that the area could be reduced without lowering the sails. A relatively short mast in relation to the hull length would lower the centre of effort and thus the heeling leverage which the wind could exert on the hull, so full sail might be carried in somewhat stronger breezes than in a racing dinghy of the same length, and this aided by the fine design of the hull would permit quite good speed under sail alone. Unfortunately the limitations of the boat and its gear would mean that it would not point as closely to the wind as might be desirable; so a centreboard or daggerplate would need to be part of the design in order to reduce leeway under sail, to help the boat maintain a straighter course under power and by its sideways pressure on the water help reduce the heeling effect of the sail. The foregoing is only a very simplified description of the rig and there would be many adjuncts to make it fully workable, but basic simplicity had to be the keynote.

Even so the initial design did not meet much approval, as is shown by a letter of 4 February 1943 to T. C. Ratsey (of the famous sailmakers) in which the writer felt that the mast was too far for'ard as 'she is a brute to bring about', and that in one set of trials 'they never succeeded in coming about but were forced to wear'. He further suggested that the mainsail should either have a boom or else a 'sheeting point' on the aft buoyancy chamber and invokes Mr Ratsey's influence to discuss improvements with Uffa Fox. We know now that this influence was almost entirely successful. Mr A. Somerville, in a letter of 11 February 1943, also shows disquiet about the sail plan but states reluctance to put forward his personal opinion against the work of a 'world expert in such matters' – referring to Uffa Fox.

Even an experienced sailor would be in no fit state to cope with an intricate rig after a ditching with probable immersion in a cold sea following on a long wearisome flight, then with cramped wet seasick hours in a rubber dinghy. Adrenalin does flow at such times and men find unknown resources of courage, strength and ability, but only those who have been through such experiences can begin to comprehend what physical and mental suffering has to be endured to survive, let alone to take constructive action when racked by nausea, when only tremendous effort can make limbs perform even the simplest movement or when the entire body is shaking convulsively with the onset of crippling hypothermia.

So the design would have progressed, each section and problem having a bearing on other sections and problems until a comprehensive whole formulated and there emerged a boat with the basic underwater outlines of a racing canoe; but with an untypical straight stem, from which came sleek, clean lines to the almost rounded stern; the plan and elevation of the drawings showing flowing waterlines and buttocks throughout, the square forefoot the only hard angle. All boat designs must have regard to the qualities and limitations of the materials to be used, so that right from the earliest stages the constructional method has to be considered, even if not finalised. Just so with the Airborne Lifeboat where weight for strength of materials was vitally important. A 'clinker' (clencher) built hull offers more integral strength and lighter construction than a carvel, but it has a higher drag factor and is liable to open at the lands if not kept constantly in the water, nor does it lend itself readily to mass production methods. A 'carvel' hull needs substantial stiffening frames and a certain thickness of plank to take caulking material and would lack the resilience to withstand the shock of splashdown; which left only one alternative, within the technology of the period, the double skin system. This method, frequently used for light racing hulls as well as for coastal lifeboats, uses two or even three layers of very thin planking laid at opposing angles to each other upon a framework of light hot-bent timbers, thus giving the strength effect of plywood; a light sanding off leaves a smooth exterior finish.

Uffa Fox adopted the double skin method for the Mark I, but with the outer planking half as thick again as the inner and running from fore to aft horizontally with a membrane of unbleached calico stretched and well dressed with linseed oil between the layers. Internally the hull was to be divided vertically from fore to aft with a watertight keelson which would also serve as support for the deck and provide housings for the centreboard and the rudder frame, as well as a strength member to which the 'bomb hook' and the parachute slings could be attached. Looking a long way back one wonders if the principle of a full length keelcase cum keelson was not the result of a meeting he had with Herbert Woods in the mid 1930s.

Herbert Woods was a founder club member and the designer of the Norfolk class of racing punts and for a number of successive years built himself a new boat and almost swept the board at each of the following season's events. Another member seeking to break this run of successes and also variations in design or price of those racing craft asked Uffa Fox to design and build a punt which could compete, on handicap, with Herbert Woods's annually more successful craft. As the existing handicap rules were based solely on length Uffa Fox produced a 17-footer, named Shrimp, and according to legend came personally to Potter Heigham to race against Woods's latest, a 22-foot boat. The match was from Potter Heigham bridge to the Hickling Pleasure Boat Inn for lunch, and then back to Broads-Haven. As expected, knowing all the vagaries of wind, tide and course, Herbert Woods was first at the Inn by a long way and was adjudged the winner even on corrected time under the handicap system. Legend further states that Woods, for a wager of a 'fiver', offered to unship his rudder and sail the twisting three or so miles back steering his punt by sail control only and still be moored up by the time Shrimp arrived. It's said that Herbert Woods kept that 'fiver' for many years as proof of his success. Uffa Fox may have remembered this and watched his rival's progress, for the following year one of the Broads-Haven punts was disqualified because the bottom had sprung; that is, the downward pressure of the mast combining with the upwind pull of the forestay and mainsheet brought too much curve into the keel. So Herbert Woods built Swallow II with a keelcase which extended the entire length of the punt, and had no more trouble from 'sagging'. The Airborne Lifeboat's keelcase cum keelson followed the same principle in providing a central member to withstand the stress of being slung (in this context 'hogging') firstly from the plane's bomb hook and then from parachutes; from this keelson individual transverse watertight bulkheads divided the interior of the craft into buoyancy chambers which also served as engine compartments and storage lockers.

This then could have been the evolution of the Mark I Airborne Lifeboat. Soon Uffa Fox's fertile brain would turn to the Mark II, a 30-footer, produced from 1944; there were also to be digressions into other sizes for the Fleet Air

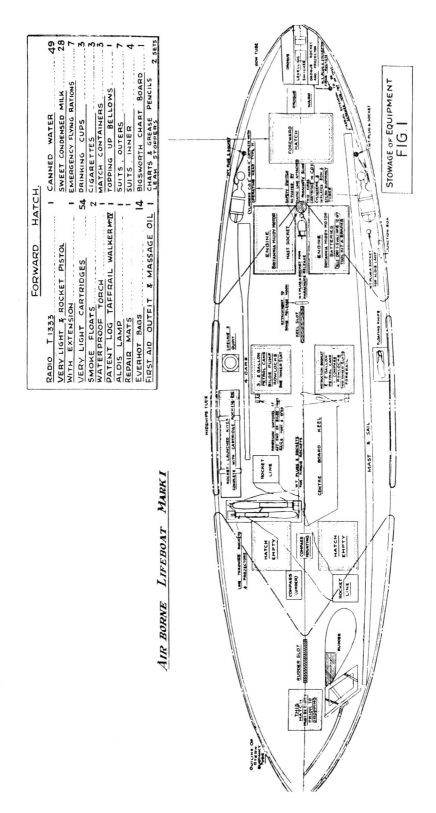

Air Borne Lifeboat Mark I

FORWARD HATCH.

RADIO T1333	1
VERY LIGHT & ROCKET PISTOL	1
WITH EXTENSION	
VERY LIGHT CARTRIDGES	54
SMOKE FLOATS	2
WATERPROOF TORCH	1
PATENT LOG TAFFRAIL WALKER MK IV	1
ALDIS LAMP	1
REPAIR MATS	
EVERHOT BAGS	14
FIRST AID OUTFIT & MASSAGE OIL	1
CANNED WATER	49
SWEET CONDENSED MILK	28
EMERGENCY FLYING RATIONS	7
DRINKING CUPS	3
CIGARETTES	3
MATCH CONTAINERS	3
TOPPING UP BELLOWS	7
SUITS , OUTERS	4
SUITS , INNER	4
BIGSWORTH CHART BOARD	1
CHARTS & GREASE PENCILS	2 SETS
LEAK STOPPERS	

STOWAGE OF EQUIPMENT

FIG 1

5   *Deck layout of the Marks I and IA*

6 *A Mark IA beneath a profusion of parachutes*

Arm, and in the distance, plans for 35, 40 and 50-foot craft to be dropped complete with coxwain and medical attendant.

All the while there were tussles with Government Departments, first to have the principle accepted, then to wrest promise of materials from the Ministry of Supply, with Manpower Authorities always on the sidelines with their demands for pairs of hands here, there and everywhere that the varying situation demanded. The building programme was therefore slow to get under way. Uffa Fox writes with strong feelings and many touches of humour about the struggles of those early days: it is impossible to reproduce his colourful writings and anecdotes within this book, so the author would recommend to you *Joys of Life*, *More Joys of Living* and *Seamanlike Sense in Powercraft*, in all of which can be found interesting photographs as well as enjoyable reading.

This was then the beginning of the Airborne Lifeboats, which when demonstrated around the bomber bases by a team led by Flying Officer Wilson, met with a very varied reception. Some RAF crews were incredulous that such an ingenious craft, with so many gadgets, had been evolved to help in rescue work, others treated the whole matter with an 'I'll never need one', attitude, echoed at the majority of American bases, where Wilson reported 'the hospitality was tremendous but aircrew interest generally sadly lacking'. In those early days the USAAF, after an initial shock of high losses, believed they had the problem licked by improved formation and fighting tactics but had not appreciated the tenacity of the Luftwaffe's fighter arm which was seen in the terrible losses of men and machines when the bomber offensive really got into its stride. Then many were to bless Gp. Capt. Waring, Lt. Robb, Uffa Fox and all who helped the wonder craft to operational use.

Even from this stage the development of the lifeboats was far from simple. Delays in design and construction, supplies of equipment etc. were so great that the Hudson was in danger of being phased out before the boats would be ready so there was heavy pressure to ditch the Mark I programme and go straight into the Mark IA production for the Warwicks. Not all these delays were attributable to the wartime situation – some sprang from the red-tape procedures within the departments concerned. Waring writes on 20 January 1943(?):

> It seems incredible that the project of an airborne lifeboat should require such a very long time to bring to fruition.
>
> The Air Staff approved of the complete scheme many months ago. Part of the essential scheme was this rocket throwing line which of course also requires cartridges to fire the rocket.
>
> It now appears that each individual item requires separate sanction and approval not only from the Air Staff but from each sub-section in the M.A.P.
>
> If we go on holding trials we won't get anywhere. The aircraft for carrying the boat will have disappeared and, above all, in the meantime we are losing lives which we need not lose.

In the event the Warwicks also were so far behind target delivery that the use of Hudsons continued to the end of the War for the Mark I, while the Warwicks carried both Marks IA and II, with Mark IIA as an adaptation for Lancasters.

3   Operations 1943

5 May   Halifax 'V' of 102 Squadron was hit by flak over Germany so that the starboard inner engine failed. As height was lost the incendiary containers and other equipment were jettisoned, but the Dutch coast was crossed at only 4000 feet. Shortly afterwards the starboard outer engine also packed up, followed by the port outer at 0308 hours; they were now down to 1500 feet and ditching was inevitable. It was a dark, moonless night, with a slight haze and a light wind from the north-east.

At 4000 feet the crew had been ordered to ditching stations, which were taken up correctly; except that the Captain was unable to fasten his 'Sutton' harness in spite of all efforts. At 0313 SOS was transmitted and the wireless operator clamped down the key. 'Gee' was out of action. No acknowledgment was received of their position fix of 5333N 0132E (85 miles east of Spurn Head, Yorkshire). The sea was approached at 45 degrees down and across the slight swell; flaps lowered and the only engine running at full revs. The impact at 75 mph was not violent by the bomb aimer was thrown from his position as the tail rose sharply. The crew left the aircraft hurriedly, one twisting his knee as he went through an upper exit.

Neither the manual release nor the immersion switch would free the dinghy until the Captain made a last despairing effort by breaking into the stowage and heaving it out. It inflated well. Once they were all aboard the bomb aimer's face was given attention and all made themselves as comfortable as possible to await rescue.

It was 0625 before any aircraft was heard; then their Very lights drew Hudson 'D' (F/L Fitchew) of 279 Squadron to circle the dinghy and transmit a new position signal of 5340N 0126E, and it remained with them until 0820 when two more of the Squadron's Hudsons arrived, 'W' (F/S Moggeridge) and 'Y' (F/O Wilson), the former carrying an Airborne Lifeboat. Then the Halifax survivors were privileged to witness the first operational drop of one of these ingenious craft. The lifeboat left its carrier plane at about 800 feet when the airspeed was 120 knots, plunging steeply away from its parent before a retarder parachute began to pull the main cluster out of its containers. One parachute was seen to develop before the others so the boat swung violently as it came down. Regrettably the drogue rocket in the bow tube did not fire so the sea anchor in the hawse pipe on the opposite side of the stem was not released, nor did the self-righting canopy chambers over the bow and stern inflate from their CO_2 cylinders. These were designed to lie flat within the boat whilst attached to the aircraft but as the parachutes opened they would inflate to provide buoyant shelters covering both the bow and the stern for a distance of about six feet with 2' 6" clearance above the gunwale height. Nevertheless the boat landed gently although at too flat an angle, some 25 yards from the dinghy. It was fortunate that it was so close for the side rockets which were intended to carry out a broadside of 175 yards of brightly coloured floating line had not fired either, although the parachutes released effectively; and the Halifax crew were able to paddle to the boat and board it easily, despite being wet, cramped and seasick for the past five hours.

The injured bomb aimer was lain on the softness of the uninflated for'ard buoyancy chamber, thus obscuring the equipment hatch and denying the crew its contents. Both the engineer and the navigator had previous small boat experience and were able to start the engines whilst the Captain shipped the rudder into place; finding it difficult to do as the after buoyancy chamber had only partly inflated. Meanwhile the W/Op had read a message from the Hudson giving them a course to steer of 214 degrees magnetic, and soon the boat was under way at 6 knots with the dinghy in tow. This soon broke free and was sunk by gunfire from one of the Hudsons.

At 1115 the planes lost sight of the lifeboat due to fog and it was whilst thus enshrouded that the shear pin on the starboard propeller broke. The engine was stopped and the mast stepped, in spite of having to be pulled clear of the supine bomb aimer on the foredeck. There was difficulty with the rigging and in setting the mainsail, again due to the foredeck complication, but the boat went well under one motor and the sail until the port motor also sheared its propeller pin and had to be stopped; both breakages were undoubtedly due to entangled cordage around the propeller blades. From then on progress was slow as the wind was light and the foresail had not been discovered inside the hidden fore compartment.

At 1300 the lifeboat was sighted by searching planes and surface craft requested to set course to intercept it. Two Naval Rescue Motor Launches and an RAF HSL responded to the call, the position now being 5330N 0116E, at 1648 hours. HSL 2579 won the race, the survivors being taken aboard and the lifeboat in tow. Cox'n Cyril Shutt of the HSL, at his Norfolk home, has been able to add to the official report:

> We were about ten miles east of the Dudgeon Light when we spotted this blue sail; we'd been told to look for a 'powered dinghy' and wondered exactly what that meant. At that time there were quite a few Danes and Norwegians escaping across the North Sea and we thought perhaps it was one of them. Anyway we went alongside and were greatly surprised to see what sort of craft we'd picked up; we'd never heard of Airborne Lifeboats. At that time we were in the middle of a minefield so didn't hang about getting the men on board. We tried all ways to tow the Lifeboat but it was very awkward, yawing about all over the place and slowing us down a lot. So our Skipper, F/L Bull, a fine bloke, had us moor it to the first swept channel buoy we came to so as we could get into Grimsby as quickly as possible, and the Navy brought it in next day. Our unit was 22 A/SR Marine Craft Unit, based at Grimsby, and our Commanding Officer

named Haines; I believe he went on to become an Air Commodore.

13 May Not a lifeboat drop but an exercise which brought the right craft to the right place at the right time. In the afternoon No. 1241 – a purpose built 60-foot A/SR pinnace – left its base at Wells on the north Norfolk coast with an Airborne Lifeboat in tow so that trials could be carried out. During these the Lifeboat, with its buoyancy chambers deflated, capsized throwing its three-man crew into the sea. All managed to regain the upturned craft and hung on to it until 1241 had turned to pick them up; it is reported that W/Cdr. Burwood managed to retain both his sun-glasses and his pipe during the ducking. About 1615 hours, just after the lifeboat had been righted, a Flying Fortress passed within sight and broke up in mid air with two parachutes seen to descend. At once the lifeboat was cut adrift and all speed cracked on by 1241 to effect a rescue. The intervening distance was rather more than anticipated but after an hour wreckage and an empty dinghy were found. A Stirling bomber joined in the search and soon signalled a direction by Aldis; minutes later Lt. Norvill Gorse (USAAF) was taken from the water but unhappily his companion, Captain Derrol Rodgers (USAAF) died shortly after being picked up by Sheringham Lifeboat. It was later learned that after taking off from its base in Lincolnshire the Fortress of 96 Bomb Group sustained damage in the air over the North Sea. The pilot at once turned back towards land and ordered his crew to bale out over the north Norfolk coast, hoping that having secured their safety he and the co-pilot would be able to set the automatic pilot so the stricken aircraft would head out to sea again. Unfortunately the damage was so severe that neither were able to leave the controls until the plane commenced breaking up. Their effort had not been in vain for all survived except Captain Derrol Rodgers.

16 June The second operational Lifeboat drop was not a success and only the bare details have been recorded. A Catalina was wrecked 150 miles north-west of Vaagar (Faeroes) whilst trying to pick up the crew of a Fortress of 206 Squadron from Benbecula (Hebrides). Hudson 'F' of 279 Squadron was sent to the Faeroes to assist in the Fortress operation, but by the time it reached there another Catalina had completed the rescue, so 'F' (F/O Sherwood) was diverted to the damaged flying boat. It arrived over the survivors' dinghy at 2013 hours; two men were evident with possibly another in the bottom of the frail craft. The lifeboat was dropped from 750 feet but the parachutes failed to open and the boat broke up on impact. Another Hudson, believed to be from Iceland, dropped a Lindholme to the distressed crew. 'F' was forced to return to base; happily the survivors were later saved by surface craft. Subsequent examination revealed that the static line, to pull out the parachutes, had not been attached.

15 July Wellington 'F' of 12 OTU was on its way to drop leaflets over the Rennes area of France when it was hit by flak in the port engine; the cargo was jettisoned as altitude was lost and the plane headed back towards the Channel. Heavy flak was again encountered as the coast was crossed near Bayeux and evading tactics cost further height. 'The moon was bright' relates W/Cdr. N. A.

N. Bray; 'with a 20 knot wind from the north-west, we could see the sea was choppy with waves about six feet high. Ditching drill was followed but no radio transmission made because of proximity to the enemy coast.'

The impact was not severe but sudden deceleration caused the Captain to injure his face on the windscreen as his harness pin broke, and because his right foot was trapped he was dragged under by the rapid ingress of water. All the crew experienced this but despite some bruising managed to free the dinghy and struggled to the surface, apart from the mid-gunner, to be quickly joined by the Captain, who assisted by the W/Op had fought his foot free. Then they went to the aid of the gunner who was badly bruised, and still caught; only by ducking back into the fuselage was he able to free himself. All then scrambled into the dinghy; fifteen minutes later the Wimpey sank and they were alone, at 2.10 in the morning, some 26 miles west of Cap de la Hève, in a stormy sea.

'W' of 279 Squadron took off from Bircham Newton at 1025 in response to a dinghy sighting by Fighter Command; wisely they picked up an escort of 12 Typhoons from Tangmere. F/O Wilson, formerly a builder, from Melbourne Australia, takes up the tale. 'We flew along the coast for about 20 minutes, searching for the dinghy, it was a fine day in France, houses on the shore being clearly visible; when we found it, about eight miles out, the crew were paddling vigorously seawards. I flew over them and then pressed the lifeboat release.' It was a perfect drop with splashdown only 30 yards from the survivors who were seen paddling towards the boat as 'W' left for home escorted by four of the 'Tiffies'; the others remaining near the dinghy. Very shortly afterwards 16 FW 190s approached and the fighters rose to meet them, managing to draw the battle some ten miles from the lifeboat. Two of the Luftwaffe planes were shot down before the arrival of a gaggle of Spitfires sent the rest rapidly homewards.

Meanwhile the survivors had boarded the lifeboat and on the Captain's orders rested, after the trailing lines had been cleared, whilst he read the Instruction Book thoroughly. All were very wet, cold and seasick, but cheerful. Again, they were fortunate in that both the bomb aimer and the W/Op had experience of two-stroke engines, so the boat was soon under way. From the Captain: 'We soon lost sight of the coast and were absorbed in the very gallant behaviour of our fighter escort; I only regret that in their anxiety to draw off the attackers they did it so thoroughly that we were unable to confirm more than one victory for the New Zealand Squadron.'

Three and an half hours later they were met by HSLs 177 and 190 from 28 A/SR Marine Craft Unit based at Newhaven; the former took them aboard, the latter the Lifeboat in tow. Doug Rushmer of Somerleyton (Suffolk), cox'n of the latter, remembers it well: 'We went out from Newhaven with a pretty heavy escort of fighters but it was 177 with Geoff Lockwood which beat us to the survivors, so we decided to tow the airborne boat home but just as we'd secured her orders came over the radio to salvage what equipment we could – quickly – and then sink her. We attacked the engine compartments with axes to try to get the motors out but found the plywood deck and double diagonal planking very tough; we'd done considerable damage before another order came over to tow the lifeboat home. We brought her up to the transom as short as possible but even then dared not open up our throttles, and running those

7   *Flt Sgt Harry Fitchett and crew 13.7.1943 (H Fitchett)*

engines at slow speed does no end of damage, but we finally got the remains back to base.'

It had been the aircrew's first flight together over enemy territory, and even forty-three years later ex-F/S Fitchett, a strong supporter of the Goldfish Club, whilst attending a reunion at RAF Museum, Hendon, could remember the experience vividly and retained a strong debt of gratitude to the Fighter lads, the A/SR Service and the staff at RN Sick Quarters, Swanborough who cared for them so well when they were brought ashore.

26 July When 279 Squadron's 'W' (W/Cdr. Corry) scrambled to a Fortress reported 'in the drink' 65 miles north of Ameland in the Frisian Islands they thought they were in for a long flight right on to the enemy's doorstep, in company with 'U' (F/L Fitchew). It was a near perfect day, with a light air of wind from the south-east, a slight swell on the sea and reasonable visibility – fortunately for the crew of Fortress K 229901 (from 94 or 388 Bomb Group) forced to ditch 35 miles north-east of Cromer when returning from a daylight raid on Germany.

It was 1445 when they hit the water and all ten men managed to get out and into the dinghies, neither of which came out of the stowage easily; one inflated well, the other had a leak. The plane took half an hour to sink, during which time the dinghies stood off about 100 yards apart. It was very shortly afterwards that 'W' and 'U' hove into sight, weighed up the situation and decided that this was an immediate need; so 'W' dropped its lifeboat into the wind, intentionally clear of the dinghies; it splashed down 80 yards from the one with six men in it. All systems worked perfectly and those six were soon aboard and rowing across to the others, two in the half inflated dinghy, the other two in the sea, hanging on to the handropes. All hands at once set about preparing the boat for the voyage home, but found two inches of water in the engine compartments and the engine instructions unreadable. None the less they managed to start the motors, but both soon stopped and would not restart, probably being flooded with unburnt fuel and excessive choke. Nothing daunted they stepped the mast and set sail on a course of 220 degrees, just one hour after ditching. All water was pumped from the boat, the US kite aerial and radio (brought from the dinghy) used for transmissions and some of the boat's supply of chocolate eaten. The log was not streamed nor used, as even after reading the instructions they could not understand its operation. For a crew who did not have a single sailing man amongst them and had previously neither seen, nor heard of, the Airborne Lifeboats, they did very well. In four hours and fifty minutes they covered almost 20 miles before being met by HSL 2551 of 24 A/SR Marine Craft Unit and taken into their base at Great Yarmouth. The lifeboat was abandoned but found afloat and brought into port the next day, where it attracted considerable interest and attention from the local boatmen.

26 July Meanwhile 279's 'U' had watched the commencement of the rescue before continuing alone to the original casualty, Fortress 'Happy Daze',

F 230206 of 94 Bomb Group; and told to keep a lookout also for a Lancaster and a Halifax, both of which had ditched; 'Happy Daze' had been attacked by two or three FW 190s whilst crossing the Danish coast, homeward from Kiel, on the 25th, the starboard wing tip was set afire and the plane dropped 25,000 feet in three minutes, pancaked onto the water and bounced three times before folding in two just abaft the radio cabin and sinking in 15 seconds. The two dinghies were released manually and all of the crew boarded them except Sgt. Thomas Brown who could not be found. The survivors only managed to take out a flare pistol, a radio, some rations and an escape kit compass. Weather conditions were not bad, but uncomfortable, with a south-east wind of 14 knots giving waves five feet high. For 19 hours the dinghies drifted tied together, 'enjoying' during the night the sight and sounds of the RAF giving Hamburg another pasting. Radio transmissions were made during daylight and paddling commenced to the westward at 0800 hours on the 26th. At 1245 two Halifaxes were seen searching five miles to the south so flares were fired which were immediately observed. The planes circled them briefly, dropping a set of Lindholme gear which was quickly recovered, the waterproof suits donned and the supplies utilised. An hour later another set was dropped, and at 1800 a third which landed much too close for comfort; all were recovered.

It was during the evening that a Hudson came into view and made a couple of dummy runs dropping smoke floats before releasing its Airborne Lifeboat. 'U' had finally arrived, done its best, and now being very short of fuel hurriedly set course for home after watching the lifeboat alight 75 yards downwind of the dinghies. The drogue had hit the sea first and checked the boat whilst the parachutes released and the side rockets fired. The buoyancy chambers had inflated during floatdown. Two of the Americans easily paddled to the boat, boarded it, and rowed to the others after hauling in the drogue and side lines. Two other Hudsons which had located the dinghies earlier, and kept contact, witnessed the drop and destroyed the dinghies by gunfire after most of the equipment had been transferred, and then signalled a course of 270 degrees to be steered. Sq. Ldr. Frank Griffiths, now a noted RAF writer, explained in a letter that it was not wise to orbit a dinghy too closely as German radar could pick up the pattern and might decide to investigate; so it was best to carry out a search pattern flight, just keeping the dinghy in view at intervals.

Aboard the lifeboat one engine was soon started but the port one proved more difficult for a while; but both stopped after 15 minutes, due to over-heating. Once cooled off they started again easily and ran all night at one-third throttle. Unhappily the rudder had not been correctly shipped and during the night the tiller broke. Quite undeterred the crew brought the whole assembly aboard, bored through the wooden blade with a knife, reinserted it and rigged steering lines through the hole. Course was maintained with the navigator making full use of the Bigsworth Chartboard. At 0730 the next day the Danish fishing vessel, *Betty*, was sighted dead ahead, and as steering was difficult with the jury steering it was decided to investigate the ship. Once alongside the welcome was not entirely friendly as the Captain was a German who took them and lifeboat aboard and insisted on heading eastwards. However, her new course was soon spotted by a searching Halifax and a burst or two of gunfire across the *Betty*'s bows quickly brought her head onto a westward course, much to Sq. Ldr. Griffiths's satisfaction, until the ship ran into a bank of fog and was lost to view. At least that was the story released at the time. The next day she was escorted into Great Yarmouth by HSLs 2551 and 184 which had met her at sea. Apparently the German skipper had been 'persuaded' by his three-man Danish crew and the Americans that discretion was the better part of valour, even if it meant sailing through the British coastal minefields in the darkness. More recent research by letters from the survivors tells a slightly different tale and it is now certain that the welcome aboard was entirely friendly but to protect the families of the Danish fishermen left at home under Nazi subjugation an element of coercion had to be introduced.

Mr Jack March, a member of one of the Halifax crews, for many years kept the Heartsease public house in Norwich, and his wife treasured as a brooch the badge which one of the Americans gave her husband when the Fortress and Halifax crews met soon afterwards. The survivors were: Lt. John Keelan, pilot; Loren E. Hubbell, co-pilot; Lt. Wm. Greulich, navigator; Thomas Nelson, bombardier; Sgt. Edward (Sunshine) Cannon, engineer; Sgt. Eugene Deyoe; Sgt. H. Kornick; Sgt. Herbert Symes.

There was a bonus on the day's operations in that 'V' of 279 Squadron whilst searching for the RAF planes came across eight American airmen in two dinghies; Lindholme gear was dropped and successfully recovered with the happy conclusion of a Walrus arriving at 1845 hours to pick up some of the survivors, followed by another 'Shagbat' rescue a few minutes later.

28 July   Whilst coming away from Kiel, Fortress 423035 of 94 Bomb Group was jumped by a number of FW 190s from Luftwaffe unit JG 1 and hit in No. 3 engine; it managed to remain in formation for a time but was again attacked with No. 1 and 4 engines knocked out, so height and formation were rapidly lost. At 7000 feet it was joined by another Fortress (on only three engines) which kept company until 423035 was forced to ditch at 0930 hours. Weather and sea conditions were both good. During the descent ammunition etc. was jettisoned and a fire in the starboard wing kept under control. This had rendered some of the controls useless and filled the cockpit with smoke and choking fumes to the extent that proper ditching stations could not be taken up, nor was one of the lower hatches resecured after the jettisoning operation. Final deceleration was very severe and only five of the crew managed to get out before the aircraft sank. At the time the engineer was trying to release one of the dinghies and was carried under with the plane; he managed to free it and was brought gasping to the surface as it inflated. The men clambered into this and promptly ditched their heavy flying gear and boots. After watching this the other Fortress climbed, circled and headed for England. Searching aircraft were seen during the afternoon but the survivors were only located after their sixth flare had been fired. These planes remained in the vicinity until at 1745 two Hudsons appeared, 279 Squadron's 'G' (F/O Myatt) and 'W' (F/S Palmer), the latter dropped her lifeboat after two preliminary runs. The survivors were astonished at how lightly it landed on the water, only 100 feet away from them, so they were able to board it very quickly.

They soon found the 'Book of Words' and started both engines before setting a course of 250 degrees as given by one of the Hudsons. Four of the survival suits were donned but the others were not located in their storage compartment; neither the sails nor the kite aerial were utilised. The port engine would not run continuously, but the starboard chugged away all night, nursed by the engineer, although he'd injured his back when releasing the dinghy. A parachute drop of 'petrol' the next morning was very welcome, and after using this the port engine decide to behave itself and ran well from then on. No rationing was set and all took food, but were sparing on the water supply. Meanwhile attendant Hudsons had contacted HSL 2551 (F/L George Lindsay) and interception was made at 2200 hours. The five airmen were taken aboard to be landed at Great Yarmouth, some 98 miles away, the next day.

31 July A Mitchell of 226 Squadron was on A/SR search about 65 miles north-west of Terschelling, one of the Frisian Islands, when it was surprised by eight enemy fighters and sent down into the sea. The pilot managed to retain control and make a form of ditching rather than a plunge, so three of the crew were able to get out and into a dinghy. The time was 1740 hours on the 30th, the weather fine with a light breeze from the south-east. A reasonably comfortable night was spent, no one was seasick and both friendly and enemy planes were seen during the evening. A sparse meal was taken in the morning of the 31st, but as all watches had stopped the time could only be guessed at. Being connected with A/SR they knew about Airborne Lifeboats and hoped that a Hudson with one was already on its way to them. About 1330 their hopes were realised as two appeared, escorted by four Beaufighters. Ten minutes later 'R' (P/O Watts) of 279 Squadron dropped its lifeboat from 700 feet, which alighted 100 yards downwind and to one side of them; all systems worked perfectly so they were able to board it without difficulty. An Aldis signal gave them a course to steer of 247 degrees.

They found the rudder frame very difficult to ship and punctured the after buoyancy chamber in the process. All lines were hauled aboard, the mast stepped and rigged with the mainsail set to supplement the engines, which had started without trouble and set to run at half throttle. During this time the weather had started to deteriorate with the wind freshening to 15 knots, then as dusk set in both engines stopped. Inspection revealed that both compartments were half full of water, as was the for'ard one, and all stores were soaked. At once all lockers were pumped out and the mainsail lowered as wind and seas continued to increase. Then the tiller carried away at the rudder post and the boat broached to, lying broadside onto the waves which continually swept over her. The drogue was streamed in an attempt to keep the boat's head to the seas, but this was inadequate so the mast and sail were also streamed as a sea anchor; which improved their situation considerably but waves still continued to break aboard and a fearful, very uncomfortable night was spent. Most movable gear was brought aft in an effort to raise the bows, but to little effect.

At dawn on Sunday 1 August the improvised drogue carried away and they were left helpless with no engines, mast, mainsail or rudder; and seas constantly sweeping the boat. Then it was found that the starboard midship compartment was again almost full, giving them a pronounced list. To correct this the boat was trimmed by allowing an equal amount of water into the opposite compartment and then steadily pumping a little out of each alternately, even whilst water continued to sweep across the deck and to well up through the centreboard slot. It took six hours to clear the boat and then they tried to rig another sea anchor by streaming the patent log with a waterproof suit lashed around it, and this made a very effective jury drogue. During the afternoon they were circled by three Hudsons, one of which carried a lifeboat; but to their intense disappointment the planes flew away without dropping it to them. The night was more comfortable than the previous one as the seas were moderating, but their situation was still distinctly parlous.

All through the weekend tension had been high at A/SR HQ as news of the lifeboat was awaited from the many searching planes. Aboard the boat efforts were made throughout the Monday to get the engines running again. The plugs were removed and dried, water pumped out of the cylinders by continuously winding the pistons over with the starting cords; the carburettors were stripped, cleaned and dried off and fuel allowed to flow to waste through the pipes to remove all traces of the salt water; but all in vain for the flywheel magnetos could not be stripped and dried as the special tools required were not aboard. Undaunted the crew rigged an oar as a jury mast and set the foresail on it so some headway was made until the wind shifted dead into their faces and all forward progress ceased. Efforts were made to fly the kite aerial by hand but it continuously dived into the sea. The spare kite was held in reserve awaiting more favourable conditions. The seas were still high but with no broken water and the boat rode well at its improvised sea anchor. All the men were very tired and took turns to sleep under the for'ard buoyancy chamber. Rations were issued at the rate of one tin of water, one tin condensed milk and nine Horlicks tablets per day between the three of them. At no time was there any seasickness. During the day several aircraft were seen, three Mitchells only half a mile to the south early in the morning, but the flares they sent up were not observed. In both the early and late afternoon Mitchells sighted and circled them but soon lost contact; but around 1800 hours a Halifax pin-pointed them and remained until joined an hour later by two Hudsons, all remaining in orbit until darkness fell.

It was around 0800 next morning (Tuesday 3rd) that three Mitchells circled and stayed nearby until relieved by a Hudson and later another Mitchell. Mitchells and Beaufighters then plied continuously between the lifeboat, now in position 5507N 0410E (230 miles east of Newcastle), and two RMLs until interception was made. The exhausted men were taken aboard and the lifeboat in tow. By late evening all were safely back at base and the four-day rescue operation involving dozens of planes, hundreds of flying hours, and the co-operation of numerous boats, was over.

In that July 139 Fortress crew were rescued by A/SR out of 196 men aboard planes forced to ditch; the 25th being top day when 78 out of 80 personnel were saved.

1 August   Any euphoria generated by the successes of July soon evaporated on

8   An HSL making a 'pick up' (practice drop)

9   A Mark IA 'Bombed Up' to a Warwick

this day. Much of its events are shrouded in mystery. There were eight men aboard a plane which was forced to ditch returning from operations; three American aircraft (out of twelve lost) had ditched on 30 July (one each from 95, 96 and 303 Bomb Groups) and had still not been found. 'N' of 279 Squadron (F/O Pederson) was airborne from Bircham Newton at 1510 and had located and circled three dinghies in position 5431N 0447E at 1647 (160 miles west nor'west of Heligoland). Two of the dinghies were British pattern and the third, in tow, was an American. There were only three survivors. It could be that the men had left a sinking plane in their own dinghy and been spotted by RAF operational planes which had dropped their own dinghies to the survivors before reporting in. 'N' dropped her lifeboat at 1653 and the three men were seen to board it, examine the hatches etc. but make no attempt to start the engines or set the sails. The boat had landed perfectly with everything, apparently, working as it should, and appeared to be completely seaworthy. Sea conditions were not bad but would have been unpleasant in a small boat. 'Bandits' then appeared and the rescuers were forced to leave, during which one Mitchell was shot down with no survivors. It is probable that the two Hudsons seen by the Mitchell survivors on the same day in the previous incident were on their way to these three men which was why a second lifeboat had not been dropped. Constant enemy presence in large numbers prevented any further contact with the three men in the lifeboat and it was then feared that they either succumbed to the North Sea or were shot up and sunk by the German planes; but they were finally picked up by HSLs of 24 A/SR Marine Craft Unit from Great Yarmouth. The real wonder is that A/SR were able to operate at all within 60 miles of the enemy coast and 200 odd miles from their own bases. It was subsequently learned that the men in the dinghies were from 303 Bomb Group.

23 August   'R' (F/S Bedford) and 'O', both of 279 Squadron, were aloft from Bircham Newton at 0749 to search for a dinghy with two men reported 50 miles north of Terschelling. At 1113 red pyrotechnics were sighted and 'R' dropped her lifeboat to survivors at 1118. One parachute opened fully, one partially, the third not at all, but the boat appeared to land and float satisfactorily within 40 yards of the dinghy. One man climbed aboard and then signalled 'Boat US' and returned to the dinghy in which a second man appeared injured. 'Q' had trouble and was forced to return to base. 'F' (F/O Clark) and 'D', sent out to help, located the dinghy at 1747 in position 5424N 0509E (120 miles north-west of Heligoland) and the former dropped her lifeboat from 700 feet at 110 knots and both men were seen to board after paddling the intervening 40 yards. An Aldis signal to steer 260 degrees was not acknowledged. Meanwhile five Fortresses and four Beaufighters had joined the circus, a dangerous show of strength right on Hitler's doorstep. It was observed that the boat's engines were started and then stopped, and the lifeboat lay motionless. 'D' left to see if an RML or HSL could be found. At 1915 the lifeboat got under way again, steering a course of 260 degrees magnetic erratically at 4 knots; apparently on one engine only. At 1930 'K' which had come out as a relief, noticed the tiller was broken and the man was steering with an oar on a wavering course

10   A Lancaster floating well

11   A Mark I sailing home, towing the aircraft dinghy

between 220 and 260 M. 'K' returned to base at 1938 leaving three Beaufighters circling the slowly moving boat. It is doubted if these men reached safety as there is no further information in 279 Records beyond that subsequent searches failed to locate the lifeboat and German radio stated that two men had been picked up from the sea by a Dornier flying boat which was subsequently shot down by a Fortress, with no survivors.

24 August   279 Squadron's 'H' (F/L Fitchew) and 'R' (F/S Bedford) took off at 1415 to seek a dinghy with five men aboard in position 5449N 0440E (160 miles north-west of Heligoland) being circled by two Stirlings. It was located and a lifeboat dropped by 'H' at 1600; the five men were seen to board just before the Stirlings left for home. At 1630 two ME 110s intervened and fired on the lifeboat. 'H' and 'R' both closed the boat and took violent defensive and evasive action on a westerly course to lead the Germans away from the survivors. 'H' was hit many times by enemy fire but survived the attacks, contact with 'R' was lost as it was apparently shot down. There was no further news of the lifeboat or its occupants.

4 September   Early morning at Docking saw 279 'H' with 'M' take off to search for Lancaster ED 385 (ZN) of 106 Squadron, or its dinghy, in position 5422N 0313E (140 miles east of Flamborough Head). It was found at 0857 and a Lindholme gear dropped, but the dinghy in the string did not open and one of the containers burst, the survivors only recovering one of the remainder. 'M' then left to find 'O' and 'W' (W/O Passlow) which were also out on the search but had spread out as dead reckonings differed by 12 and 25 miles. 'O' and 'W' were found and led to the casualty, the latter dropping its lifeboat at 1114, 50 yards downwind of the survivors, who had boarded it within ten minutes. At 1155 the lifeboat was still not under way and all the Hudsons except 'O' were forced to return to base. At 1159 RMLs were contacted and homing commenced.

Lt. Cdr. Sheppard RNR (Ret.) is able to take up the story:

Aboard RML 550 we were homed to a floating Lancaster in position 5422N 0310E with survivors in a dinghy nearby. On arrival we found six men in an Airborne Lifeboat with a dead companion still in the dinghy. We took them all aboard but before heading for home attempted to sink the Lancaster by gunfire – totally without success; apparently its tanks were completely empty. I decided therefore to drop a depth charge alongside it, at minimum setting, but whilst we were at FULL speed. We came in, flat out, along its port side, sliding past the tail plane and close in to the wing tip. The operation was completely successful, the plane heeling over to starboard and slipping beneath the waves. Probably the only occasion when an aircraft was destroyed by a depth charge. We took the lifeboat in tow and headed back for Immingham. On the way, just into the defensive minefield – some 40 miles wide – we saw a glimmer of light in the darkness to the nor'ard. We knew that nothing, absolutely nothing, should be there so Action Stations was sounded and the lifeboat cast adrift. We made the

'Challenge' by light; there was a sudden glow where previously there'd been a glimmer – then complete and utter darkness. We made 'Enemy Report' and turned towards the position, saying our prayers, but found nothing, nor could aircraft sent out at dawn find anything which could account for the sudden glow of lights.

A Lancaster of 49 Squadron (JB 126) was later reported lost near this area and the sudden glow could well have been the final moments of this aircraft.

6 September At 1659 hours 279 'W' (F/O Clark) with an escort of four Mustang 1A of 168 Squadron RAF was over an H type dinghy with a K type attached in position 4941N 0005W. A run into the wind was attempted but as this approach was blinded by the sun the lifeboat was dropped on a crosswind run. Unfortunately the boat alighted 100 yards downwind from the dinghy and the men in it were seen to be paddling towards the boat, but not to board it. 'W' was forced to return hurriedly to base and contact was lost. Neither the survivors, believed to be from 106 Squadron's Lancaster DV 182, nor the lifeboat were heard of again; which is hardly surprising as the given position is right close in to the mouth of the River Seine.

4 October 'N' of 279 Squadron took off on a routine flight during which its lifeboat fell off for no apparent reason. It was recovered by surface vessels.

15 October Whilst on a search operation the crew of 279 Squadron's 'Z' found the aircraft yawing badly and vibrating in a most alarming manner. It was discovered that the drogue of the Airborne Lifeboat had come out of its housing and had wrapped itself round the plane's rudder and port fin. The lifeboat was jettisoned and base reached with a great sense of relief.

11 November Warwick 'W' of 280 Squadron crashed into a hillside near Whitby and all the crew were killed.

24 November Whilst 'O' of 279 Squadron was airborne in poor conditions on a routine search north-west of Lands End, having taken off from Harrowbeer, it observed an Airborne Lifeboat dropped by a Warwick to five men in a dinghy in position 5058N 0606W (65 miles north-north-west of Lands End). This was the crew of a Wellington from Haverfordwest and the survivors were seen paddling towards the lifeboat which had a bad list, as the aft buoyancy chamber had not inflated. The men boarded the lifeboat and their dinghy went adrift. At 1335 the lifeboat was seen to be sinking and efforts were made to drop Lindholmes, but in the circuit the position of the boat was lost and no further trace could be found despite continued searching by a Wellington and the Warwick. The drop had been made by 280 'J' (F/S Chesher) which had taken off from Portreath at 1034, finding itself over the dinghy at 1130, and dropped its lifeboat at 1137. 'J's crew had also observed that the lifeboat was damaged and that the survivors were not able to reach it, so had released a Lindholme which had failed to open. At 1310 another Lindholme was sent down, the dinghy of which opened successfully but the survivors could not manage to board it. At 1312 Hudson 'O' arrived on the scene but the two planes could not communicate owing to an unserviceable Aldis lamp. After continual strenuous paddling the survivors reached and boarded first one of the Lindholmes and then the lifeboat only to realise that their efforts were largely in vain as the boat was partly waterlogged. It was then that 'J' intercepted a message from Control asking the Hudson to drop another Lindholme, but it landed out of reach. At 1502 contact with the lifeboat was lost so the Wellington which came on the scene at 1508 joined in an organised square search, which continued until 1535 when failing light and dangerously low fuel reserves caused it to be called off. A tragic sequence of mishaps. Searches continued in very bad weather conditions until 2 January, but to no avail.

4 Operations 1944 January–June

6 January   The first report spoke of a Lancaster of 622 Squadron down on the sea at position 5348N 0245E (80 miles north-east of Great Yarmouth), so 'N' of 279 Squadron (F/O Gaze) took off from Bircham Newton at 1057 hours. At 1220 it was circling a dinghy with seven occupants at 5444N 0245E, quite a way further north than the original given position. Visibility was poor and the sea very rough at the time, so conditions were not good, added to which it was very cold. The lifeboat was dropped at 1225 and landed 200 feet downwind, but the port rocket did not fire and as the survivors were on this side they could not reach the boat. 'N' maintained contact for three hours until relieved by 'E', also from 279, which dropped a Lindholme within 50 yards of the dinghy at 1542. The man paddled to within a few yards of this but still failed to reach it, despite every effort, so it drifted away and was lost in the gloom. The early dusk came down and blotted out everything from the watchers in the sky.

Meanwhile an HSL had been despatched despite protests by the crew about the roughness of the night and the expected conditions in the area. (The seas do tend to stand up on end over the 'North Sea' shoals when it's blowing hard.) HSLs were not generally regarded as particularly good sea boats in bad weather, and have to reduce their speed so much that they become very nearly uncontrollable; also protracted running at low speeds causes almost as many engineering problems as prolonged periods 'flat out'; which is one of the reasons why coastal lifeboats of that era were relatively slow at 7–9 knots. Nevertheless, they did set out. Meanwhile 'Y' of 280 had joined the search and about midnight sighted a red flare so dropped a marker buoy and flares as near as possible to the position, and reported their action by radio. The transmission of this incident probably assisted the HSL from 24 A/SR Marine Craft Unit, which arrived at 0055 on the 7th and took the survivors, probably from Lancaster ME 577 of 626 Squadron, aboard to land them at Great Yarmouth later in the day.

8 January   On the 7th two JU 88 intruders were being chased away by four Mosquitos from Predannack when one of the enemy was shot down, and one of the attackers forced to ditch very shortly afterwards, some 170 miles south of Lands End. Both crewmen got out safely and into a dinghy each, which they prudently kept tethered together. The aerial battle had moved away from them and they drifted alone throughout the night on a great expanse of ocean. At daylight they hoisted their scraps of sails and made headway towards Britain at about one knot. When the sun was at its zenith they were sighted by four

Mosquitos of their own Squadron and soon afterwards by five Beaufighters; raising high hopes of rescue. Just before 2 pm in position 4734N 0639W (175 miles west of St Nazaire) a very welcome Warwick of 280 Squadron ('E', F/L Chesher) successfully dropped an Airborne Lifeboat to them but a freak of wind sent one of the releasing parachutes underneath the boat so that its cords fouled the propellers. Both men had boarded easily and realising the position the Captain stripped off and dived overboard into the icy water with the boat's knife; after considerable effort and his navigator sitting on the opposite gunwale to list the boat he managed to cut away the entangling lines.

They soon set a course of 350 degrees for home, using the starboard motor only, but after a while this stopped so they brought the port one into use, making northwards at 3 knots. Early on the 9th the port engine also stopped and they found that the trailing drogue wire was fouling both propellers, but they were unable to cut it away. Neither had any experience of boats or sailing but working entirely from the Instruction Book and diagrams they rigged the mast and set the sails. No aircraft were seen during that day and as the wind and sea increased in the evening they lowered the sails and rode out an uncomfortable night on the spare drogue.

Morning brought a moderation in wind strength so the sails were set again; both men were very tired but had eaten some rations and managed to keep warm in the waterproof suits provided. Their fatigue factor progressively rose until they reached the point of debating whether to alter course for the French coast, and certain captivity, but finally rejected the idea and pressed on using the favourable wind, now resolved to sail right into Mounts Bay. During the afternoon they were sighted by a Mosquito which then flew due north. This they interpreted as meaning they were south of the Scilly Isles and altered course accordingly. Later a Liberator overflew them but did not see their red star signals. By now the wind had changed and they had to alter course again, pressing on until the wind eased and finally died at midnight. The sails were taken in and turns taken at resting. It was fortunate that one stayed on watch for in the early hours of the morning engines were heard, and hoping they were not German E-boats, signals were fired to attract attention. Within minutes three RMLs were circling and 534 took them aboard, while the lifeboat was towed in by 526. They had motored and sailed about 100 miles to within 40 miles of the Lizard since ditching 103 hours earlier, and in spite of their privations were disappointed in not making the voyage all the way home.

28 January   It was a pitch black night when the crew of Lancaster 'Q' of 61 Squadron from Skellingthorpe faced the prospect of ditching into a heavy swell and gale force wind about 35 miles to the west of Guernsey; but they had no choice and only five of their number managed to reach the dinghy before the plane vanished. The Captain considered himself very lucky to get out at all, so rapid was the entry of water that he was carried down a depth of 15 feet before managing to extricate himself from the controls and struggle to an exit. Normally the Lancaster was a fair 'floater' but probably this one was badly damaged in the ditching – in the darkness there was no way of knowing. To aid them 280 Squadron's Warwick 'C' (F/O Williamson) was scrambled from

Davidstow Moor just after noon the same day, acting on a chance 'possible' sighting of a dinghy. This was found in position 4942N 0311W at 1310 hours and an Airborne Lifeboat duly released at 1325. It alighted 30 yards downwind from the dinghy but two of the parachutes did not release, although they partially collapsed, allowing the drogue to check the drift, and then finally blew clear after several minutes so the survivors were then able to reach one of the rocket lines and pull themselves to the lifeboat. This they found in a sorry state, having landed on one side and been pulled over so the engine compartments filled with water, either through the breathers or damaged hatches. From the Warwick the men appeared fatigued and once aboard made no effort to start the engines or make sail; but did stream the heavy drogue and lay hove to on this. 'C's fuel was now low so they were forced to return to base, leaving ten Spitfires in orbit. During the day visibility decreased and at times contact was lost. At 1745 two MTBs came into sight, guided through the darkness by the Spitfires; the survivors were taken aboard and the lifeboat destroyed. The voyage back to Dartmouth may have been uncomfortable but heavenly compared to their recent ordeal.

9 March   When F/L Wilson and his crew took off from Bircham Newton in Hudson 'B' of 279 Squadron at 1340 hours, accompanied by 'K', they were to patrol an area off Haisborough (or Happisburgh), Norfolk in poor conditions and heavy low cloud. The patrol was almost completed when 'B' was directed to a new area where a dinghy had been reported, so 'K' continued its task alone resulting in three survivors from a Liberator of 448 Bomb Group being rescued. 'B's search area was around 5250N 0355E (40 miles west of Texel), but it was not until 1742 that the rear gunner sighted pyrotechnics and a 300 degree change of course brought them over two United States type 5251 dinghies with nine or ten men aboard. At 1750 the lifeboat was successfully dropped 50 yards downwind of the dinghies, both of which managed to reach it within five minutes and all occupants boarded, apparently fit and well. At 1855, when 'B' left, having exceeded PLE, no attempt had been made to start the engines or hoist the sails, although a course had been given. Delayed action sea markers were dropped and a report made.

The next day 'J' (F/O Bedford) and 'G', both of 279 Squadron resumed the operation at first light, later to be joined by 'L' piloted by F/L Wilson. When the search area had been almost completely covered 'L' was detached to investigate one of the HSLs which were also out for a similar purpose, and was relieved to see a lifeboat fastened alongside and two aircraft dinghies on its deck; thus the ten men from the B17 of 447 USAAF Bomb Group sighted by 'B' were saved. 'J' and 'G' not knowing this completed their search pattern and returned to base. The HSL, of 24 A/SR Marine Craft Unit, took the lifeboat in tow at position 5241N 0325E. Thus F/L Wilson and his crew had the satisfaction of seeing the completion of the rescue they'd commenced the previous day.

Subsequent examination of the boat revealed that no use at all had been made of its resources, the survivors not even bothering to unpack and wear the protective clothing; and this in March weather on a very chilly North Sea.

12   'Splash Down' with parachutes still attached

13   The parachutes blow clear and drop from a Mark I

Perhaps they were some of the personnel of Framlingham or Sudbury to whom the Airborne Lifeboat demonstrations had seemed a waste of time and not worth attending. Obviously they were quite confident that A/SR would pluck them off Hitler's doorstep without any effort at all on their part. As a Squadron Leader in A/SR said, 'quite sure they'd be picked up – and so they were – BUT.' Unfortunately the lifeboat did not reach home, HSL 2678 being forced to transfer the tow to another HSL so the survivors could be brought ashore as quickly as possible, landing at Great Yarmouth at 1645. The boat had to be cut adrift when it developed trouble under tow, and was used for target practice.

11 March   A Mosquito was forced to ditch off the northern Adriatic coast of Italy and the plane drifted ashore inside the minefields of the enemy coast. The pilot waded through the shallows, leaving his dead navigator in the wreckage, and from a searching Walrus was spotted waving on the beach. Realising it would be suicide to land close to the shore the Walrus crew set down outside the minefield, launched their rubber dinghy and tried to paddle through the mines to the Mosquito pilot, but found the current far too strong. Meanwhile a Warwick had appeared, complete with Airborne Lifeboat, almost certainly from 293 Squadron. The Captain quickly summed up the situation and dropped his lifeboat alongside the Walrus, whose crew boarded it, cleared away the lines, started the engines and negotiated the minefield into the beach. There they took the stranded pilot aboard, wended a very, very, careful way back to their plane and calmly took off for home base. The lifeboat had to be abandoned.

14 March   281 Squadron were requested to prepare an Airborne Lifeboat to fly to Lagens in the Azores to assist in the search for survivors seen in a dinghy in position 4710N 2220W (almost 1000 miles out into the Atlantic); but no order to proceed was given.

23 March   Whilst not a lifeboat incident this gives an insight into the work of A/SR and the co-operation between different Forces. 'D' of 280 Squadron was out searching a designated area looking for 'float lights'. When two ship's masthead lights were seen; 'D' dropped flares and a distant light on the water was then seen flashing SOS. 'D' replied 'R' (message received and understood) with its landing lights and remained over the position until surface vessels closed. More flares revealed trawlers, one of which signalled by lamp 'All saved'. 'D' replied 'Who are you?' The reply was 'H. M. Trawler'. 'D' then asked 'Are they aircrew?', to which they received the answer 'Yes – Cheerio'. 'D' closed the interchange with 'Goodnight'. Subsequent enquiry revealed that the rescued men were the crew of Sunderland 'M' of 461 Squadron which was attacked and shot down in position 4525N 0958W. Eight men survived the ditching and were picked up from their dinghies at 4442N 1002W (400 miles south-west of Lands End).

8 April   Not a night operation this time but broad daylight in the stormy waters 180 miles south-south-west of Lands End, with two men adrift in a dinghy apiece, and too near to the French coast for comfort. 280 Squadron's 'E' (F/L Chesher) from Davidstow Moor prudently picked up an escort of six Beaufighters before leaving British shores. It was at 1301, in position 4734N 0721W, that they sighted the survivors and dropped them a lifeboat at 1310. It was a successful drop but a trifle too far from the dinghies for easy boarding; only with considerable difficulty was this managed by 1335; after which it took the two men only five minutes to get under way and head towards the Cornish coast. Interception was later made by surface vessels but no details were recorded in the 280 Squadron report.

As Airborne Lifeboats became less of a 'seven days wonder' the reports of operations in which they were used tended to become less detailed and informative, even basic particulars of positions, times and eventual outcome sometimes being omitted.

11 April It was into a moderately rough sea off the north-east coast of Scotland that an Anson from Wick was forced to ditch and Warwick 'P' of 281 Squadron (F/S Corney), took off with its Airborne Lifeboat from the same station at 1925 to attempt a rescue. The dinghy was located at 2002 hours and the lifeboat dropped. Whether the boat was damaged or the parachutes did not release properly is not noted, but the four survivors did eventually manage to board it before being picked up by a Walrus at 2045, which was then unable to take off, possibly due to overload; so it started to taxi home, towing the lifeboat astern. Happily an HSL had also been sent out and this took the Anson crew aboard. What happened to the Walrus and the lifeboat is not related.

27 April 282 Squadron come into the picture with 'C' (F/O Williamson) accompanied by 'Q' (Lt. Vallieres) being called out from Davidstow Moor at 0822 to take part in a search for survivors of Halifax JD 176 of 58 Squadron which had taken off from St Davids on an anti-submarine patrol but forced to ditch at 0515 in 5003N 0771W (just west of the Scilly Isles) following an inexplicable loss of petrol. Fixes and navigation were obviously very good for by 0915 hours, following a remarkable sighting by Rear Gunner F/S J. Davies of the smoke trail of the second Very fired, 'Q' was dropping its lifeboat within 60 yards of the six or seven survivors, who were seen to transfer to it. Its duty done the Warwick then left for base, to land at 1032, leaving Hurricanes to maintain air cover. Until recent publicity regarding research for this book, F/S Davies had been under the impression that the lifeboat was dropped too far distant for the survivors to reach, probably being much too busy watching the sky for unwelcome intruders than following the drama below, so was extremely pleased to learn that the day's effort had been crowned with success. 'C's crew were not too sure about the outcome, possibly being 'down sun' from the dinghy, but the rescued crew had no doubts whatsoever.

F/O Burroughs and his men had a big welcome for the lifeboat when it splashed down with all systems functioning perfectly. In the past few hours they'd had a very difficult time, apart from being shot down. On ditching the immersion switch which should have released the dinghy failed to operate;

though the manual release did when the F/E attacked it; there had been some confusion because ditching drill had taught the crew to await the second impact before operating it – and this time there was only one impact. A fire and minor explosions inside the fuselage made matters even more difficult and immediate evacuation of the aircraft essential. On checking the Captain discovered the ASR operator was missing; search was made for him but the fire and explosions made re-entry of more than a small portion of the body of the plane impossible. The navigator and rear gunner, both badly burned, had escaped onto the starboard wing and did not realise that the dinghy was off the port side, so feared they'd been left, but the others managed to paddle round the front of the plane to take them off. All wore their 'Mae Wests', some of which had inflated automatically, others had to be blown up; all watches had stopped. Shortly after ditching several friendly aircraft were seen and red flares fired, to no avail, so they commenced paddling eastwards, which kept them occupied and warm. The arrival of the Warwick was greeted with cheers. The lifeboat was successfully boarded and all hands helped to get it under way without any difficulties. 'G' 282, which was also out searching, had sighted an HSL in position 4956N 0615W at 1046 and in response to 'Q's radio call commenced homing this vessel onto the lifeboat. W/O J. Smith of Cleethorpes relates that the day after the rescue the F/E went into a bar and was addressed by an unknown airman who said: 'We dropped a lifeboat to some of your boys yesterday'; and was astounded when the Welshman said 'Yes – me.'

29 April   It was late in the evening when 'F' of 279 Squadron (F/O Brown) took off for position 5138N 0325E to search for a dinghy. Later flares and a small light were observed, possibly that of a dinghy radio. In his endeavours to position the momentary gleam the observer inadvertently put pressure on the 'Drop' button shield, which in turn actuated the release so the lifeboat was dropped a quarter a mile from the dinghy's estimated position. Soon afterwards searchlights from Schouwen Island (Holland) swept the area, even illuminating the dinghy on one occasion; 'F' used this dubious aid to drop a message to its occupants saying 'Lifeboat dropped bearing 320 degrees – 1/4 mile from you'. It was too dark to observe further results although the boat was seen floating satisfactorily during later circuits. No further sightings or report filed. BUT on

30 April,   during a search and rescue patrol a P38 sighted two dinghies containing survivors, believed to be from an American bomber, in position 5138N 0325E, which is about 20 miles north of Walcheren (the island to the north of the mouth of the River Schelde). An Airborne Lifeboat was dropped to them in a strong north-westerly wind, and successfully boarded. It is believed that this craft with the men aboard later drifted onto the Dutch coast and that the aircrew were taken prisoner. This operation is quoted in PRO Air 15/598 and has not been traced in the records of any RAF Squadron operating in the area. There are frequent discrepancies in dates of operations as quoted in the memos of Air 15/598 and the Squadron records of Air 27. For the purposes of this book the latter have generally been deemed the more reliable, as they were compiled on the spot.

Subsequent examination of USAAF records suggest that this mission of 30th is a continuation of the 29th's and that a second lifeboat was *not* dropped, which explains why its Squadron was not traced; the survivors were men of a Fortress of 447 Bomb Group.

20 May Following a report that a Flying Fortress had ditched in position 5440N 0540E (some 70 miles west-north-west of Heligoland) search aircraft of 279 squadron took off from Bircham Newton from 1557 hours onwards. The three-quarters Canadian crew of 'K' under F/O Reade was the first to sight the survivors and dropped a lifeboat to them at 1812 and after watching them board it and set a course of 250 degrees at 1835 had to return to base, due to shortage of fuel. In the fading light another Warwick took over surveillance despite poor visibility. At 0600 on the 21st three Danish trawlers were observed to approach the lifeboat, one taking the men aboard and the boat in tow, before setting a course of 100 degrees towards the southern part of the coast of Denmark. W/O Oakes signalled them to change course and put a burst of machine-gun fire across their bows to emphasise the point. This brought all three vessels to a stop. Then from 0855 hours until 1600 hours aerial cover was laid on in the form of four P 47s of the USAAF Emergency Squadron from Boxted doing two-hour stints in pairs. At 0930 HSL 2551 had arrived and taken the survivors aboard, reaching its base at Great Yarmouth at 1640 hours. The sea being too rough for the lifeboat to be towed it was used for target practice. The rescued men were from a B 17 of 100 Bomber Group, piloted by Lt. J. R. Rogers USAAF; he reported being very hospitably received by the Danes who were prepared to remain in the area for two days to await the arrival of the expected rescue craft. At this stage in the War the Royal Navy and the RAF had achieved a famous reputation in occupied Europe for attempting long and dangerous missions and for using every ingenuity and effort to rescue ditched airmen – regardless of nationality.

2 June Two deplorable failures of equipment totally negated the efforts made by two Warwick crews of 276 Squadron from Portreath. Lifeboats were dropped by HF 960 (F/O Virgo) and BV 531 under heavy anti-aircraft fire from shore batteries on Guernsey during the afternoon of this day. The parachutes did not release from the first boat so it was carried away by the strong breeze, and one only opened on the second drop; the lifeboat after hitting the water at considerable speed was extensively damaged and sank. Both planes were hit by flak from the German batteries, but remained in the area long enough to see the RAF pilot they'd come to rescue picked up by a fishing boat from Guernsey; they then destroyed both lifeboats by machine-gun fire before returning to base.

6 June This operation gives an insight into the painstaking monotony of a typical A/SR search. Take off for 'R' (W/O King) of 282 Squadron was at 0813 hours for a 'creeping line ahead' search, using one-mile visibility over an area bounded by 4840N 0457W – 4842N 0425W – 4852N 0503W – 4852 N 0446W.

At 1016 a dinghy was sighted in position 4846N 0447W (not far from Ushant) but contact was lost and not regained until 1140, so that a lifeboat could be released at 1157. This was a very precise drop, the boat landing only 40 yards from the dinghy with its two occupants, who were seen to climb aboard at 1204 hours. The lifeboat was soon under way, probably on one engine only by the estimated speed of 3 knots on a course of 350 degrees true. Although visibility was patchy the sea conditions were good so it is not surprising that a successful rendezvous was later made with surface rescue craft, when it was learned that the men were the three survivors from Lancaster LL 833 of 101 Squadron which had been forced to ditch in the early hours of the same morning.

On this day an American of 78 Fighter Group baled out in this area of the Channel and was rescued, but it is not thought that the two incidents were related; although the following may be the answer.

7 June Started early for Warwick HF 940 (F/O Gamper) of 276 Squadron, stationed at Portreath, with take-off at 0554 hours, to find one man in a dinghy in an approximate position of 4924N 0528W (not far from the search area of the previous day). Success ultimately attended their efforts for the dinghy was located and their lifeboat dropped in position 4925N 0528W. Then things went wrong for one parachute of the cluster failed to release, or snagged and did not collapse, so the boat was blown away downwind. After dropping another dinghy to the unfortunate man HF 940 was forced to return to base. As this incident was on the extreme edge of the tremendous cross-Channel operations following D-Day on the 6th there could have been many naval and other craft in the vicinity, so one can hope there was a successful outcome.

7 June This meagre report concerns Warwick BV 531 (F/O Rushton) of 276 Squadron. Take-off from Portreath was at 2130 hours for a search approximately 20 miles south of the Lizard where nine men were adrift in dinghies. Conditions must have been good for they were vectored direct to the survivors and the lifeboat dropped and successfully boarded by all the men, the crew of a B 17 of 381 Bomb Group. An HSL was also speeding to the rescue so the Warwick returned to base; as it went home so soon it can be assumed that other aircraft were orbiting and would have homed the HSL. This was later confirmed.

8 June A less happy occasion, but fortunately no loss of life. Warwick 'D' of 282 Squadron (F/O Wise) took off from Davidstow Moor to carry out a search around position 4950N 0023W. On the outward flight pressure dropped on the port engine which stopped at 1500 hours, but picked up again; then the starboard engine failed. Control was informed of the circumstances and the crew ordered to ditching stations; unfortunately the plane was already too low to drop its lifeboat. A successful landing was made on the water at 1520 in position 5035N 0246W and all the crew left the aircraft safely. It sank within three minutes and they were adrift in the Channel, west of Portland Bill. Ten minutes later two Spitfires were seen and their attention attracted by firing two distress flares. The fighters returned within 20 minutes homing two RAF seaplane tenders, Nos 1506 and 1515, which picked up the survivors at 1601. Two appears to have been their lucky number that day; a bonus on the rescue was the pick-up on the way home of a Mustang pilot of 357 Fighter Group (USAAF) based at Leiston.

13 June   Catalina T 9816, of the Canadian Squadron 162, piloted by W/Cdr. G. Chapman, was east of the Faeroe Islands, when the periscopes of a submerged submarine were sighted just after 1000 hours; an immediate attack was made with the result that U-715 sank bows first with several of the crew jumping overboard, but this successful attack was not accomplished without severe damage to the Catalina and a ditching was inevitable in position 6244N 0166W. It sank within 20 minutes, just allowing the two dinghies to be got out. One was badly holed and the other burst on inflation. Two of the crew boarded the holed dinghy whilst the other six hung on to the lifelines. They were soon seen by a Liberator and then by a Sunderland, both of which flew away again. The Warwick of 281 Squadron, skippered by P/O Duthie, which they had summoned then appeared and released its Airborne Lifeboat which splashed down about 100 yards distant. The Catalina navigator P/O Waterbury managed to shed some of his outer garments and swam to the lifeboat and more than an hour later brought it back to his companions, although too late for the F/E who had lost his hold and drifted away. Even after boarding the lifeboat their plight was not much improved for it was damaged and barely afloat. Another Warwick then dropped Lindholme gear, but the connecting lines parted and the major parts, including the inflatable dinghy, were lost. Fortunately the survivors managed to remain aboard the lifeboat, even though the deck was awash, until an A/SR launch appeared to take them back to Lerwick in the Shetlands; unfortunately the two W/Ops succumbed to exposure on the way in.

14 June   This was a sad operation for Warwick 'G' (F/O Mathieson) of 282 Squadron. They took off from Davidstow Moor at 1626 hours for a flight to the mouth of the English Channel, south of the Scillies, where Liberator 'V' 53 was reported down in position 4920N 0600W. In company with two Mosquitos they eventually found a Carley (?) float at 1650 in position 4519N 0603W. Although no survivors could be seen the lifeboat was dropped in case any men might be lying unseen in the bottom of the float. This was in vain for a frigate later brought to the scene by the Mosquitos signalled there were no survivors on the 'floats' and took the lifeboat on board. One would not expect a rigid raft such as a Carley float to be carried on an aircraft so the plural used by the frigate suggests that 'it' or 'they' were actually aircraft dinghies.

20 June   Another operation in which the eventual outcome is not known. 280 Squadron's Warwick 'L' (W/O Delgazio) was airborne from Thornaby at 1333 hours bound for a position off the Dutch island of Texel where men were reported adrift in dinghies. With a heavy fighter escort two 'Q' type dinghies with seven occupants were eventually sighted in position 5327N 0338E and the Lifeboat dropped to them from 400 feet to land within 20 yards of the survivors who were able to board easily as all systems functioned perfectly. The altitude of 400 feet instead of the recommended 750 suggests that cloud level was very low and as there is no mention of enemy intervention this could explain why no outcome is mentioned in the reports. As it was not unusual for HSLs, RMLs, MTBs and MGBs to operate almost within sight of the enemy coast the men could have been picked up but no operational link has been established. It is known that Lancaster ED938 of 635 Squadron was shot down in this area on 13 June so these men could well have been the survivors.

21/22 June   This operation absorbed most of the aircraft of 279 Squadron from Bircham Newton. On the 21st 'J' (Simpson) and 'G' were circling a dinghy in position 5439N 0540E (120 miles west of Heligoland) until relieved by 'Q' (W/O Palmer) with an Airborne Lifeboat. This was dropped and alighted 50 yards downwind of the survivors, but one parachute failed to release so the boat blew away downwind and in spite of hard paddling the men in the dinghy were unable to catch up with it. Presumably this was late in the day for the report is resumed on the 22nd when 'K' (F/O Carmichael), 'Z' (F/S Hill), 'U' (F/L Welpby), 'D' (F/L Ashby) and 'B' (P/O Curtis) were out. 'U' made the first sighting at 0700 hours reporting a lifeboat, a 'Q' type dinghy and a Lindholme, so just to be helpful another Lindholme was dropped whilst search was made for a rescue craft. An HSL was contacted and air cover maintained until it homed on to the dinghies and took four men aboard at 1050 hours; without doubt these were the sole survivors of the crew of a B 24 (Liberator) of 445 Bomb Group shot down on 21st.

24 June   Whilst in circuit over Sumburgh (Shetland), after a transit flight from Wick, 'U' of 281 Squadron was requested to proceed to a position almost equidistant between the Shetlands, the Faeroes and Alesund in Norway, where a Liberator was circling the survivors of Catalina 162 P which had been shot down whilst attacking a U-Boat. The crew of the flying boat were found in position 6255N 0001E at 1250 hours and the lifeboat dropped downwind of them at 1255. David E. Duthie, of Manchester, the pilot of the Warwick, is able to add to the official report as he later met the six rescued men at Wick. 'The navigator swam to the lifeboat and boarded it in order to row to his comrades. This must have been quite a feat for the lifeboat's back was broken; but it remained afloat until we left the scene. Later, an HSL believed to be 2723 arrived from Lerwick to pick them up.' On the Warwick's return flight a group of men seen in the water were identified as survivors of U-1225, which the Catalina had attacked; so Lindholmes were dropped to them by both 'U' and 'V' which was in company. Seventeen German sub-mariners were later picked up by surface craft.

These few words compiled from a very brief entry in the Squadron Daily Report and supplemented by a letter from the Warwick's Captain are but a prelude to one of the most horrifying, yet indomitable, rescues of the survivors of a warplane's ditching ever made; the whole episode resulting in the award of a posthumous VC. The following paragraphs are as near to a full reporting of the whole operation as can be obtained from various official records as well as researches personally and by other interested parties.

Canso A F9754P of 162 Squadron RCAF serving at Wick took off early in the morning on a routine operational patrol over the hostile northern waters in the Faeroes to Norwegian coastline area north of the Shetland Isles. An uneventful day followed until just after the return flight home had begun in the evening, when a U-boat was spotted. At that time of the year in these northern latitudes daylight lasts the entire twenty-four hours so with the sun still well up the crew of U-1225 sighted Catalina only a minute after it had commenced its attack run from five miles away. The submarine's 'flak' guns opened fire at extreme range and almost immediately scored hits knocking out first the aerials and then severely damaging one of the wings to the extent that the starboard engine caught fire. F/L David Hornell of Ontario, Canada, at 34 was rather older than most pilots so could not be accused of youthful bravado in continuing to press home his attack with the utmost determination. The flames rapidly spread along the damaged wing and smoke from this, as well as from a cannon shell which had burst inside the fuselage, filled the cockpit making breathing and seeing very difficult. In many ways a flying boat was at considerable disadvantage when attacking a violently resisting surfaced submarine. The basis of its entire design is a buoyant hull which will speed over the water for take-off, therefore it can have no downward pointing weaponry beyond the nose guns in a diving attack; so it was not until close range had been achieved that retaliatory fire was opened and hits scored on the enemy's conning tower. Approaching now from directly abeam the Canso, needing all the pilot's strength and skill to maintain the attack, roared over the U-boat and released its entire load of depth charges, two of which achieved a perfect straddle, each within a fathom of the pressure hull. Aided by the sudden release of the considerable weight of the explosives F/L Hornell tried to bring the nose of the plane up in attempt to limp home but the added stress on the damaged wing caused the burning engine to fall completely away. With half the wing gone and the flames spreading towards the fuselage it was now obvious that there was no alternative but to ditch, so with only 250 feet of altitude the pilot trimmed the plane for an into the wind landing on the relatively calm sea. The appearance was deceptive for a series of heavy impacts with the swells were experienced before way stopped and the two aircraft dinghies could be launched and vital supplies transferred in the few minutes before the amphibian sank.

Now the nightmare began. One dinghy was completely useless so all eight of the crew were forced to rely on the remaining 'four man' one. Seven were just able to get into it, but the eighth had to hang on to the side. Although high summer the water temperature would be only around the 40–50 °F mark, for the Gulf Stream/North Atlantic Drift has shed much of its warmth by the time it reaches the Faeroes and normally survival time in such waters might be measured in minutes rather than hours.

To add to their troubles the wind began to freshen with the swells building up and commencing to break, tossing the tiny dinghy in sickeningly lurching swoops. Fortunately their luck had not entirely deserted them for around midnight, when the sun was at its lowest a Norwegian Catalina of 333 Squadron, Captained by Lt. Carl Krafft, spotted red 'tracer' from three miles distant, turned towards it, and then flew almost over them and plainly saw seven men in RAF uniforms. Although homeward bound this plane, after sending a signal to base, dropped flame floats and sea markers and stayed circling the dinghy until its limit of endurance had been reached, despite a cloud base now down to some 50 feet and experiencing extreme difficulty in banking the Catalina with a wing span of 104 feet between the clouds and the sea. When it finally touched down back at Sullum Voe it had been airborne for 17 hours and 40 minutes, including 13 hours circling the survivors' dinghy, a monumental flight involving 100% concentration the whole time.

During the waiting time Sgt. F. St Laurent succumbed to the terrible conditions and was lowered into the sea so that Sgt. Scott could take his place although he was by now terribly weakened and suffering from exposure, miraculously he managed to hang on to life until almost mid morning of the next day, when his body too was committed to the deep.

It was shortly after this that a Warwick hove into sight, but could not locate the dinghy owing to bad visibility and radar equipment 'on the blink'; but its companion spotted them instantly although the wind had increased to 50 knots with very high waves. After dropping the smoke floats on a dummy run it released its Mark IA airborne lifeboat. Let the Warwick's pilot as spokesman for the crew take up the tale.

> The drop was a good one in that the lifeboat splashed down quite close to the dinghy, but unfortunately, although it was not observed, there must have been a parachute malfunction for when we came round again the boat's back appeared to be broken. Despite this one of the survivors swam to the wreckage and managed to paddle it back to his companions. Having done all we could and being well down on fuel we turned and headed for base in company with our companion 281V which did not carry a lifeboat. On sighting the U-boat survivors we both dropped Lindholmes to them.

Within 20 minutes of the Warwick's departure the airborne lifeboat broke up and had to be abandoned for the overcrowded dinghy and although realising that other aid would be on its way the survivors began to have serious doubts if it would arrive in time. The failure of the lifeboat drop had been a bitter blow to their hopes. All through the long, soaked, convulsively shivering, hours of their dreadful ordeal F/L Hornell, although very weak and almost sightless, worked hard to maintain the spirits of his crew, leading them in feeble singing and exercises to keep some movement in their bloodstreams and limbs; but it was not until mid-afternoon that relief came over the horizon in the form of HSL 2507 guided to them by an aircraft. Three planes claimed this honour, a Warwick, a Liberator and a Sunderland; probably all three were closely involved and within minutes of flying time of each other. The story now continues as seen by HSL 2507.

> At our Shetland briefing just after midnight we were given an aiming point not far from the Arctic Circle and set off as rapidly as we could. Our craft was a Vosper with Thornycroft engines, not one of the fastest type in the Service but considered much the better sea boat for these far north waters.

Unfortunately ours had seen an awful lot of hard sea miles and soon we experienced trouble with one of the engines and the Skipper was faced with making a decision to either press on with one engine or make course back for base. In reality there was no question at all, we just could not leave those blokes and hope another craft would reach them in time. As the weather deteriorated speed had to be further reduced and in the wallowing; climbing up one swell and swooping down its back; seasickness set in for some of the crew. In the early afternoon we had reached the position given by the 333 Squadron Catalina; of course there was no sign of the dinghy and after a conference on possible wind and current drift a search was started which had only just got under way when a Warwick was seen in the distance. Owing to the violent motion it was impossible to read the aircraft's morse signals so F/O Garrett decided the situation was desperate enough to warrant breaking radio silence. We immediately got the 'Follow me' instruction and headed off after the plane, plugging away on the one engine and praying it would not pack up. Happily the distance to cover was not too great and a small cheer went up as the yellow dinghy was sighted. Getting the almost helpless survivors aboard was very difficult in the rough seas but it was finally accomplished without loss or injury and we turned thankfully for home. Despite all our attentions F/L Hornell died five hours later. The remaining survivors were subsequently landed at Lerwick and whisked off to hospital.

There was an ironic twist to the rescue in that F/O Garrett was reprimanded for breaking radio silence, but also awarded the MBE; and F/L David Hornell was awarded a posthumous Victoria Cross.

29 June   At 0534 hours, Beaufighter 'S' of 489 Squadron reported it was over a dinghy in position 5203N 0400E (close in to the coast just north of the Hook of Holland). Accordingly Warwick 'W' 280 (F/O Myatt) took off from Strubby and proceeded to the location with a fighter escort of two P 47s. Whilst searching close in to the coast for the 'pinprick' on the surface of the sea it encountered heavy and accurate anti-aircraft fire, was hit in the port engine and forced to head back to base; unfortunately it had not reported in some seven hours later. Meanwhile other fighters, returning to base, had spotted the dinghy ten miles off the Hook of Holland so 'H' and 'W' of 279 Squadron and an HSL were sent out, the former with a heavy fighter escort. At 1215 the 279 aircraft sighted their objective and at the same time observed enemy surface vessels in the distance. 'H' (F/O Carmichael) circled and dropped her lifeboat whilst 'W' went off to seek an HSL. The Australian Beaufighter pilot in the dinghy was paddling frantically to reach the lifeboat and had only just boarded it when the rescue craft, HSL 132 (F/O Clarke) from 24 A/SR, Gorleston (Great Yarmouth), arrived, so he was quite happy to transfer to this from the smaller boat. The HSL only stopped to recover the body of the navigator before heading back to England, leaving the lifeboat to be destroyed from the air rather than have it fall into enemy hands.

A minor contradiction appears regarding this incident. According to a report filed by F/O Clarke, the survivor was in the Airborne Lifeboat at position 5157N 0342E, quite a distance further south and west than the original position, and his companion's body was recovered from the sea not far away.

During this time 'W' 280, which had last been seen with its port engine smoking, had ditched at 5205N 0225E (30 miles east-south-east of Great Yarmouth). The leader of the US 56 Fighter Group returning home had reported being over a dinghy containing several men, so an HSL stationed at Felixstowe was contacted and given the position. 65 USAAF Control Wing at Saffron Walden then gave the fighter leader a course to intercept the HSL from Felixstowe, which he did and led it to the Warwick crew for a successful rescue.

29 June   To illustrate the hazards of A/SR apart from the weather etc., in response to a call from 'E for Easy' of 390 Bomber Group (piloted by F/L Edgar W. Moody), timed 1135 hours, stating that ditching was imminent, 'Q' and 'G' of 280 Squadron were sent to a position 150 miles east-south-east of Flamborough Head, and within 20 miles of the Dutch coast, where eight men were reported in two dinghies, but was unsuccessful in its search. An HSL meanwhile made the pick-up several miles away and took the ten survivors on board to make all speed back to base at Great Yarmouth. This was the day HSL 2551's luck ran out and its outstanding career came to an end. It would appear that the position given to the Warwicks was not very accurate for 2551 was still very close to the Dutch coast after picking up its human cargo when it was attacked by enemy aircraft believed to be either JU 88, ME 210 or ME 410 and set on fire. Four of its crew were killed and two of the American survivors were unaccounted for having been either lost in the strafing or killed during the action when their plane was shot down; seven others were injured. The remaining 15 men took to the boat's Carley float and various aircraft dinghies, happily soon to be picked up by HSL's 158 (F/O Sutch) and 184 (F/O Clark) from Gorleston and brought safely into their home base.

A naval surgeon was taken out aboard HSL 2679 (F/O Herrick) and with two American medical officers flown out in a Walrus transferred to HSL 158 to assist the HSL's sick bay attendant. The sea conditions were such that the Walrus had a hazardous landing and was unable to take off again, so was escorted by HSL 2555 (F/O Muir) as it taxied all the way to Yarmouth.

Here again there are variations in reporting; at the official enquiry into the loss of HSL 2551 it was stated by one witness that HSL 158 had 15 survivors and one body aboard, another mentioned ten survivors, another ten survivors and one body and that two American airmen, believed to be the navigator and the rear gunner, were drowned or killed in action. As there is no listing of USAAF survivors in the file it is now very difficult to check these statements. What is certain is that Cpl. Stewart, LAC Sykes and LAC Woods of HSL 2551 were lost with their Skipper.

But with the help from a researcher (Sid Harvey) into USAAF operations a few more details have emerged. Flying Fortress 42/97830 was forced to ditch about ten miles off the Dutch coast. The pilot, 1st Lt. E. W. Moody, was killed but the rest of the crew escaped from the plane before it sank, although 2nd Lt. J. S. Mayall Jnr was drowned whilst swimming from one liferaft to another.

Then reading between the lines and appreciating from experiences of both German warfare and the North Sea, and digging deeper into the recollections of contemporaries from the June 1942 days, it would seem that the skipper of HSL 2551, F/L Lindsay, and his crew were not actually on duty at the A/SR base on the corner of Baker Street and Riverside Road in Gorleston when the news came through about the Flying Fortress crew, but learning that the other 'Crash' boats were already out after other ditched airmen he called his men together and soon their plumed wake was heading out between the piers, leaving the drawn aside naval boom wallowing in their wash. The coastline of East Anglia is fringed by offshore sandbanks with 'Gats' or passages through which vessels can pass to reach the relatively open water. Some of these sands dry out at low water, especially with the twice monthly spring tides, whilst others treacherously hidden await unsuspecting passing vessels. The local lifeboat crews and fishermen know the Gats well and also several other minor channels which can be navigated if the vessel, tide and sea conditions are all compatible; but 2551 would have had to stick to the major, swept, fairway before setting course for the given position just off the coast of Holland. A 63-foot 'Whaleback' draws about four feet of water when stationary but does pull her stern down at high speed so it would have been with some minor trepidation that F/L Lindsay unhesitatingly took his craft and crew into the German minefield where the USAAF men from the B 17 of 390 BG were helpless in their two dinghies. Cecil Featherstone later described the rescue operation:

> We were some twenty miles off the Dutch coast, clear sky, sea fairly calm and good visibility, too good in some senses. Instructions were radioed to us to proceed to pick up an American aircrew in a dinghy. On plotting this position I made it almost inside Ijmuiden harbour. After consulting with the Skipper I asked the wireless operator to call back for a check. It came back exactly the same. I couldn't believe this, so asked again. I was told in no uncertain terms to get on with the job and not to disbelieve their accuracy. So it was tin hats on and in we went. German soldiers could be seen walking along the harbour walls; why they did not fire is a mystery, but sure enough there was the dinghy with eight Americans. Over went the crash nets and all eight were hauled aboard as quickly as possible, as was the body of 2nd Lt. Mayall; then with the three engines flat out we headed due west.

Overhead the usual slight haze was sufficient for two escorting USAAF fighters to maintain contact but not enough for enemy aircraft to hide in; although there can be little doubt that the operation was being watched from a very discreet distance. So all went well for about ten minutes by which time a freshening wind had brought up thicker clouds, but these were fairly high with no sea mist to conceal the wake of an HSL heading for home with the rescued Americans as if the hounds of hell were after it. As indeed they were in the form of the JU 88 (or ME 210 or ME 410) which came diving down on them within a few minutes of the escorting fighters being forced to leave because their limit of endurance had been reached. Their replacements were not yet in evidence, which is probably why the German pilot seized his opportunity and came down with all guns blazing. In that initial attack 2551 was not only rendered helpless but shattered and set ablaze from stem to stern. Those who could took to the water but one American, Sgt. G. S. Downie Jnr (ball turret gunner), was killed, F/O D. R. Simpson (bombardier), and Staff Sgt. D. J. Beeson (top turret gunner) were wounded as well as at least one of the HSL's crew killed and up to seven of the others badly wounded. With the remaining half of his total complement assisting, the Skipper led the efforts to get the injured onto anything which would float sufficiently to support them and was last seen swimming away to fetch a dinghy which had drifted away a little distance. Other HSLs from Gorleston were also active in the eastern part of the North Sea, for there had been a heavy RAF raid the previous night, and picked up the brief attack report which was all the 'Sparks' had been able to get off. Immediately two of them, 158 and 184, headed for the casualty and were fortunate in making a quick sighting and thus enabled to take the survivors from the cold waters, and pick up the body of F/L George Lindsay, who had died of exposure. All were later landed at Great Yarmouth, some spending considerable time in the Naval Hospital there. Lindsay's body was landed at HMS *Miranda*, the 'sweeper' unit, based across the river from the RAF boats, in and around the former 'Klondyke' wharf and the herring oil reduction plant. An Honour Guard of four sailors with reversed weapons was posted around the coffin and the entire base came to Attention when at 1030 hours on 4 July the 68ft HSL 2679 (F/O Herrick) came alongside to accept its sad load and lead the cortege over the harbour bar at 1045. It was a fine 'crisp' day with a light south-easterly breeze as the convoy threaded its way out between the battered wooden piers and headed out in a lively sea through the familiar swept channels between the sandbanks and the protective minefields to a rendezvous some miles off the coast escorted by HSLs 184, 158, 2555 and RMLs 499 and 498.

Aboard the accompanying craft were those relatively well survivors of HSL 2551, many Base friends, Sq. Ldr. Lawrence (C/O 24 A/SRU), Sq. Ldr. Scott (16 Group), Sq. Ldr. Lawledge (?) (C/O 969 Squadron), Lt. Cdr. Harbutt (SOO – FOIC Great Yarmouth), F/O Herrick, F/O Clark, F/O Sutch and Capt. Croft (USAAF) with other associated RAF and USAAF officers and naval officers from the three Great Yarmouth bases HMS *Watchful*, *Midge* and *Miranda*. As the lead boat stopped engines the other craft formed a circle around her and joined in the Committal Service, restarting their engines in turn to pass slowly by to cast their tributes at the spot where the first wreaths floated. Overhead three Coastal Command Warwicks led a dipping salute 'fly past' of three United States Flying Fortresses and three Thunderbolts. LAC Wood, ex-W/Op of 2551, was buried at Bungay.

The Board of Enquiry report does not reconcile the statements of ten survivors picked up and two American airmen killed or drowned, with the report that HSL 158 had 15 survivors aboard and the mention also of ten US survivors, one injured. There is no listing of the American survivors.

During June 1944, 279 Squadron flew 112 search and/or rescue sorties, logging a total of 434 day and three night operational hours over the North Sea and English Channel. This was the peak period for A/SR operations, although many more fine rescues were carried out before, and even after, the end of the War. It is noteworthy to observe that 24 Air/Sea Rescue Unit at Gorleston celebrated their 300th pick-up with a party at the Cliff Hotel on 11 November 1944, at which time there were 13 HSLs on the Gorleston strength. A reunion of men of the Gorleston and Lowestoft bases was held at the same hotel over the Armistice weekend of 11–13 November 1988, 44 years later to the day.

That more operational Airborne Lifeboats came into or were dropped within the Great Yarmouth area than to any other port emphasises the importance of the No. 24 A/SR Unit which during its operational life at Gorleston lists the following HSLs and other craft: 108 (lost by enemy action), 125, 132, 134, 144, 149, 158*, 168, 184, 185, 1679, 2550, 2551 (lost by enemy action), 2555*, 2556*, 2559, 2560*, 2572, 2579, 2594*, 2616, 2631*, 2677*, 2678, 2679*, 2691*, 2694*, 2696*, 2706 (lost in action), 2707*. (Those with asterisk were on strength at the time of the 300th pickup.) Much of the USAAF bomber flight paths was over this area, as was a high proportion of the Royal Air Force's operations.

5 How the Lifeboats Were Built

A complex craft like the Airborne Lifeboat, built to critical standards of purpose, dimensions and weight called for considerable planning to put into quantity production; there had to be a stack of blueprints covering every detail of construction from the keel to the smallest gimp pin; every item had to have an exact specification; else the end results coming from of a number of scattered boatyards would have varied considerably, thereby causing endless confusion and frustration when the boats went operational. A nucleus of highly skilled labour was also necessary to interpret the drawings and do,the 'laying off' necessary before actual building could start. The writer can speak only of the methods used on the yard at which he worked; other firms may have done things differently but the end result had to be the same, standardisation had to be the keynote of wartime production. This was not always easy for traditional boatbuilders who tend to be highly individualistic, many of the older journeymen still being disciples of the discipline 'Let your eye be your guide'; though even that code still had a place, especially in 'fairing up' and finishing off. Unfortunately there were too few skilled boatbuilders to meet the demands of the new Service craft necessary to pursue the War to a successful conclusion, so dilution of labour was a necessity with many men from other wood trades coming onto boat work for the first time in their lives; suddenly having to forget about 'squares and levels' and think instead of 'curves and bevels'. Many women also joined the industry, some in such work as cleaning out but others becoming very proficient woodworkers, mechanics, painters, electricians etc. in a remarkably short space of time.

The writer, having been concerned mainly with building small naval craft and ships' lifeboats since the outbreak of the War, as well as their repair and equipping, was drafted early in 1944 to the boatyard at which he'd served the first five of a seven years' apprenticeship, and was amazed at the extent and concentration of the work being carried out in sheds, which in happier times had been used for building and maintaining holiday yachts and cruisers. The yard, fortunately, had a high reputation for building quality boats, including One Design classes of racing dinghies and punts, so the principles and practice of complicated drawings, standardisation and precise scantlings were not difficult to embrace. Around the open central wet dock new sheds and a large hanger had been erected and in these as well as in the older ones Motor Torpedo Boats, Harbour Defence Launches, Motor Gunboats and High Speed Rescue Launches for the RAF were on the slips. Airborne Lifeboats had to be sandwiched into a section of what had been the 'Long Shop', next to the wood machining mill, with the stores to the east and one of the covered wet docks to the west. Coming from London's 'blitzed' dockland it was a wonderfully peaceful place to work, even if Jerry had strafed it during the previous autumn. Coming back also meant meeting again many old friends; but under very different working conditions. Gone were the peacetime days of starting when the wall clock showed the hour and downing tools when the minute hand was noticeably past the appropriate time – and eating our 'elevenses' and 'fourses' as we worked. Now there was a timeclock to punch, ten-minute tea breaks morning and afternoon and a cooked midday meal in the canteen instead of sandwiches in the Mess Room. The hours now were longer: 7.30 am to 5.30 pm each weekday, occasionally Sundays for an urgent job, plus an hour or more's travelling at each end of the day. Firewatching and Home Guard duties had to be fitted into the leisure hours, so it was small wonder that many of us spent half the lunch hour and most of the train journey in sleep.

Initially assigned to planking up Mark Is on one of the eight building berths, the author soon dropped into the work and found the pattern of labour to be, broadly, one boatbuilder and two ancillary workers to each hull or section of construction, though very flexibly operated to suit the flow of available labour, work and materials. But there were several stages to be gone through before building the hull could actually commence, so it may be as well to follow all the steps from the designs to the completed boat.

When a new set of drawings comes onto the yard they have to be 'proved' by the foreman, by reproducing them in full size, in French chalk, on the 'matt black' painted mould loft floor – an almost sacred area – plimsols only and 'DON'T walk on the chalk lines'. It's also a great place to develop a dose of 'housemaid's knee'. This scaling up usually calls for some uncomplimentary remarks about the designer; such as 'how does the ——— expect us to make a piece of wood do that without breaking' etc. No one pays much regard to this; it's all part of the age old game of rivalry between the 'brains' and the 'brawn'. I know, I've been in both positions. Although whether this actually happened with Uffa Fox's drawings I don't know, I wasn't there then, but I expect so. The reason for this full-sized drawing is to 'fair' the lines accurately, for to make up moulds etc. directly from a 1:12 blueprint would be to invite errors, for even the finest pencil line can be 1/4″ thick when scaled up.

The 'lines' of a boat are composed of three separate views of and through the hull. In practice none of these can stand alone; they have to 'prove' each other. The 'plan' is as if the hull were seen from above, cut horizontally in equal layers; these are called 'waterlines'. The 'elevation' shows the hull as if it were cut vertically from fore to aft all the way along from the centreline in equally spaced divisions; the resulting lines named 'buttocks'; this dimension also gives the keel and sheer lines. The third view, the 'section' is as if the hull were cut from port to starboard vertically, at predetermined positions which are not necessarily equal. Note that the forward stations are 27″ apart in Plate **14** whilst the aft ones are 30″, with 12″ subdivisions at bow and stern. By cross-referencing the three drawings it is obvious that what is a series of athwartships boat shaped lines on the section shows as straight lines on both the plan and elevation. Conversely the same applies to the waterlines and buttocks where

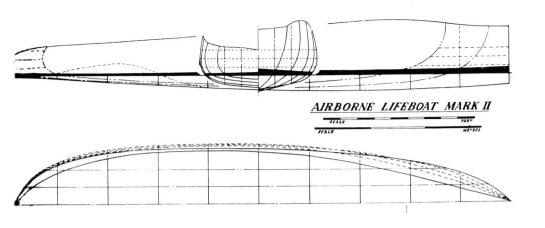

14a   'The Lines' showing section, elevation and plan, with stations, buttocks and waterlines of Mark II

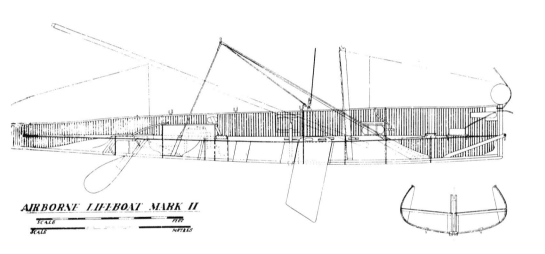

14b   Diagrams to show construction and fitting positions of Mark II

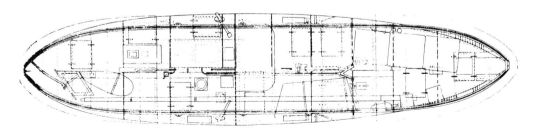

14c   Deck layout of Mark II. Planned range 500 miles

15   *Half the building line at Broads-Haven (J Turner)*

they appear on the other views, the waterlines LWL, 1LL, 2LL and crosspole being straight athwartships on the section, straight lengthwise on the elevation but long flowing curves on the plan. The buttocks are straight verticals, 8″ apart, on the section, longitudinal curves on the elevation and long straight lines on the plan. Thus the beam can be more accurately measured at LWL and above on the waterlines but vertically on the buttocks as well below LWL. Take station 5 as an example: on the section the beam at crosspole is exactly the same as the outside line on station 5 on the plan, with 2LL, 1LL and LWL all appearing at the same distances from either the vertical or horizontal centre lines on the views; whilst the buttocks A, B and C are translated from straight verticals on the section to long curves on the elevation. Initially this may seem a little difficult to follow but it is the only way to understand the precise location of positions on compound curves.

Once the points, i.e. waterlines at stations, depths at buttocks etc. have been marked on the mould loft floor, long springy wooden battens, held on locations by 'hutchicks' (movable wooden grips), are used to join appropriate points without humps or hollows; this is known as 'fairing'. Because of scaling up, two perspectives which should give an identical position for a given point frequently show a discrepancy on the floor and the skill of a good 'lofter' lies in an accurate reconciliation, taking a little in here, giving a little out there, always in the knowledge that to alter a waterline on the section will also mean moving it on the plan, probably over a number of stations. In translation from drawing to floor there can only be one correct interpretation; finding it by adjustments in any or all the three dimensions without provoking distortions is the secret of the lofter's craft; but is can be terribly hard on the knees. You will notice on the illustrations that Uffa Fox introduced another complication, a 'diagonal'; this is normal in naval architecture. Here the diagonal commences at the centre line on the section, at a point 16″ above LWL and from there declines at an angle through the turn of the bilges on the stations. This is another cross-reference. If all the points at which this line cuts the stations were translated to the plan the result should yield another 'fair' outline; thus complicating matters by the use of a fourth dimension but improving accuracy at the turn of the bilges which so frequently seem to have a critical shape midway between a buttock and a waterline. I remember one 65-foot seagoing yacht we laid off, in peacetime, had three diagonals to reconcile to the maze of other chalk lines on the mould loft floor.

Once the lines have been faired the boatbuilders can make up the moulds around which the hull can be constructed. These consist of light wooden formers, the exact shape of the inside of the hull at certain stations and can clearly be seen inside the first hull on Plate **15**. In my early days wooden boats were generally built right way up but when using double or treble skin planking it is easier to work small boats inverted; and today, with mechanical handling available, more and larger boats are built this way. The Plate shows one half of the Mark II building line at Herbert Woods's Broads-Haven Yard. In this, sturdy stools serve as supports for a broad plank base roughly following the extreme outline of the hull, with the inverted moulds firmly secured at their respective positions. The moulds are far enough above the base boards to allow the stem and stern posts to be secured, yet still leaving working room for planking to the gunwale level. This photograph illustrates beautifully the progress of the hull through four stages of construction which would follow on from making up the keel, stem and stern post assembly. Both the latter with their respective aprons would have had their plank rebates chiselled out to the correct depth and angle on the bench before being attached to the keel; which would also have been rebated (rabbetted) with changing bevels to accommodate the differing angles of the planking along its length; thus leaving a minimum amount of fairing and reconciliation to be done on the building berth. These prime members were fastened to each other with brass screws, laminated wooden knees being used for reinforcing, through clenched with copper fastenings.

Of the ten men in the photograph seen working on Mark II hulls only two are boatbuilders, another two are apprentices (or 'boys') the remainder coming from allied trades. The other five building berths, which were to the right of the picture, had a dozen men, and it can be safely assumed that at least another five (some of them ladies) would have been engaged on bench work or in the mill preparing wood, part of their time anyway for the lifeboats; regrettably none of the 'ladies' are shown for they were very much members of the teams.

The reverse sheer line and considerable tumblehome are obvious, as is the supporting staging beneath and around the moulds of the first hull, which has the keel and stem assembly trued up and secured to the building matrix. The pre-bevelled deck riser (or stringer) of rock elm has been steamed until supple and fitted into slots already cut into the moulds, and fixed with brass screws into housings in the aprons, stem and stern posts. This is the stoutest of the longitudinals seen passing along the turn of the bilge; the other, lighter, ribands over the rest of the hull are temporary, having a dual purpose; firstly they tie the moulds firmly into their respective relative positions, and secondly, by having slots precisely cut into their outward facing surfaces ensure the accurate positioning of the $3/8'' \times 1/4''$ rock elm timbers when they are steam bent in at 1 3/4'' centres; which would be the next operation on this hull. The wood for these would have been carefully selected for straightness of grain, then sawn and machine planed to exact dimensions. Just out of the picture stood a long wooden box on waist high trestles, beneath the centre of which was a metal cylinder atop a burner fed with bottled gas. Steam from the cylinder rose into the base of the box (known locally as a 'kell' or kiln) and circulated freely around the timbers which were to be bent as they lay spaced out on the metal racks inside the kell. Some there are who hold the opinion that ideally wood could be bent better by boiling rather than steaming, believing that it permitted a higher moisture penetration and thus allowed the individual cells to slide over each other more easily, but steaming was almost universally used throughout Norfolk.

More often than not production was behind schedule, not only on our yard but also on all the others, judging by correspondence on file at the Public Record Office, though seldom through building causes. Herbert Woods wrote some very irate letters to the Ministries of Aircraft Production and Supply urging immediate release of necessary materials so that his current contracts for 64 Airborne Lifeboats and five High Speed Launches could be commenced – and later, proceeded with. This same situation apparently prevailed at most boatyards during the War, due mainly to the many conflicting demands on very scarce materials; although the allegedly overpaid and underworked 'paper shufflers' in far distant offices came in for most of the criticism where shop floor workers were concerned. I, too, well remember our anger and frustration in my London yard when, with an urgent order for ten boats for the Admiralty we had to wait for silver spruce rejected by the aircraft industry before we could get on with the job. Undoubtedly the boys in light blue needed those Mosquitos just as much as the dark blue lads needed the boats. It was very frustrating though. Uffa Fox expressed himself more forcefully by appending the following four lines in his own handwriting to a drawing sent to Sir Stafford Cripps in an effort to get Airborne Lifeboats into production:

> The Bee is such a busy soul
> It has no time for birth control;
> That is why, at times like these,
> There are so many sons of 'B's.

On withdrawal from the kell a hot timber would be passed directly over to the building jig; the receiver to set one end into the pre-cut housing in the keel and then align the timber in the appropriate slot in the first riband before fastening it to the keel with a 1″ brass panel pin, positioning it so that it would be clear of where the final fastening copper nail would come through. Then the still hot timber would be gently, but firmly, eased downwards in the ribands and stringer slots towards the gunwale, being secured on the way, where necessary, by 3/4″ oval brads. A third worker would assist by holding a 'dolly' beneath the springy ribands whilst his colleague drove in the brads. A similar process would be going on at the other side of the hull, the work progressing almost in parallel down both sides of the boat. Any over length of timber would be cut off with Rolcut secateurs, the pieces of useful size being retained for resteaming and use at other positions in the hull where short ends might be required, such as a propeller tunnel or at the extremes of bow or stern. The unplanked sections of the second hull illustrate clearly the closeness and precision of the timbers. The lad at the kell had to be careful to load the material accordingly to the varying lengths required at different places along the boat, in order to make best usage of the wood, and then extract them in the correct order; as well as keep a sharp eye on the quality and quantity of the steam.

On the next jig the first layer of 1/8″ mahogany diagonal planking is being fixed, each plank having a maximum width of 3″ at or between the gunwale and the bilge, and tapering from thence to approximately 2″ at the keel. This planking up is usually done in sections so as to preserve the correct angle of lay, one plank being fastened at a given number of maximum widths, the intervening spaces then being filled with equi-width pieces; usually the 'marker' planks would be straight on both edges so the abutting edge of the next would be shaped to fit, with its opposite edge left straight for the same procedure to be followed. The 'filler' at the end of each run always needed extra attention as both edges would have to be shaped. It was vitally necessary that each plank should lie completely flat against the timbers and be fitted exactly to its neighbour, for the slightest attempt to 'pull' a plank to tighten a joint would produce a pucker and thus completely ruin the strength of the lay. Securing whilst fitting was with 3/8" brass gimp pins, their shortness and smooth finish, with consequent low holding power, being an effective guard against any malpractice. Any wood which shew short grain, lightning shakes or other defect was discarded, the good portions to be utilised at either end of the hull or in the tunnel where length or width had diminished sufficiently for faulty portions of the material to be cut away before use.

The third hull shows two further stages of construction. The second layer of diagonals (of the same scantlings as the first) is clearly seen being worked aft over the membrane of unbleached calico which went between the layers. This cloth was smoothed into place and well dressed with linseed oil as each plank was fixed, again with 3/8" brass gimp pins at requisite places. So far as was practicable both sides of the hull were progressed equally so that no undue stress was built in; therefore it is unlikely that the two men on the far side of the boat would already be laying the third skin of fore and aft planking which finished off the exterior to the hull, as can be seen on the fourth boat. The calico membrane had a two-fold purpose, firstly as a water barrier should there be any seepage through a skin and secondly as a powerful reinforcing for the very thin wood. The fourth boat, which appears to have the horizontal planking completed, would have been worked from the keel towards the gunwale for this process and apparently all that needs to be done here is to have the trailing ends of calico trimmed off. The fifth berth is back to the beginning of the process again as it shows the keel assembly draped across the top of the moulds, ready for setting up, ribanding etc. It seems appropriate that the Mark II was to be carried by the Warwick for there is an obvious affinity between the double diagonal of the inner planking and the geodetic framework of the plane.

The 3/16" exterior planks were mainly pre-cut and shaped in the mill; first sawn out on a bandsaw and then finished to shape and size on a spindle moulder working against a template, so that only minimal fitting would be required at the hooded ends, the butt joints and along the length. When fitted onto the hull the planks appear to have only a slight curvature along their length and one could wonder why any joints would be necessary, but when seen as flat material on Blueprint 2-2020/3 the wide sweep of curve is obvious, as is also the reason for the butt joints; apart from the fact that without joins a 30-foot boat would need boards 33 feet long, which would be neither practical nor economic. So the joints were permitted at certain specified positions, there having to be at least three 'passing' strakes between butts with at least twelve timbers between joints in adjacent strakes. Each had to be 'back-strapped' inside the diagonal skins with a piece of rock elm fitted closely up to the timbers at each side of the butt, the faying side of the strap being planed to the contour of the inside of the hull. As each exterior plank was fitted it was drawn firmly up to its neighbour before being secured. Final fastening was very time consuming; the 'hooded ends', that is where the plank fits on the aprons to the rebates in the stem and stern posts, were secured with 3/4″ by 5 gauge brass countersunk screws turned very carefully into the oak beneath. Along the lower edge of the garboard strake 1 3/4″ by 16 gauge copper boat nails passed through the plank, the diagonals, the hog and the steamed timber to tie the whole bottom structure together. The through fastening of the planks to the timbers, clear of the keel, were 3/4″ by 16 gauge copper boat nails, two to each exterior plank at each timber, with extra nails in way of the butt joints. Every hole had to be drilled, to eliminate any chance of the materials being split when the nail was driven; but always slightly under nail thickness, so there could be no seepage through the hole. Once this was done the interior of the hull resembled a veritable hedgehog of protruding nail ends; every one of which had later to be turned or rooved and clenched, for there is virtually no frictional hold in a square copper boat nail.

Once planked up no further work would be possible until the shell had been removed from the moulds, quite a delicate task for the hulls were very flexible without gunwales to stiffen the topsides. During planking up the builders would have progressively removed the oval brads which had secured the bent timbers to the ribands, so there would be nothing securing the shell apart from some screws from the moulds to the keel and others holding the stem and stern posts to the jig. Once these were withdrawn the whole structure could be gently lifted, turned the correct way up and settled into pre-shaped hull formers so that the true shape could be preserved with no hogging, sagging or spreading. Then temporary cross members were screwed from deck rising to deck rising across the hull, after widths had been checked. Much of a boat's integral strength lies in the shape of the hull, i.e. in the rise of the sides from the bottom. Just as a steel channel girder has greater resistance to bending than a flat bar of the same weight, so the up-rising sides of the hull impart resistance to bending the keel in either direction – providing the sides are not allowed to move inwards or outwards from the designed width. Thus the temporary athwartships members.

The sheerline marked on the moulds would have been worked to as the free edge of the larboard and starboard strakes, which was the gunwale line, and the ragged ends of the diagonal planking could now be cut down to this to allow the gunwales to be fitted. For lightness and strength these were formed in two parts, one inside and one outside the hull so that the treble layer of planks with their steamed timbers were sandwiched between them; the outer one usually being known as the 'rubber' (short for rubbing strake). Both of the same scantlings, they had to be steamed into shape and position to follow the curvature of the hull outwards and the rise of the sheer upwards without exerting undue pressure at any point and being only 3/4″ × 3/4″ were quite light to handle. Once withdrawn from the kell the inner one would have its pre-fitted fore end brought up against the stem apron and then be handled along the inside of the boat with restraining clamps and pegs. Experience and a good eye were vitally necessary to trim the aft end so that it would butt neatly against the stern apron at the right length and angles whilst still hot. Sometimes it had to be unclamped and partly resteamed to make the aft end a first class fit. Both 'inners' would be fitted and temporarily fastened before the 'rubbers' were steamed on. As the gunwales were fitted atop the timbers the nails in the top two planks would have been turned whilst it was still possible to get at them. The two parts of the gunwales were fastened together, and to the shell, by 14 gauge copper nails driven through drilled holes at alternate timbers. The ends were fastened to the posts and to their opposite numbers with steamed timber laminated breasthooks, glued up in similar fashion to the stem and stern post knees, and through secured with 7" × 12 gauge copper nails. To drill for these from the centreline of the rubber through to the centreline of the breasthook called for a good eye and a steady hand, and even to drive a copper nail of that length and thickness is a skilled job, for the diameter of the drilled hole must not exceed, even by a whisker, the width across the flat of the nail. A slack hole could 'weep' and would allow the nail to 'work' and thus reduce its life as well as its holding strength.

Now would be the time for the 'girls' to take over for a while; to painstakingly turn or clench (clink), as stipulated, the hundreds of copper nails. On a Mark I (23-foot) lifeboat there were 21 strakes and 153 timbers each side; at two nails per strake per timber that works out at 6600 nails when extras for butt joints, gunwales, keel, etc. are taken into account. On the Mark II (30-foot) we've watched building in this chapter there would be proportionately more in the strakes, plus extras to fasten the slender planks around the propeller tunnel, as well as the fastenings in the other places. In clinking, a domed copper washer is driven over the protruding nail point and brought firmly down onto the wood with a hollow punch whilst a dolly is held against the nail head to prevent it being driven back. The nail is then shortened, by using a pair of fine 'end cutters', to just above the roove; and then with the dolly again held outside the cut off nail is spread over the roove by angled tapping with a light hammer to build up a dome of tempered copper over the roove – which will automatically tighten it against the timber inside and draw the nail head slightly below the outside surface of the planking.

All the nails in the steamed timbers were 'hook' turned by cutting off the protruding tip at a sharp angle and tapping over the point thus formed so that as it rolled down into the grain of the wood it formed a staple-like arch pulling the two portions together under tension. Naturally a dolly has to be held against the head to prevent the nail from being driven back. As in clenching the tapping hardens the copper, transforming the original soft, pliable metal into an unyielding fastening. The 'girls' were adept at this, and fast too. Working in pairs, often out of sight of each other with a wall of wood between them, they had to have a pattern of working so that the nail turner on the inside and the dolly holder on the outside both attacked the same nail simultaneously, and then moved together to the correct next nail. The sound made by the hammer held the key to the system, a well worked fastening giving off a sharp metallic sound, a poorly held nail-head echoing hollowly; 'move' was signalled by a single light tap on the wood. At Broads-Haven the hulls were slung on pivots afixed to the stem and stern posts on trestle-supported gymbals for this job, and others, thus allowing the workers easy access to their task without uncomfortable positions on beds of nails or lying flat on the floor beneath. Even this simple measure sped production and increased efficiency.

With nailing completed the boat could be completely cleaned out of nail ends, shavings, dust etc. so that a primer coat of paint could be applied to the inside before the exterior was sanded off. Brushes, 'ticklers' and a vacuum cleaner were used for the former job and a belt sander for the latter. This took off the slight irregularities of the surface of the plank edges and gave a smooth finish ready for the application of the exterior primer paint. It also served to highlight, by polishing the head, any nails which had not been worked slightly below the wood surface, and therefore may not have been fully tensioned. As the strakes were close jointed there was no caulking to be done, except along the bottom edges of the garboards and up the hooded ends; a few strands of cotton worked into these seams took care of this, the gap later being filled with paint mixed putty.

Once the boat was clad in sombre grey the boatbuilders could again take possession of the hull to commence fitting out. The first, and most essential, job would be to fit the keelson cum keelcase, which would already have been made up by bench workers. This was a composite multipurpose member serving as a fore and aft watertight bulkhead over the greater part of the length of the boat; as a central support for the deckbeams and deck; as housings for the centreboard and the rudder frame; and most importantly as a longitudinal strength member when the boat was suspended from the plane or the parachutes; as well as, by its construction, a way of draining shipped water from the deck through the centreboard slot. To this would be fastened the bomb hook, the parachute sling plates, the towing bar and the mast tabernacle. It would be impossible to hoist a normal boat by a single suspension point to the underside of a plane so tightly that pressured air (at 200 mph) was excluded, so this fore and aft central member had to be strong enough to prevent the ends of the boat sagging, and it had to be very thoroughly fastened throughout its entire length. From the time the operational lifeboat left its trolley on the tarmac until it rested on the sea its entire weight and all the flight and drop stresses would be borne by either the bomb hook or the sling plates and thus by the keelson; likewise if the boat were to be towed home after dropping the stress would come on the towing bar and the keelson. It fulfilled the same purpose in both Marks I and II but its design could not be the same because of the entirely different engine systems. Whilst we've worked on the Mark II hull so far because of the excellent supporting photograph it is now necessary to explain the main differences in construction between the two.

For the Mark I the keelson started on the bench as one wide piece of 3/4" mahogany almost 20 feet long, designed to extend from just abaft the stem knee to midway between stations 9 and 10. To the side of this was attached a shorter piece of similar width to commence between stations 2 and 3 and carry full length aft. 1" and 1 1/4" spacers between the two sections delineated the slots for the centreboard and the rudder frame respectively, with necessary packing pieces at other places; copper through fastenings were clenched to build a sturdy central member which could be screwed in place upwards through the keel; to which it had to be 'paint' fitted. This involved lowering the keelson onto a thin coat of wet paint on the keel, and where paint transferred the wood had to be eased away and the process repeated until the entire underside of the member bore transferred paint, only then could the 144

4″ brass screws be used to secure it home. As the 'Middy' engines were mounted each side of the centre line this member could extend the entire length of the boat.

The Mark IIs had to be different as they had a single, centrally mounted engine and an arched propeller tunnel in the underside of the hull. (The first Uffa Fox design for the Mark II had the engine mounted off centre to preserve the through-length central keelson or keelcase, as in the Mark I. No drawings of this have come to light so one assumes that the propeller also was to one side, rather than in a tunnel.) The keelson in the Mark II, although similarly formed for'ard as a single built-up unit from just aft of number 2 station, went only to the foreside of the engine compartment bulkhead midway between stations 6 and 7; with twin engine-bearers set the width of the engine apart, overlapping in length to carry the lateral strength the rest of the way aft. These were partly mounted on the twin tunnel chines which commenced for'ard of number 5 station to continue aft to form edges of the propeller tunnel before terminating at number 12 station, being integral members of the hull construction. Atop of these the engine-bearers rose gradually to full height so that where the keelson terminated they took over the role of deck support thus forming three athwartships watertight compartments, the engine being mounted in the most forward, with the tunnel rising into the next aft. Where the keelson and the engine-bearers overlapped they were linked and stressed with cross-bearers. A watertight bulkhead at each end of the engine compartment assisted this support structure. The engine itself was mounted on four shock-absorbing brackets fastened to the bearers. At all places where the keelson and engine-bearers met the transverse bulkheads triangular strengthening blocks were fitted on all four angles, being both glued and screwed into position.

The propeller tunnel rising from station 7 to a high arch reached its maximum at station 9, where its camber intruded slightly into the deck, from which point it declined to be lost in the stern curve aft of station 10. Its narrow planks were a boatbuilder's dream, or nightmare, as its shape had to allow the vulnerable propeller blades to rotate without showing below the natural contour of the bottom. The exterior (fore and aft) planking of this tunnel comprised 24 separate strakes, of which ten were 'stealers', that is, they tapered off to nothing in less than the length of the tunnel. Another significant difference in the two boats to be emphasised was in the planking; because of its very light engine system and smaller size the Mark I had only a single thickness of diagonal planking beneath the horizontal strakes whereas the Mark II was double diagonal beneath the horizontal; and in the former the keel and planking ran uninterrupted over the entire length.

On the Mark I the engines were fitted down onto mahogany pads fixed to the interior of the hull where they were to be mounted. These 1 1/2″ blocks tapered to nothing at the bilge, resting on tingles used for filling the narrow spaces between the bent timbers, the whole mounting being set down onto white lead paste after paint fitting. Further blocks could then be added to bring the engines up to the correct height for the spigots to take the exterior propeller units. Clenched copper nails at alternate timbers and around the keyhole-shaped shaft-holes ensured that the mountings were firm and well fastened to take the engines.

There were several other major items of structural work still to be done which would be basically common to both types of lifeboat, but with variation in size and positioning. One would be the hand/grab rails outside the hull. With the Mark I they were virtually bilge keels with hand-sized slots cut in for survivors to hold on to should the boat capsize, but by the time the Mark II was on the drawing board it was realised that there were difficulties in climbing aboard from the water, so two sets were fitted, the lower, still termed handrails, were right under the boat, just 16″ out from the centreline, extending between positions ten and fifteen feet from the bows. The second set, now called side handrails, commenced 14′ 1 5/8″ from the bow for 3′ 3″ only, about 8″ below the gunwale. Their positioning brought them aft of the port access door and for'ard of the starboard one, thus giving maximum assistance to anyone attempting to climb aboard via either of these. It is assumed that the lower hand rail was so positioned that if the boat capsized there would be something for the crew to hang onto whilst they righted it, the other set would then provide a foot grip or rest. These were through secured with clenched copper nails to internal false stringers joggled over the timbers.

Another important task would be securing the fore and aft galvanised sling plates which would take the entire weight of the boat whilst it parachuted down. The centre of the sling shackle hole on the for'ard one of the Mark II was 7′ 3″ from the bow, with the aft one at 22′ 9″. Both were made to be fitted to the keelcase at different angles so that the odd legged wire slings would transmit a straight pull as the boat descended with its bows pointing 30 degrees downwards. Equally important was the rather misnamed bomb hook, an incongruous name for a lifesaving craft. By this single point attachment the lifeboat was secured to its carrying aircraft. It was a two legged fitment, secured both through the bottom of the boat and to the keelcase, which it spanned. This same central member also provided the anchorage for the towing bar, again made of galvanised steel and mounted at an angle on the keelcase so that the line of pull could be true from its projection through the stem to the body of the lifeboat.

On each side of the boat betwixt gunwale and deck the access doors had to be cut through the shell planking; originally they were solely to allow the riggers to get an arm inside the boat when securing the lifeboat to the bomb hoist and hook etc. before take-off; but later they were enlarged to 18″ × 12″ so that a survivor (smallish) could climb through to gain the deck, using the bilge hand rail of the Mark I as a step, rather than attempting to climb over the much higher gunwale. On the Mark II the lower handrail was too far below the turn of the bilge to be used for a foothold so the upper handrails were positioned to give a firm handgrip whilst releasing and opening the door. Later it was proposed that a boarding ladder, similar to that used on the Hurricane fighter plane, should be fitted. Closing on to a rubber seating these doors were watertight when secured by a brass clip on the exterior of the hull, easily accessible to a man in the water.

Then there were the chain plates to take the mast shrouds; these inverted

'V' fittings needed a firm anchorage, so doubling pieces had to be fitted inside the boat before the securing bolts were fitted.

Meanwhile work could proceed on the interior, firstly fitting the deck beams in way of the watertight bulkheads. Both types had four of these bulkheads extending across the boat, from the hull planking to the keelson each side, and upwards to the deckhead; there being one each for'ard and abaft the engine compartment(s), another just foreside of the aft sling plates and one foreside of the rudder slot. A fifth bulkhead for'ard of the towing bar did not extend completely to the deckhead, acting as a stiffener and compartment baffle, watertight only up to a certain level. These were quite light, of 1/4" seawater-resisting plywood, fitted tightly to the inside of the hull, between two steamed timbers, one an especially positioned extra, the keelson and a deck beam; to all of which they were secured. The deckbeams of 3/4" mahogany, sided 1 1/4" at bulkheads, 1 3/4" elsewhere, were single dovetailed into the top edges of the keelson and the deck risings; spacings varied according to positioning of the deck hatches, but clear of these they were never more than 13 1/2" centres apart. In way of the hatches a light carling, dovetailed into the deckbeams at each end added strength to the extended spacings. The deck, of 1/4" seawater-resisting plywood, covered all joints and was fitted tight up to the inside of the planking so as to form a watertight seal to the lower part of the boat, broken only at the hatches and the centreboard drainage slots in the keelson, which needs explaining. Conventional deckbeams are 'cropped' so that the centre is higher than the ends, encouraging deck water to drain overside through relieving ports or scuppers. The low deck level of these lifeboats, relative to the outside water-level, would not permit this so the deck was made lower at the centreline for water to drain away through the centreboard slots. Later versions of the Mark II had a recess built into the deck immediately forward of the engine compartment, which averaged 4" in depth and was 46" wide just for'ard of station 6, extending across the centre of the boat, with sloping sides to the regular deck level at the exterior planking. This recess was built in to take the 'Cox'n's Bag', but all boats so fitted had a continuous flush deck fitted above it, so they could be rapidly adapted for use if the bag (and coxwain) system were introduced.

There were eight hatches and their coamings through the deck of the Mark I, as can be seen on Plate 5, which also gives their sizes. The 'forward' compartment contained most of the boat's stores as it extended from the bow to the for'ard engine bulkhead, right across the boat, with a single central hatch. Next came those for the twin engines, followed by a pair almost amidships for spare fuel as well as the heavy drogue, inner suits, compass and foresail. The next pair aft were similar in size and used mainly as spares for additional gear or stores, whilst the aftermost one, situated on the centreline, was kept empty to decrease stern weight. With the hatches closed all the compartments became buoyancy chambers except those containing the engines, where the engine breathers prevented a full seal. The hatch covers were made of 7/32" marine plywood on mahogany frames; the midship ones being hinge mounted, and all fitted with quick-release clamps, which when engaged, pulled the cover down tightly onto expanded rubber sealing strips. All were flat-topped, except those over the engines, which were convex for drainage and being removable were fitted with retaining lanyards.

The Mark II had nine hatches in the deck; the two for'ard ones both being to starboard, the midship pair being one each side of the keelson abreast of the centreboard slot, another pair were situated in the 'wing' compartments each side of the engine space with a similar pair each side of the tunnel, the ninth being to port adjacent to the rudder slot. All were 18″ × 13 1/8″, some having their maximum dimension fore and aft, whilst others were athwartships. All had watertight clamping devices, similar to the Mark I. Each had its compartment contents stencilled on the outside:

No. 1 – Chart Board. Charts

No. 2 – 2 Signalling Lamps
1 Waterproof Torch
1 Signal Pistol
81 Signal Cartridges in tins of 3
1 Heliograph
2 Kites and Containers

No. 3 Port – 65 Tins of Water
50 Tins of Condensed Milk

No. 3 Starboard – 35 Tins of Water
20 Tins of Soup
3 Drinking Cups
10 Flying Rations
4 Tins Cigarettes
2 Fishing Kits
3 Tins Matches

No. 4 Port – 6 Inner Suits
6 Outer Suits
10 Everhot Bags
First Aid Outfit

No. 4 Starboard – 15 Deck Cushions
Awning

No. 5 Port – 10 Safety Belts
Foresail

No. 5 Starboard – Instruction Booklet
Dinghy Repair Outfit
Bellows
Knife
Heavy Sea Drogue

4 Blue Suits

2 Sets Leak Stoppers

No. 6 – Empty

In addition there were two small hatches to the cox'n's recess and two similar ones to the petrol tank compartments just abaft the mast tabernacle. The engine had a convex-topped hatch of its own, mounted above low coamings, with, at its for'ard end, a separate, smaller, hatch beneath which was the starting handle, the two-way petrol cock, primer and choke. Even the propeller tunnel had a removable observation 'window' through which any fouling could be seen and cleared away.

All these fittings were made up on the benches, as was the 44 1/2" by 15/16" Mark I centreboard (60" for the Mark II), with its carefully streamlined underwater section and self-sealing handgrip top.

The presence of tail fins on the lifeboats seen in some of the photographs may be cause to wonder. In the early dropping trials it was found that on release the boats dropped sharply by the head, allowing the stern to kick upwards with possible damage to the tail planes and fin of the carrier aircraft. Experiments were made fitting plywood fins to the quarters of the lifeboats and these succeeded in keeping the stern of the boat level long enough for gravity to do its duty. These fins also reduced yawing whilst the boat was on the parachutes and helped it to be on an even keel at splashdown. They were secured by 'Oddie' keys which could easily be withdrawn once the boat was afloat; to attempt to sail with them in position would be to court disaster. No mention is anywhere made of the effect thay had on the carrier plane so one must assume it was either neutral or beneficial.

The mahogany rudders, 1" thickness for the Mark I and 1 1/4" for the Mark II, were each built into an unwieldy locating and retaining frame, because they had to be shipped after splashdown. In operation the rudder was inserted down through its slot in the aft deck so that the frame around the galvanised steel stock provided a mounting within the hollow keelson, which could be held in position by retaining clips. Frequently survivors omitted to use these properly and consequently had steering troubles. During building various other fittings had also to be installed. The 3" tubular brass socket into which the mast had to be stepped needed to be set into the deck of the Mark I at a rake on the port side of the keelson, whilst the tabernacle for the pivoted mast of the Mark II had to be built in on the port side of the keelson, with its centre 8' 1" from the bow.

Then there was the teaser of a job cutting the exactly sized elliptical holes in the planking each side of the stem so the drogue and rocket boxes could be positioned on the deck. Each box was 24" long, with a 5" internal diameter at the open (for'ard) end, tapering to 4" at the inboard end and made from 1/16" resin-bonded plywood, rolled around formers so that the two edges overlapped and could be riveted together with 16 gauge rose-headed burrs. Once the formers had been withdrawn the aft ends were closed off with substantial blocks; for the starboard one had to withstand the thrust of the line rocket when it fired whilst the port one merely provided a suitable receptacle for the folded drogue. Where the bow planking was cut for the boxes an inside strengthening pad was fitted, the boxes themselves being fastened to the deck as well as to the planking reinforcements. Both types of lifeboat also had side rockets to carry floating lines out to port and starboard when the craft came to rest after its descent. The actual projectors were designed and made by the Schermuly Pistol Rocket Company, but it was vitally necessary that deck strengthening should be built into the boats during fitting out ready for the projectors to be mounted. Initially both Marks had the projectors mounted on the after deck, but a modification of the Mark II altered the design so they were enclosed in boxes mounted at an angle on a false stringer in the bottom of the boat and passing through the deck to discharge through circular holes immediately below the gunwale, 24 feet from the stem; the floating lines were stored in special 'run free' boxes on the after deck.

The rowlock blocks had to be fitted onto the gunwales, as well as dozens of other minor jobs not coming in any particular order; with the painters hovering around all the time awaiting a chance to get a coat of protective paint on every part before it was fitted or sealed in. The electricians were frequently on the job also as they contrived to get their wiring in place as the construction progressed.

Now would be the opportunity for the engine fitters to come aboard, able to call on a 'chippy' to assist them for woodwork, when required, as they mounted the two motors of the Mark I on the blocks, fitted the exhaust pipes and offered up the propeller units for final bolting together of the two portions of the power units. With the hatches closed during operational running 'breathers' were necessary, so in the form of inverted 'U' tubes they were fitted at the edge of the deck, close up under the gunwales, where even a deluge through would discharge harmlessly into the bilge clear of the engines. On the Mark II the engine fitting would involve much more work than on the smaller boats. The power unit chosen was the Austin 8 hp Marine, which had necessitated a change in the compartments and hatches arrangement. The Austin engine had its own 'room', which because of its height required coamings raised above the deck and an openable lid for access; but as this could not be guaranteed watertight the whole engine was enclosed in a flexible rubber bag which opened along the top for maintenance or servicing. Installing this power unit would involve boatbuilders first for a slanting hole would need to be cut through the keel for fitting the shaft log; this had to be at the correct angle so that a line straight through it would lead exactly from the centre of the propeller shaft flange at the gearbox to the centre of the hole in the shaft skeg. The brass shaft log, with its waterproof sealing gland, was designed and made by Bruntons of Sudbury, and was through bolted to the upper side of the tunnel planking where it rose steeply. The propeller shaft would pass through this to be supported just forward of the propeller by a skeg, with a 'cutless' rubber, water lubricated bearing, also bolted to the tunnel roof further aft. Then there would be watertight glands to be fitted in the bulkheads for the petrol leads and wiring to come through, and also in the deck where the exhaust pipe emerged to lead along to the port quarter for discharge overside. One disadvantage in fitting the conventional marine engine was that the boats' centre of gravity was raised – so they rolled more.

Meanwhile the mast would have been made up on the bench; for the Mark I from two pieces of 3″ by 1 1/2″ silver spruce 16′ 5″ long. These were glued together before being shaped and rounded, but prior to this a half-round groove had to be ploughed along the centre of each faying surface, so that when completed there was a hole through its entire length for the aerial lead which connected the aerial attachment at the truck to the socket at the foot. The main halyard sheave fitted into and through the mast just below the head, so in way of this the aerial lead hole had to be chiselled in a curve around both the sheave slot and the sheave pin. To the lower portion of the mast were attached rock elm cleats for securing the jib and main halyards whilst the boat was under sail. A brass track for the luff of the 71 square feet, loose footed, mainsail was screwed the length of the mast on the aft side, the single hoist, double sheeted foresail being just over 40 square feet.

As the mast for the Mark II was pivot mounted in a tabernacle it was built differently to that of the Mark I and the greater length of the boat allowed it to be 20′ 2″overall; 4″ square at the foot before coming into a round above deck level and tapering to 2″ at the head. Again it was built from two pieces but was hollow, the wall thickness above the square portion reducing to below the sheave slot where the aerial lead hole had to contort itself clear of both the slot and the pin. This time no sail track was fitted, the mainsail being secured to the mast by rope toggles, the upper four of which were fitted with four wooden parrels each to assist in smooth hoisting and lowering. All standing and running rigging was made up in the riggers shop and had only to be fitted to the boats as the builders completed them.

A letter from Uffa Fox to Gp. Capt. Waring, dated 26 February 1943 relates to five enclosed sail plans for this boat: the first as if the boat were to be used for racing, and thus impractical for Air/Sea Rescue purposes; then two for single-masted cutter rig and two for schooner. The single-mast design, without spars, similar to that used for the Mark I as described in Chapter 2, was the basis for final choice, with a four-gored mainsail of 141.75 square feet, the upper half of the gores being sky blue, the lower azure blue as was the three-gored foresail of 67.5 square feet.

Stowage compartment usage could differ. Appendix I gives some idea of the scale of equipment, but cannot be taken as completely standard at any one time for this varied in both types of boat with new developments, locations and seasons of the year.

Only after engine fitting had been completed, the electrical circuits install-ed, the CO_2 bottles for inflating the buoyancy chambers fastened in their racks and all tested, could the woodworkers come onto the boat again to affix the two-inch thick rubberised felt and canvas cushioning on top of the gunwales and fasten the inflatable buoyancy chambers at bow and stern with copper tacks on the inner and outer surface flaps, after liberally applying an adhesive, before capping both flaps with screwed-on wooden battens. Then final coats of paint were applied and the lifeboat readied for engine and sailing trials.

These were carried out in the presence of an Aeronautical Inspection

16   *A Mark II ready for trials (Jeanne Lee, the eldest daughter of Herbert Woods)*

17   *Sailing trials with a Mark II on the River Thurne (Jimmy Turner)*

18   *A Mark II being crated for overseas shipment at Broads-Haven (Jeanne Lee)*

Directorate representative, usually the one who had watched supervision of all the RAF boats on the yard throughout their building. Normally two boats went out together, on a pre-set day, regardless of weather; only severe icing would be a valid reason for an adjournment. Our trials were on the River Thurne, the crew a cox'n and engineer in each boat, with the Inspector changing craft, without stopping, during the four-hour run, part of which over the measured mile had to be with fixed throttle. It was on one of these runs that we nearly had a casualty because of the fixed throttles. Along the river bank were several summertime bungalows which had been pressed into all-year use because of heavy bombing of nearby Great Yarmouth. There was an elderly 'marshman' who earned a few extra coppers by carrying bags of coal in his small rowing boat to these outlying dwellings. Seeing him in the distance I asked if we could reduce speed whilst passing him, and received a negative reply; so there was nothing to do but zig-zag all over the river in an effort to reduce our bow wave and wash and then pull within inches of the bank furthest from him as we passed, standing by to go about in a hurry if the worst happened. It didn't, but gave us some anxious moments as the top of the wash just slopped over his gunwale; I don't think he ever really forgave me.

A Mark I Airborne Lifeboat numbered AB 3 (4030) is on display at the RAF Museum at Hendon and a Mark II is on display at the Imperial War Museum at Duxford. Parts of three 'Middy' engines have recently been found for the former, also a set of rigging has been made and plans for a suit of sails submitted to a sailmaker.

6 Operations 1944 July–December

The second half of 1944 brought just as much work for the Air/Sea Rescue Service; but some of the reports made out were even scantier on details; perhaps this was due to a certain amount of familiarity causing the reporting officer to feel that it was unnecessary to record all the information he received, having no inkling that professional and amateur historians in future years would find an interest in his writings far beyond a bare recital of facts required for official forms; perhaps 'war weariness' was rearing its insidious head, for after reading some reports there are elements of doubt as to all the exact circumstances. The following is an example.

5 July   A Warwick of 281 Squadron was sent out from Wick to search for, and succour, the crew of a Liberator who might be in a dinghy within 100 miles of Stavanger in Norway. At 1753 a sighting was made of a dinghy containing one man in position 5745N 0435E. It appears that an Airborne Lifeboat was dropped very close to him but he just drifted over the extended floating lines. A Lindholme dinghy was also sent down but to no avail. Long range surface assistance was sent for and a watch maintained but at 1835 hours the man fell out of his dinghy and floated away face down.

6 July   At 1020 hours 'Y' of 280 Squadron (F/O Wallace) accompanied by 'J' (F/L Schaffer) took off from Thornaby to search a specific area for survivors of a ditched bomber and within a few hours had found seven or eight men wearing Mae Wests floating in the sea in position 5416N 0538E (about 110 miles west of Heligoland); much too close to that highly defended island for comfort. The group were slightly scattered so it was to a pair less than 50 yards apart that 'Y' dropped its lifeboat. All the systems of the craft functioned perfectly as it landed within 30 yards of the two men who made no more than a perfunctory effort to reach it; probably being already too weakened by the cold and exposure to do more. By 1410 hours all the men in the water had ceased movement and it was feared they were either unconscious or already dead. It was 1602 when the Warwicks landed back at Thornaby to make their sorrowful report. Happily their news was wrong for a surface vessel also on the operation picked up all seven men of a 492 Bomb Group Flying Fortress alive but unconscious.

12 July   This operation, six days later, did little to raise 280 Squadron's morale, even though Strubby was enjoying a wonderful summer's day. Warwick 'E' took off from the Coastal Command aerodrome at 1113 hours,

W/Cdr. McIntosh scarcely pausing to admire the flat countryside with its foretaste of harvest spread out beneath the wings. The sun was high on the starboard hand as course was set to take them out over the North Sea to commence Patrol Pattern 'A' off the Belgian and Dutch coasts seeking any possible survivors of earlier American Air Force raids. The previous day's clouds had dispersed and he knew that although Lancasters and Mosquitos had been hammering flying bomb sites, storage depots and marshalling yards not far away to the south and west there were no reports of RAF planes missing. The tedious eye-straining hours passed slowly as the methodical search pattern was flown until at 1610, in position 5140N 0228E (about 15 miles north-west of Dunkirk) the wreckage of a Liberator was sighted with four Lightning aircraft circling six aircrew in the water. Quickly sizing up the situation he made a dummy run dropping smoke floats to gauge the direction and strength of the wind before making a perfect lifeboat drop at 1628 from a height of 700 feet; but although the boat settled safely 100 yards downwind of the men and they slowly drifted towards it no attempt was made to reach or board it.

Meanwhile, 'Q' (F/O Thomson) had taken off from Thornaby to assist and arrived at the casualty scene just before 1650; observing that the lifeboat was not being used and fearing that the survivors were seriously weakened he dropped a Lindholme Gear from 50 feet. This splashed down amongst the men, fortunately without actually hitting any of them, being rewarded by some signs of activity, although none of the men reached any of the parts of the gear. At 1715 another Lindholme was released, this time with more positive results as very soon one man reached the inflated dinghy and was observed attempting to drag two of his comrades aboard. Watching this, the crew of 'E' must have felt rather helpless for W/Cdr. McIntosh took them off to seek a surface rescue craft but soon returned and, being near the Permitted Limit of Endurance (PLE), dropped marine markers and headed off for an East Anglian base. Whilst on the way, at 1735, in position 5152N 0214E, an RML was sighted with supporting and guiding Thunderbolts apparently trying to direct it to where 'E' and 'Q' had been operating all the afternoon. On the way, at 1745, RML 547 picked up ten survivors from the sea, which neither 'E' nor 'Q' had sighted, with HSL 2578, which also arrived on the scene from a different direction, recovering one man from a Lindholme dinghy and five bodies from the water. All were from two Liberators which had collided in mid-air earlier in the day. During the afternoon HF 968 of 278 Squadron from Bradwell Bay had been patrolling and searching east of Felixstowe at altitudes of between 1800 to 3000 feet. Apparently, as so often happens on a hot day with a westerly wind, clouds were forming off the Suffolk coast, and the altitude was allowed to permit close searching.

On this day 24 bombers went missing.

12 July   Warwick BV 478 of 278 Squadron from Bradwell Bay was on patrol over the sea when it came across a Fortress at 5000 feet flying homewards with its wheels down, so decided to escort it in case of trouble. Trouble was indeed encountered – but in the Warwick, for 'gremlins' took over the port engine stopping it completely so the Fortress drew ahead and the erstwhile rescue plane limped home alone on one engine; sadly the B 17 of 457 Bomb Group did not make the English coast but ditched off Felixstowe. Nine of the crew were picked up by an HSL from the nearby 26 A/SR unit at Felixstowe.

16 July   There is reference in some unrelated papers to an Airborne Lifeboat being dropped by a plane from St Eval to the wreckage of an RAF Liberator with only one survivor seen, who was too weak to board the lifeboat; but no account of this has been found in records of Squadrons at St Eval (or in the area) at that time.

16 July   Warwick HF 968 of 278 Squadron aloft from Bradwell Bay came across a ditched Fortress of 381 Bomber Group in position 5152N 0222E (50 miles east of Felixstowe); but just as it was about to drop its lifeboat an HSL from 26 A/SR Marine Craft Unit appeared on the horizon so the Warwick circled to watch the launch pick up the nine survivors from their dinghies at 1324 hours.

19 July   The Spitfires of 'B' flight of 278 Squadron whilst on routine search and rescue patrol sighted a waterlogged Airborne Lifeboat in the southern North Sea.

21 July   'A' Flight of 278 Squadron was ordered off from Bradwell Bay at 0530 to undertake creeping line ahead patrol on positions R9991, R8860, S4566 and S7192, with an escort of two USAAF Thunderbolts. But let John Sumner, navigator of 278 'J', tell the story, supplemented by extracts from the official report and comments by M. C. McVeigh, the pilot; the former an Australian, as were three others of the crew, the latter a New Zealander, but now both resident in the United Kingdom.

On July 20th a B 24 of 493 Bomber Group USAAF, was damaged during a raid on Germany and forced to ditch in the southern North Sea (actually a few miles north-west of Ostend). RAF Coastal Command and the USAAF flew 80 sorties during that afternoon and evening to try to locate the crew who were all thought to have survived the ditching. Arrangements were made for a Warwick of 278 to continue the search at first light the next morning. Take off was at 0525; visibility beneath a solid cloud base at 1000 feet was very poor and the wind had whipped up quite a rough sea. The escort was necessary because the search area was adjacent to the Dutch/Belgian coast.

A creeping line ahead search pattern was carried out and as we turned at one extreme corner of the area the rear gunner said he thought he'd seen a faint light some way off. Our pilot, W/O McVeigh, altered course visually toward the position of the light whilst I took a Gee Fix to establish our exact position at the time. By calculation based on our heading and the relative bearing and distance of the light I arrived at a probable answer. A further Gee Fix showed that our position was, by then, some twenty miles away and I gave the pilot a course to bring us back to the spot. By sheer good fortune we passed directly over two dinghies containing the nine crew members of the Liberator . . .

This was my first and only drop, in fact, I believe it was our Squadron's first, so with fingers crossed I pressed the release. Everything worked perfectly and within minutes the survivors were aboard the boat and getting stuck into the cans of self-heating soup. Unfortunately the lifeboat must have suffered some damage as the crew had no luck in starting either of the engines and we had to call up the RAF HSLs from Dover. As we were only eight miles north-west of Ostend and flying lazy circles at 300 feet we were very relieved two hours later when the launches came charging over the horizon to complete the job. So that they could make a quick exit they rammed and sank our lifeboat, a sad sight we did not see as we were dashing home on near empty tanks.

W/O McVeigh adds humorously: 'They were left-handed circles we were doing and I was getting quite dizzy after two hours of it – what with looking out for Jerry at the same time; we landed at 1140.'

22 July The scene shifts to the warmer waters of the Mediterranean for a search and rescue operation for a Spitfire pilot of 184 Squadron who, after a brush with a JU 88, developed engine trouble and was forced to bale out south-east of Malta. Warwick 'E' of 283 Squadron took off initially and located the man in his dinghy at 1931 in position 3553N 1618E with another Spitfire loyally orbiting the lonely survivor. A larger dinghy was successfully dropped and the man seen to board, so 'E' climbed and remained in the vicinity whilst homing Warwick 'B' 283 (Sq. Ldr. Crampton) which was on the way out carrying an Airborne Lifeboat. It was 2019 when 'B' arrived to drop its lifeboat at 2023 from 750 feet. Unfortunately only one parachute opened and the rescue craft broke up on impact and sank at 2028. 'E' was then asked to climb to 5000 feet to home an HSL. 'B' had to return to base leaving 'E' orbiting until relieved at 2322 by 'X' which had taken off at 2140. Eventually the HSL arrived and picked up the fortunate pilot at 2320. (283 Squadron operated from bases all along the North African coastline and Malta during the course of the Middle Sea campaigns; base in the above operation was probably Malta.)

24 July It was 1110 when Warwick BV 475 of 278 Squadron (F/O Whitely) took off from Bradwell Bay to patrol 15 miles south-south-west of St Albans Head (Dorset). It commenced at 5000 feet and from this height observed a Fortress and two Lightnings circling and on closing to investigate saw four men in the sea, position 5009N 0245W, also a Walrus of 278 Squadron (from Martlesham Heath) on the sea. Smoke floats were dropped to mark this position whilst the Airborne Lifeboat was dropped to a man some two miles to the north at 1440. This landed some 60 yards away but he swam to it and with considerable difficulty ultimately managed to climb aboard. The report adds that the four men near the Walrus were picked up by 1600 hours by an HSL but the man aboard the lifeboat is not mentioned again. Being almost in sight of the Walrus and watched over by the Warwick, and not quite in mid-Channel, so well within the Coastal Command Rescue network, it can be reasonably assumed that he was safely picked up. These men were survivors of Lancaster PB 211 of 630 Squadron which had been out minelaying but had hit the sea when flying in very low cloud.

26 July   269 Squadron, stationed at Lagens in the Azores now comes into the picture with a successful lifeboat drop. 'V' (F/O Smith) was scrambled at 0445 to go to the aid of ditched Fortress 'Z' of 220 Squadron RAF. Another Fortress, 'A' 220, searching during the night, had located two dinghies after sighting a Very light and homed its companion 'K', and Hudson 269 'F', so that they were over the dinghies at 0609; one of which contained nine men, the other empty. Their position was 3723N 2404W, approximately 300 miles south-east of the Azores base. At 0631 after two dummy runs the Hudson dropped her lifeboat 150 yards upwind of the survivors, who had reached and boarded it within nine minutes. A visual signal of the course to steer was given at 0710 and 'F' left to contact a Portuguese merchant ship, the *Lourenço Marques*, seen some miles away, leaving 'K' to watch over the survivors. Contact being made the vessel turned off course and at 0943 was alongside the lifeboat. At first the Portuguese were very reluctant to take the survivors aboard, thinking them to be from a sunken U-boat; but the difficulty was soon and happily resolved. A footnote to the report says 'Hudsons almost worn out, promised Warwicks eagerly awaited'. A long letter from Mr Harry King of Thundersley in Essex sums up the hopes and fears of all who were forced to ditch; his experiences flow with all the ease of a natural story-teller so it will be best to quote him with a minimum of editing:

> We left St Eval June 14th 1944 bound for the Azores; a 'sproggy' NCO crew. The Skipper, F/S Macilwick, a Scot; P/O Lamb, 2nd Pilot; 2nd AG Sgt. Cousins, both Canadians; 4th W/O AG Ryan an Australian; Warrant Officer Taylor, 1st W/O AG; 5th W/O AG Lyle and myself [F/E], all British and 3rd W/O AG Domininco (?). We always flew alone, the Squadron motto was 'Observe Unseen'; we were a reasonably happy crew considering each of us came from different backgrounds and education; but we all had a similar trait, which was 'Slow to anger or panic', and an unexpressed thankfulness that we'd not been posted to Bomber Command where the casualty rates were rarely under 25%, more often higher, I lost two cousins in Bomber. Also we were better off for food.
>
> The morning of the 25th we assembled about 0900 for our pre-flight meal, which was always better than Mess meals. The two cooks did nothing but cater for operational aircrew; they also packed our in-flight snacks – four spam sandwiches, one banana or orange, a bar of chocolate each plus a gallon of coffee or pineapple juice to sustain us for 12 to 13 hours; on one occasion the Americans supplied us with in-flight rations; what luxury, even an individual fruit salad.
>
> At the pre-flight meal the Skipper asked 'Where's Dom?' Cousins answered 'Sick'; we did not realise that Providence was beginning to smile on us. We were boarding the aircraft when Dom appeared, with the cheeky grin on his face which the majority of women could not resist. Before

anyone could speak he announced in a jovial voice, 'I have the old complaint; excused all duties – the MO did not say not to start a poker school. So long you guys.'

After completing the pre-flight checks we took off to commence the patrol of 'creeping line ahead' (in other words ploughing a field) to sweep an area of 10000 square miles of sea. Depending on wind speed and direction, slightly above stalling speed the four engines consumed around 160 gallons per hour; all fuel consumed meant ditching. We had been aloft approximately ten hours on the homeward leg and I was in the Skipper's seat listening to the sound of No. 1 engine; which was at a higher pitch than the other three. The pilot shouted to me 'It looks as through we shall make it tonight'; I replied that I was not happy with the sound from No. 1, then just as the Skipper returned No. 1 engine screamed – the rev. counter shot up to well over 4000 in a few seconds. It was shut down at once; we, like the other crews, were accustomed to returning on three engines. 'Not to worry, three are still working OK.' About an hour later No. 4 screamed off the rev. counter, identical with No. 1. I tried starting up No. 1 but with no result. Meanwhile the Skipper had told the WO/AG to send out the SOS and the rest of the crew to throw every movable article overboard. As I opened the bomb doors the Skipper pressed the bomb release button 'Bombs away'. I calculated we had used about six tons of fuel which plus the weight thrown overboard should make us ten tons lighter, so at 1000 feet on two engines we should be able to make the landing strip on San Miguel which was about 90 miles nearer than base. There had been no reply to our distress signals. Twenty minutes later after No. 2 engine had screamed up to 4000 revs plus, the Skipper announced, in his best Scottish accent, 'Ditching stations'. On a dry land rehearsal we had taken just 19 seconds from the bell to all out so we didn't waste any time; I grabbed the signalling pistol from its holster with three cartridges and pushed the lot into the blouse of my battle-dress as I made my way to my place in the now empty bomb bay. I was the last to take up position and already Cousins was relaying heights over the intercom. The last I heard him say was '100 feet – for Christ's sake – Pull'. He promptly pulled the dinghy release himself and then we hit the water. I did not know any more until I was aware of someone pulling me out of the bomb bay which was three-quarters full of water. It was the 2nd pilot who realised that I was not in the dinghy and came back for me and managed to lodge me on the radar aerial which broke under my weight; fortunately I came up beside the fuselage, not underneath it, so I was hauled into the dinghy somewhat revived by the cold water. The Skipper had landed the plane very well in the darkness with no flare path, an uneven surface and only one engine, which itself caused instability. He made an excellent job of it and I can't remember any of the crew thanking him.

A few words about the dinghies that the Fortress carried. Each was housed in a rectangular compartment to port and starboard in the top of the fuselage, above the bomb bay; by sharp pulls on the two release handles the CO_2 cylinders were activated to inflate the dinghies and thus force them out of their storage.

It was a dark night with a slight drizzle and a heavy swell and I had just settled into the dinghy when we heard a shout from the port dinghy 'We are sinking'. We paddled towards them with our hands and took the other four aboard which made us eight in a four-man craft and so low that we shipped some water. The port dinghy had been cut in its buoyancy chambers. We were equipped with a wireless, which was 'US', a salt-water purifier, two Star Reds for signalling, plus rations etc. Not one of our distress signals had been answered and now we were adrift with a useless radio; we were alone at the mercy of the sea, with eight aboard and only two inches to spare, a light breeze would have swamped us; an inquisitive shark could have sunk us with ease – on a warm sunny day they sunbathe. Just as the Skipper arranged a lookout watch, Taylor to the south and I to the north, the rest to go to sleep – if possible, the plane broke into two at the beam windows and both portions slipped soundlessly beneath the water. Would we be next? I don't know how long I'd been looking into the dark sky when I saw a short beam of light. I told the Skipper; this brought a laugh from someone 'George has gone crazy'. I pulled out the pistol from my blouse and fired it; again I fired it, yes there it was again, a short beam of light; I fired all the cartridges. By then the 2nd Pilot had got the Star Reds out and commenced firing whilst we all looked. It seemed a long time before aircraft engines became music to our ears; the plane was lit up, the outline one of our B 17s. A message in Aldis – 'Who are you?'

I should explain that the Fortress was conducting an experiment with multiple candlepower flares; that's what I saw. One of the WO/AG, not on duty, was leaning out of a beam window, smoking, when he spotted the colour flare I sent up and reported it to his Skipper, who advised base. Base ordered 'Investigate'. Providence had smiled again, we had been found. If Dom had been with us the extra man would have sunk our dinghy.

The B 17 kept vigil and soon after dawn a Hudson appeared and dropped an Airborne Lifeboat; a textbook drop, about 150 yards away. We climbed aboard, eight of us 'tenderfoots'; wet, but relieved and in a boat which if handled correctly would survive very rough seas. It fell to me to start the engines and they went away at once, but soon overheated; I assumed the cooling inlet ducts were blocked. The Skipper said 'Jump overboard and clean the openings'. I could not swim, nor could any of the others, so they said – I knew otherwise, so did the Skipper. The engines were shut down and the Skipper said 'Raise the sails' – no response; we all had the same thought; if a squall sprang up anything could happen with exhausted 'tenderfoots'. Discipline was not so dogmatic in the RAF as in the Army and Navy. There were a number of reasons for this. One, I say, was a crew of all ranks confined for a number of hours in a small area; we ate our pre-flight meals together; briefed on operations together; lectured together; drank and got drunk together. I have wartime experience in mind – 'Familiarity is a broody hen and her chicks'.

Anyway we each took an available oar whilst the navigator sorted out

19   Flt Sgt Macilwick and crew just boarding their heaven sent Lifeboat 26.7.1944

20   SS Lourenço Marques which entertained them royally

the appropriate chart and began to plot a course for base from the last known position. Again a few words of explanation will not come amiss. The procedure on 'Creeping Line Ahead' was that every 15 minutes the navigator informed the W/Op of our position; in the event of attacking or being attacked; the W/Op duly informed base of the position and time; but our distress signals which carried the same information were not acknowledged. The plotting was started on the memorised last position, and I must add that when the whole episode was analysed he was found to be only 15 miles out, very good indeed considering that we'd drifted for two hours without benefit of moon or stars to take a 'fix'.

Sometime later another B 17 took over and after a period they signalled that a ship was approaching from an easterly direction and finally the *Lourenço Marques* drew gently alongside; a rope ladder was thrown down to us. The Skipper was first up (the RAF tradition is different to the Navy's); I was the last. For the first time during this episode I felt an apprehension of fear seeing that swaying ladder but with all the anxious faces looking down at me I overcame my fear and climbed up. The Captain and a Portuguese Army MO and, of course, the rest of the crew, awaited me. The MO said in good English, 'You are wounded'. Apparently I had blood all over my face, but no one had told me. 'Come to the surgery.' Whilst he was checking me over he told me the Captain was under the impression that we were Germans. He told the orderly to prepare a hot salty bath and a bunk. When I awoke my uniform had been replaced with a pair of blue flannel trousers and a silk shirt, a luxury which I treasured for many years, and I went up to the Bridge where the rest of our crew had gathered except the Skipper. Whilst I'd been asleep the ship had docked at Ponta del Garda on the island of San Miguel. The British Consul had come aboard to persuade the Captain to release us from internment, which he managed to do, but the Captain upheld International Maritime Law and kept the lifeboat and all its equipment.

Later I went down to the lower deck to look for my uniform, for I had over £20 in Portuguese currency in my wallet. I found all the uniforms laid out on deck to dry – under guard; I indicated that I wanted to check my pockets and much to my relief the wallet was there intact. He, in turn, indicated that he'd like the whistle attached to my lapel, which I gladly gave to him. I returned to the Bridge just in time for drinks and snacks all round. When the Consul led the way off the ship I hastily finished the half tumbler of Scotch whisky given to me by the steward under the Captain's orders; fortunately, seeing the state I was in, it was a gangplank which had to be negotiated, not a rope ladder. We were billeted in a small house in the city and were all in 'civvies', for the Mission to Seamen had kitted us out very well. The following day, about lunchtime, the Skipper told us that the British Consul had invited us to a private dinner party at his Residence. It was a dinner party I will always remember; he and his wife a perfect host and hostess, his 17-year-old daughter, a lady with manners that alas have passed into history. I named my elder daughter after her, much to my wife's disgust. The Portuguese staff were very good, it was a seven-course dinner; before we went in from the garden we had two champagne cocktails and at dinner four appropriate wines suitable to the course served. I was a bit concerned as I had not eaten a reasonable meal for two days; the champagne was already having an effect. I'm pleased to record that we did not let down the Royal Air Force. Sometime before midnight we all had a bottle of British beer. The next day we went to the Emergency Landing Strip which we had attempted to make two nights before; Providence had smiled again. To make a satisfactory landing there in darkness meant an approach between two hills, the runway starting on the edge of a 200-foot cliff and ending with a hill at the other end; what with this, a poor flare path and no reserve engine power to climb, it was indeed providential that we'd not had to try to land there.

By 1100 hours we were on a C 54 Skymaster and heading for base to undergo a medical. The Skipper and I were questioned separately as to how we managed to lose one of His Majesty's aircraft. I did not learn the result until four months later. My Skipper was commissioned and posted to the Squadron's Liberators and the officer who questioned me was now my Skipper and Flight Commander. I asked him the result of the enquiry; he was a man of few words and bluntly replied 'Sabotage'.

31 July   Warwick 'H' of 282 Squadron (F/L Gwynn) took off from Davidstow Moor at 1120 to search for the survivors of a ditched Coastal Command Liberator. Either it was a lucky day or else 'fixes', navigation and visibility were all perfect for just over an hour later they sighted wreckage in position 5051N 0515W (north-north-west of Padstow in Cornwall) with two men clinging to debris and another two floating nearby in Mae Wests. At 1144 the lifeboat was dropped into the wind from 700 feet at 140 knots; but there the goodness of the day ended abruptly, for the parachutes failed to open and the lifeboat partially broke up on impact, although it remained floating with the bows submerged. Back up support was, however, already on the way and at 1203 a Walrus landed, its crew requesting that as some of the survivors were badly injured a launch be sent out. At 1347 a rescue craft arrived, the men were taken aboard to be rapidly on their way to Padstow. Unfortunately the Walrus was unable to take off owing to damage and a waterlogged float, so it taxied all the way into Padstow in the wake of the launch, escorted by 'H' which had maintained contact throughout. On debriefing the crew of 'H' complained of 'continual hindrance by an Anson which continually flew across the scene at a low altitude and prevented useful photography'.

5 August   'M' (F/O Ayres) and 'J' (F/L Schaffer) of 280 Squadron had the afternoon patrol from Strubby with an escort of seven Lightnings to cover the tracks of returning USAAF bombers. 'M' wasn't long in making a sighting at 5422N 0704E (about 35 miles to the north-west of Heligoland) of two aircraft dinghies with four or five men. There were several Danish fishing vessels in the vicinity although none at that time had made any effort to pick up the men; possibly they'd not seen them. 'M' released her lifeboat from 700 feet across the wind and had the satisfaction of seeing it successfully boarded before being forced to return to base with a faulty engine gauge, leaving 'J' with a watching brief. No explanation was given regarding this unorthodox dropping approach, but it may have had something to do with the faulty instrument. Neither 'M' nor 'J' observed any attempt by the survivors either to start the lifeboat's engines or to hoist the sails. The aerial activity obviously attracted the attention of the Danes and the fishing vessel *Erika* (FV 311 or FN 311) soon came alongside the lifeboat and then took her crew and the craft on board before resolutely, and very courageously, turning her bows westwards and heading for England, subsequently making Great Yarmouth where she received a cordial reception. Seeing the course of events 'J' resumed her patrol to make it a double for the Squadron that day, in the following manner.

5 August   One B 24 from each of 448, 458 and 489 Bomb Groups ditched on this day and it is not stated from which planes the men rescued in these two operations came. After 'J' had witnessed the pick-up by the *Erika* it continued its patrol, ranging well away to the northwards until at 1630 the aircrew sighted two aircraft dinghies containing nine men in position 5428N 0655E (50 miles north-west of Heligoland); to them it dropped its lifeboat some minutes later. It landed within 30 yards of the survivors and the watchers had the satisfaction of seeing it promptly boarded. Contact was continually maintained by signal lamp until the limit of endurance was reached and 'J' was forced to turn for home; arriving at 1838. During the 6th continued searches were made for the lifeboat and its occupants without success and it was feared they had been captured by the enemy. All hope had not been abandoned and at 1210 on the 7th the lifeboat was sighted by 'M' on a course of 215/220 degrees at 5 knots, in position 5406N 0015E. Rescue craft were sought and homed so that at 1505 HSL 2732 took two (?) men aboard. It would seem they had made an epic voyage of about 270 miles in the lifeboat in less than 43 hours, an average speed of over 6 knots, and were heading gamely for Bridlington; moreover they undoubtedly stood a very good chance of reaching there that day. The report makes no mention of the initial sighting quoting nine men seen in the dinghies but only two being recovered – therein lies a mystery. Both these rescues were made within 20 and 90 miles respectively of the German island fortress of Heligoland.

15 August   280 Squadron were busy again, 'Z' (Sq. Ldr. Easton) and 'K' (P/O Hagg) taking off from Strubby at 1025 to search for the survivors of Lancaster PB 358 of 97 Squadron reported to have ditched close to the Dutch coast. The position given as centre of the search area was 5221N 0407E, but it was some hours later before seven men were found in a dinghy at 5224N 0405E, several miles further north and closer into the Dutch coast than previously reported. Without any further preliminaries 'Z' dropped its lifeboat and all the survivors were seen to board and efficiently get the boat under way at 1437, then head westwards as rapidly as possible. Meanwhile 'K' had spotted an HSL some 15 miles distant and homed it to intercept the lifeboat's course. The meet-up at 1538 was followed by a hasty transfer to the larger boat leaving the hapless Air-borne Lifeboat to be sunk by gunfire as it was so close to the enemy-held shore.

19 August   The Air/Sea Rescue Squadrons had their costs in the lives of their crews. Whilst flying at 500 feet on line ahead search for a dinghy to the north of Great Yarmouth, Hudson 'P' of 279 Squadron operating from Docking, piloted by F/O 'Bofa' Blake, was seen by her neighbour searcher, piloted by F/L Frank Goff, to go into a vertical climb before flipping over at 1000 feet and spiralling into the sea. One of the WOp/AG, a Canadian, was the only survivor to be picked up by a minesweeper.

24 August   As the armies fought their way up the peninsula of Italy the RAF went with them, the planes operating ahead of the troops with their bases to the rear. So it was that 293 Squadron were stationed at Brindisi with Warwicks to help in A/SR duties in the Adriatic, which was being increasingly flown over by bombers thrusting into the underbelly of the Axis Powers and by fighters, light bombers and suchlike strafing the communication routes of Yugoslavia or carrying supplies to the Partisans. 'B' (F/L James) took off at 1602 to search for the survivors of a B 24 which had reported imminent ditching in position 4223N 1543E (north of the Tremiti Isles). Guided by aircraft 'blips' on ASV they came into visual range of two Spitfires orbiting an oil patch with fluorescin traces. Further search revealed, at 1640, one survivor only and an empty dinghy some miles further east. Endeavour was made, without success, to contact an HSL, so the Airborne Lifeboat was dropped at 1650. By this time Warwick 'A' 293, on its way back from another operation, had joined the group and observed the action before going off to search for an HSL. The lifeboat splashed down within 75 yards of the survivor but he was having extreme difficulty in reaching it and had not done so by the time 'A' had found a rescue craft and homed it to the lifeboat at 1710. The badly injured man was taken from the sea five minutes later and hurried to Brindisi.

27 August   Hudsons 'L' (P/O Curtis) and 'E' (F/L Ashby) of 279 Squadron patrolling over the path of returning bombers spotted a 'J' type dinghy with seven occupants in position 5420N 0410E (approximately 180 miles east of Scarborough). These were the crew of a Pathfinder Lancaster, P of either 156 Sqdn or Pathfinder Force OTU from Upwood in Cambridgeshire, unlucky in sustaining damage but fortunate to get well clear of enemy-held territory. An Airborne Lifeboat was dropped, apparently successfully, but drifted away unreached; soon 'J', 'H' (P/O Gaze) and 'B' also arrived on the scene and assisted in maintaining watch over the dinghy. The subsequent arrival of 'U' with its lifeboat in the gathering dusk led to another drop, this time within 30 yards of the distressed crew, but lowering clouds and darkness hampered observation so contact was lost without knowledge as to whether the lifeboat had been boarded. The following day 'B' went out again, with other searching aircraft, and located the lifeboat with all the survivors aboard and observed the engines started at 0750; although the boat came to a stop an hour later. All guns were manned and avoiding action taken when a JU 88 hove into sight, but it was apparently blind in all eyes and flew on unaware of the drama in the sea beneath its wings. Meanwhile attempts were being made to home an HSL without success. 'W', also on watch, reported Danish fishing vessels heading for the lifeboat and the survivors were seen to board one of these so 'W' fired a burst across its bows to discourage an easterly course. 'K' then reported an empty Airborne Lifeboat in position 5434N 0426E and another alongside a Danish vessel. 'J' and 'E' had also been busy, although unobserved, and had contacted an HSL but were unable to home her onto the Dane. Later 'O' saw the fishing vessel on a course of 250 degrees at 6 knots but lost her in low cloud, drizzle and rain; she appeared to be making for the Humber. On the 29th 'J' sighted her, still at 6 knots, but now on a course of 270 degrees in position 5404N 0209E. After circling 'J' went off to find an HSL and watched it proceed in the correct direction, but then developed engine trouble and had to wing slowly home without observing the end of this three-day operation which had involved at least the eight Hudsons mentioned as well as numerous other planes. It is worth pausing to appreciate exactly what this rescue must have cost the Danish fishermen and the hardships it probably brought on the families they left behind under the Nazi oppressors.

Lancaster ND 807 of 97 Squadron was also shot down into the sea on 26th but no sighting of her crew has been traced.

8 September   Warwicks 'O' (F/O Chesher) and 'L' (F/L Proctor) of 280 Squadron took off from Langham in the evening to search for a dinghy with four men from a USAAF Liberator of 453 Bomb Group reported down in position 5458N 0040E (about 60 miles east of Sunderland), to whom a Lindholme dinghy had already been dropped. Also nearby was an Airborne Lifeboat which had not been used, maybe because it was not seaworthy or else the survivors were too weak to reach and board it. Possibly, as no other Squadron reports dropping a lifeboat at this time, it could have been the one which 279 dropped on 27th of the previous month, which had drifted about for the previous ten days and just happened to be in the vicinity of the Liberator men? The ultimate outcome of the rescue operation is not stated, but records speak of four men saved in this area.

13 September   282 Squadron started off exceedingly well in Airborne Lifeboat operations by making two drops in the same day, both with total success. Chivenor was the take-off base for four aircraft, 'D' (Sq. Ldr. Burge) at 0742, 'N' (F/L Gwynn) at 0751, and 'B' with another unrecorded. They were sent on creeping line ahead search for survivors midway between Lundy Island and Cork in Eire. Out of sight of each other two Warwicks carried out successful rescues with their lifeboats although three actually feature in the report. 'B' sighted an Airborne Lifeboat in position 5112N 0650W at 0850 and after investigating and finding it empty, with no wreckage or survivors in the area, resumed its search pattern. At 0948, in position 5121N 0646W, the rear gunner of 'N', W/O Clayton, spotted a dinghy some five miles distant on a bearing of 035 degrees true. Course was immediately altered and at 1000 hours they, with 'D', were over five survivors; 'D' dropped its lifeboat at 1015 and with all systems functioning perfectly the men were climbing aboard at 1037 after paddling to one of the extended floating rocket lines. At 1050 the destroyer HMS *Inconstant* came into view, probably attracted by the aerial activity, and took the survivors aboard. They were Art Henderson, Pilot, from Edmonton; Jack Hackett from Montreal; Butch Whale from Lakeside, Ontario; Keith Woods from St Jean-sur-Richelieu, Quebec and Fred Platts (British), who from his present home in Califonia supplied depth for this report.

Meanwhile 'N' had also sighted a dinghy in position 5122N 0654W at 1015 hours. Its lifeboat was then dropped into the wind from 700 feet at an airspeed of 133 knots, on a bearing of 120 degrees true. Either the aim was not particularly good or the wind was playing tricks for it landed 200 yards from the dinghy, nevertheless it was reached and boarded. Another destroyer of the same flotilla picked up the survivors within a very short time for it radioed to the plane that the five men taken aboard were alive and well. 'N' landed at Chivenor at 1151 whilst 'D' came into Davidstow Moor at 1150.

13 September   'F' of 280 Squadron (F/O Harvey) was scrambled at 1956 hours to find a ditched Mustang of 357 Group in position 5218N 0236E (about 40 miles off the Suffolk coast at Aldeburgh). All during the search around the given position the daylight was rapidly fading but lights were sighted on the water so an Airborne Lifeboat was dropped in the darkness, though the results could not be observed. An HSL was a few miles away but it was found to be impossible to contact her, so 'F' remained circling the drop area until endurance was reached at 0035 on the 14th. It was subsequently learned that the HSL had picked up the pilot of the Mustang as well as the crew of a Walrus, which attracted by flame floats dropped by 'F', had attempted a sea landing in the darkness and had, itself, become a casualty. These same flame floats had ultimately drawn the attention of the HSL to the fact that something important was happening just over the horizon. Whether the lifeboat was boarded or used is not reported.

17 September   Whilst not a lifeboat operation this date is worthy of note. 'M' of 280 Squadron whilst on routine patrol sighted a ditched glider approximately six miles west-north-west of Walcheren and on finding an RML, skippered by Lt. D. Harding RNVR, brought it to the casualty where the survivors, one officer and seven enlisted men, were rescued despite heavy fire from shore batteries. Later 'M' found one man in a dinghy and contacted an HSL to bring it to a second successful pick-up.

20 September   From Pognaliero in Italy 'J', 'D' and 'G' of 293 Squadron were all aloft during the day to search for survivors. 'J' took off at 1150 and at 1504 received a message to contact an HSL and proceed to the Pianosa Isles in the Adriatic (almost 100 miles south-south-west of Split in Yugoslavia). There, at 1514, they found a Catalina and two Fortresses circling wreckage, and three fluorescence patches, to the east of the islands; and further downwind a man, apparently dead, being dragged through the sea by a billowing parachute. Survivors in one of the fluorescence patches were seen waving, their position being 4212N 1549E. It being far too rough for the Catalina to alight and the HSL being nowhere in sight 'J' (F/O Goldspink) dropped its Airborne Lifeboat to the men; it landed 75 yards downwind from them, but the parachutes failed to release from the boat and dragged it away at speed in the 20-knot wind. 'J' could do nothing other than radio for another Warwick, preferably with Lindholme dinghies, continue to circle the area looking for other survivors and maintain contact with the man (or body) still being dragged by the parachute. 'D' (F/O Cornwall) with an Airborne Lifeboat took off at 1610 and was soon in the area, likewise the HSL. At 1630 a sole survivor was picked up before the Catalina guided the launch to other bodies. By 1700 Corvette L 65 had joined in the search. During this period 'J' lost contact with the errant parachute but 'D' had found it again 16 miles north of the Tremiti Islands roughly halfway in to the Italian coast; the man had his face above water so 'D' dropped her lifeboat 50 yards away, directly in his path, but once again the parachutes did not release and the boat moved downwind at about 5 knots, soon to be overtaken by the inflated parachute still towing its helpless burden, who made no visible attempt to reach or board the lifeboat. 'G', now also on the scene, kept watch whilst 'D' went back to find the Corvette. From then on the two planes worked hard to bring the Corvette and the inflated parachute together, dropping smoke and flame floats in the gathering darkness. Twice white flares were seen and the aircraft fired replies, but received no answers, having a vessel, believed to be the Corvette, on their screens just six miles away but impervious to their signals. At 2005 hours they were recalled to base and landed at 2043. Apparently both lifeboats were dropped well, but by the rate of drift it would seem that the drogue rocket of the first one did not fire and neither of the parachute releases functioned. One of these lifeboats was found capsized and waterlogged by 'D' on the 23rd in position 4225N 1549E and an HSL asked to bring it in, but the tow parted and the boat was lost.

25 September   281 Squadron's Warwick 'P' (F/O Murray) was airborne from Thornaby at 1522 for the long flight, almost to the Norwegian coast off Stavanger, to search for a missing aircraft, reported to be an RAF Liberator, and to attempt to rescue its crew. Wreckage and a single survivor were ultimately found in position 5745N 0435E (90 miles south-west of Stavanger) at 1753. The Airborne Lifeboat was dropped but the man was apparently too weak to attempt to reach it. In a further effort a Lindholme dinghy was sent down as closely to him as they dared, but still there was no positive response, the man just drifted past it and over the extended rocket lines of the lifeboat, to fall out of his dinghy at 1835 and float away face down. 'P' landed back at 2045, its crew very crestfallen. On consulting aircraft reports the only plane missing in this area around the relevant time was Lancaster PA 974 of 97 Squadron which ditched on the 24th.

3 October   279 Squadron were still at Bircham Newton on this date and it was from there that 'U' (F/L Goff) took off just after midday to seek one man in a dinghy off the Dutch coast; an escort of Thunderbolts being provided. The survivor was found in position 5323N 0503E (close to the Frisian island of Schiermonnikoog). The Hudson dropped her Airborne Lifeboat 100 yards down wind of him in a moderate westerly breeze, the parachutes pulling evenly and the release and rocket gears functioning correctly. The survivor was seen to board it and then flop down in the stern utterly exhausted; and although shadowed and watched by the Thunderbolts until darkness fell had made no attempt to start the engines. Contact was then lost and it is feared that he drifted onto enemy-held territory during the night. Neither the nationality, nor the aircraft from which this man came have been ascertained but two American Flying Fortresses collided over the enemy-held coast on 30 September. This was 279's last operational drop with Hudsons for on the 31st they moved to Thornaby for conversion to Warwicks, but by a temporary diversion to Banff were sent out, still with their Hudsons, to the Norwegian Sea to assist in the search for a Mosquito crew.

6 October   Two Warwicks of 'A' Flight 278 Squadron stationed at Martlesham Heath took off in the early light to seek two dinghies, one with three men, the other a single; the reported position was about 60 miles east-south-east of Harwich. After almost two hours of searching the three were found by HF 968 (F/O McWilliams) in position 5152N 0243E and the Airborne Lifeboat dropped to them. For reasons not stated (possibly parachute malfunction) it had started to break up by 0845, for the survivors had made no attempt to board it. The lone man, located in 5157N 0257E, was seen to fall out of his dinghy and be lost within a few minutes of sighting. Another Warwick, BV 528 (F/O Garden), now took over the operation and attempted to drop her lifeboat, but the release gear refused to work so the endeavour had to be abandoned. RML 550 had been on the way in case of need and this was now guided to the three survivors who, with the other man, were the four survivors of a German Heinkel 111 shot down by a nightfighter.

6 October   280 Squadron were also busy on this day, 'Y' (F/O Pull) taking off from Langham at 1234 bound for an indefinite spot some 200 miles or so east of Flamborough Head, where six men were adrift in an aircraft dinghy. It was half-way through the afternoon before they were found in position 5410N 0425E and an Airborne Lifeboat dropped to them at 1624 from 550 feet at 126 knots, which landed close enough for them to grasp one of the floating rocket lines and pull themselves alongside for boarding, all having accomplished this by 1635. By 1705 they had studied the instruction book and started the engines to get under way on a course of 270 degrees for the Yorkshire coast. Later a course of 240 degrees was passed by Aldis lamp, with Control advising at 1820 that 'Launches were on the way'. 'Y' was forced by shortage of fuel to return to base but despite darkness contact was made by 'G' which located the lifeboat at 1735 on the 7th and assisted an RML to an interception so that the men could be taken aboard for a speedier trip home.

More details of this rescue are supplied by Mr W. K. Boxell of Doubleview in Western Australia who now devotes his spare hours to the Western Australian Aviation Museum. At the time he was a crew member of Lancaster DV 373 of 467 Squadron based at Waddington. Below is the report filed by the Captain, F/O Feddersen:

5.10.44 Bombing Wilhelmshaven. Sortie completed. At 5450N 0540E at

1500 ft boost on port engine fell right off. Engineer tried all drills but best that could be got was – 2 boost. At 0950 port outer was feathered. Down to 1000 ft but held height on 2650 × 6. At this time being about two miles behind Squadron, I turned for base. During turn engineer reported fuel warning light on port inner, and boost dropped to zero. Height now 800 ft and losing steadily despite full power on starboard. Port inner engine not feathered. Realised ditching was imminent, instructed crew accordingly, made quick examination of possibility of jettisoning bombs, owing to height and available trim decided this was impracticable. Ordered bomb aimer to defuse which was done and opened fuel jettison cock. Gave order to take up ditching stations and W/Op fired 2 red Verys and sent out 3 SOS sig. Made good ditching across swell. Crew out in roughly 20 secs and A/C sank in approx 1 min. 'J' type lifeboat inflated and released OK. No trouble getting into it. Later formations of British and American A/C were seen passing over us that day and night. Our ditching was seen by a Liberator from 20,000 feet we were told later. At 1600 hours on 6th Oct. 1944 an airborne lifeboat was dropped nearby by a Warwick A/C of A/SR. We boarded this which greatly increased our comfort, this Warwick patrolled over us until 2200 hrs. Another Warwick came out at 0900 hours on the 7th followed by Fortresses and Mustangs of American A/SR. We were finally picked up by 2 A/SR motor launches at 1700 hrs on the 7th which took us to Yarmouth after collecting the crew of a Fortress of 487 Bomb Group on the way, which was seen to ditch just in front of the launch.

An addition to this personal narrative made by an unnamed member of one of the rescue boat's crew says: 'Just how lucky can you get, this B 17 ditched right in front of us and so close that we were alongside as the crew got out and they were able to walk along the wing to board us, and didn't even get their feet wet.' Two pilots of 479 Fighter Group were also picked up by the same launch; there must have been quite a party aboard the boat.

On F/L Feddersen's next operation to Hamburg on 11.11.44 he and his crew (Sgt E. F. Vevers, F/S I. R. Gray, F/S M. R. Stedman, F/S W. I. Houston, Sgt. G. E. Carrington and Sgt. R. W. G. Heath) were all killed in action flying NN 714, the only Lancaster lost that day. Mr Boxell was also very lucky not to be in the crew that day.

7 October   On this day 281 Squadron lost one of their lifeboats through enemy action. Whilst on patrol 'P' was surprised by seven JU 88s suddenly coming out of cloud with apparent aggressive intent. In an effort to reach similar cover the lifeboat was jettisoned, and although a deadly game of hide and seek ensued in the clouds 'P' reached Wick safely.

7 October   A very busy week for the lifeboat carriers. In response to a sighting report 280 Squadron's 'A' (P/O Hagg) left Langham at 0804 in company with 'E' (F/O Harvey), bound for the Dutch Frisian Islands, where two dinghies, containing two and seven men believed to be either from a B 17 of 92 Bomb

Group which ditched on the 5th, or the crew of Lancaster PB 412 of 626 Squadron lost whilst mine-laying during the night of 4/5th, had been seen. The first dinghy was found in position 5327N 0445E, about 20 miles north-east of Terschelling, and a lifeboat was dropped by 'A' which splashed down successfully 150 yards from the survivors who made no attempt to reach or board it, obviously too weak from cold and exposure. They were later rescued by HSL 2679 from Λ/SR Unit 24 at Gorleston, commanded by F/O David Ross. A call had come into Bircham Newton precisely at midday from a Mustang escorting a 279 Squadron A/SR flight, giving position 5327N 0445E . . . an hour an an half later the HSL found the empty lifeboat, and then set off for the dinghy, guided by the Mustang circling overhead. In the dinghy were Douglas Mann and Donald Kennedy of 626 Squadron Lancaster PB 412 shot down on the 5th; they had seen the Mustang two hours previously but had only one signal cartridge left, Mann was unable to make the effort to pull the trigger to fire the red star signal, but Kennedy managed it and it was seen by the Mustang pilot. The survivors were very weak and suffering from chronic immersion hypothermia after their five long days ordeal and on landing were taken to the Royal Naval Hospital at Great Yarmouth. Attempts to tow the Lifeboat home were unsuccessful so it was sunk by gunfire from an escorting Mustang. These Beaufighter men had survived almost a week in rubber dinghies and had drifted, sailed and paddled in horrifying conditions of wind and sea in winter weather apporximately 100 miles towards England in that time.

'A' was then diverted to 5400N 0635E (some 30 miles north-east of Juist in the German Frisians) soon to be joined by 'E', where the seven were sitting out their ordeal. As neither Warwick had a lifeboat, 'E' dropped a Lindholme which was boarded with difficulty as the men appeared very weak also. Both planes were now forced to return to base.

On the 8th 'Z' with Sq. Ldr. Bill Harper at the controls and my correspondent Frank Clark as rear gunner, resumed the search and rescue operation commenced the previous day and having found the dinghies containing the seven men dropped a lifeboat 100 yards downwind of them in the late afternoon; with results unobserved due to bad light in the falling darkness. Later red pyros were observed, believed to be from the lifeboat, more or less confirmed by seeing the Lindholme empty in the light of a flare. 'Z' returned to base to learn that 'L' (F/O Chesher), which had taken off at 1055 hours, was missing after reporting sighting four dinghies containing ten men in position 5401N 0634E with wind at 10–15 knots, 270 degrees, 2/10ths cloud, and had dropped her lifeboat to these survivors, undoubtedly the 457 Bomb Group crew, at 1250 hours. After reporting the drop and that the lifeboat had malfunctioned, for it landed capsized and did not recover itself, and the men in the dinghy had made no attempt to right it, 'L' went off the air and was apparently shot down within ten minutes of releasing its lifeboat.

'A', 'C', 'F' and 'G' had all taken off around 1000 hours to go to the Frisians to assist. At 1220 'A' (F/O Rhodes) sighted a dinghy, dropped its lifeboat, which was very promptly boarded, the engines started in record time and the signal sent aloft 'This is Chesher's crew' ('L'). 'C' went off to search for a rescue launch and sighting one at 1311 directed it to 'L's crew. At 1558 enemy aircraft appeared – as might be expected, the whole operation being conducted literally on their doorstep – so the launch was stopped. When the enemy planes first appeared 'A' was attacked by two ME 410s of KG 51 but managed to make cloud cover in the nick of time, accompanied at top speed by 'G'. A fighter escort was called for and 'A' landed back at Langham at 1752. 'G' failed to return. In formal official parlance 'One of our aircraft is missing'.

F/O Chesher making his report on the 10th wrote:

Take-off was at 1055 with the search area concentrated around 5410N 0634E for two dinghies. At 1245 four dinghies were sighted lashed together with an estimated ten men in them. We dropped our lifeboat and the survivors started to board it. During this phase of the rescue we were attacked by two ME 410 planes. Our rear and upper gunners damaged one 410 so that it broke off the attack with one engine on fire. Continued attacks by the other led to the rear gunner being injured; the hydraulics were shot up, the rudder and ailerons rendered useless and the undercarriage dropped. When we reached cloud cover we thought we might still have a chance to get away with it, but after being in the murk for eleven minutes were unlucky to emerge within sight of an ME 410. We managed to drive off or evade his first eight attacks, but the ninth was one too many for us, so we were forced to ditch at 1303. 'L' broke up and sank within ten seconds but the dinghy released and inflated automatically, allowing all the crew to board. We spent a miserable night in the dinghy, baling most of the time; my navigator, F/S Jones and the air gunner, W/O Donley were both badly wounded and I had shrapnel in my leg, but none of the lads complained. At 1515 the next day two Mosquitos sighted us and we cheered when a Warwick later dropped us a lifeboat, which we were quickly able to board and get under way. A Dornier gave us some unwelcome attention at one stage, but the boys above us managed to drive it off. We motored for seventeen hours before the fuel ran out and we were forced to step the mast and set sails, making 75–80 miles of homeward journey from right under the Germans' noses, before being picked up.

9 October 'O' (or 'D' – bad writing) piloted by F/L Thomson was airborne from 0737 to 1120 and during the flight sighted an Airborne Lifeboat under sail with six aboard, in position 5315N 0308E. One of the Yarmouth RMLs was seen about seven miles away and homed onto the lifeboat; at 0908 the crew were taken aboard. Now on the scene as well was HSL 2697, also from Yarmouth, which tried all ways to tow the lifeboat in, but it became damaged so was sunk by gunfire.

17 November Flying from Banff 'H' (W/O Bolton) and 'Q' (F/O Jenner) of 281 Squadron were on operations over the Shetland Isles when 'Q' developed trouble and was forced to ditch in West Voe, near Sumburgh. The weather at the time was reported to be 'very high winds'. Having lived for many years in the Northern Isles and knowing just how hard it can blow there the author can appreciate the extent of that understatement. 'H' observed the ditching at 1350 and immediately dropped her lifeboat to the survivors – but the parachutes did not release and the boat blew away downwind at an alarming rate, finally to strike the rocky shoreline. The whole operation had been seen from land and small boats put out which picked up five of the men alive, and recovered one body.

9 December   Also operating from Banff, Warwick 'G' of 279 Squadron (Lt. Shanks) took off to continue the search in an area around 6025N 0025E (40–50 miles east of Fetlar in the Shetlands) for two men from Beaufighter 'R' 489 which had been shot down on the 7th, and were thrilled to make a sighting in the mid afternoon. They immediately prepared to drop their Airborne Lifeboat and saw it successfully boarded at 1600 hours with a westerly course set very soon afterwards. These observations must have been made by the light of flares for in that latitude darkness would have fallen at that time of year. Searching for further aid 'G' came across the trawler *Molde* and homed her on an intercepting course so the Beaufighter men were taken from their lifeboat at 2050 to be landed in Shetland.

16 December   279's spirits touched a low ebb over this operation. 'P' (Sq. Ldr. Levin-Raw) had taken off from Banff at 1336 to go 70 miles north-north-west of Bergen in an effort to find two men of the crew of Lysander 'R' of 268 Squadron reported down in the sea in position 6100N 0400E. Success attended the search and their lifeboat was dropped at 1512, but the parachutes failed to release and the boat was blown to leeward in the near gale force wind, bumping from wave to wave until it was wrecked, only then did the release gear actuate. 'F' (F/O Reilly) now also on the scene dropped her lifeboat at 1602 but this time the opposite happened, the parachutes released in mid air and the boat broke up on impact with the sea. There seemed little more the plane crews could do beyond summon further aid, and drop an extra dinghy with full survival equipment to the men who had twice seen their hopes of life dashed; which 'F' did. One man was seen to reach and board this and then paddle to the wreck-age of 'P's lifeboat. Worsening visibility and darkness prevented further observation that day. On the 17th the planes went out again and in spite of the constant presence of enemy aircraft found one man dead in a dinghy, with no sign of the other or the remains of the lifeboats.

One wonders just what a light aircraft like a Lysander was doing so far from Scotland and can only assume taking part in a clandestine operation.

21 December   A very sad Christmas for the relatives and friends of the crew of 'U' 282 for, at 1630, she was observed to crash in flames into the sea five miles from the Fastnet Rock lighthouse. There were no survivors.

24 December   'D' 281 (W/O Stevens) were lucky to be able to celebrate their

Christmas after taking off from Sumburgh at 1042 to search for a Mustang between 6018 and 6038N and 0030 and 0558E, an area of stormy desolate northern waters almost 200 × 50 miles. Having operated without success almost to the limit of their endurance they were returning to base when they encountered 10/10 cloud at very low altitude and in this struck an unknown object which sheared six feet off their port wing, forcing them to jettison the Airborne Lifeboat at 1624 and consider themselves fortunate to reach Wick at 1652.

31 December 'B' 279 (P/O Grimston) left Fraserburgh in the fading light at 1409 to make the long flight to 5754N 0310E to seek a dinghy with one man from a Mosquito about 110 miles south-west of Stavanger. As usual, the wind was very strong and 'B's crew was very sharp eyed to spot him amid the wave crests at 1558. Their lifeboat was dropped at 1616 by the light of flares, but the parachutes failed to release and the boat blew away beyond reach of the survivor. 'G' (P/O Duthie) had also taken off for the mission and now reached the scene to assist if necessary. Their arrival was most welcome and their lifeboat dropped at 1625, but again the parachute release gear failed to operate. The boat was very close to the survivor and the floating lines well within his reach as it blew downwind; but P/O Duthie of 'G', remembering the incident, sadly recalled that no effort was made to grasp them or to board the boat. 'I formed the opinion he was injured, which with the cold rendered him either unconscious or completely helpless.'

7　Operations 1945 to VE Day

1 January　280 Squadron started the New Year off in style with two lifeboat drops; the success of the second fortunately offsetting the failure of the first. 'B' (F/L Gray) was away from Beccles at 1140 with three Mustangs as escort to seek three dinghies containing six aircrew of a 603 Squadron Flying Fortress of 398 Bomber Group USAAF, who were reported by Thunderbolts to be drifting 95 miles north-west of Texel, with 100 miles east of Hull given as a cross-bearing. Whilst searching they were diverted to 5357N 0330E (some 50 miles to the east) to assist 'A' (F/O Wyatt), which after taking off at 1437, had quickly found the missing aircrew in their three dinghies lashed together. 'B' arrived in the area in time to watch 'A' drop marine markers and then her Airborne Lifeboat at 1533 from 750 feet with an airspeed of 120 knots. To the horror of all the watchers the parachutes failed to open and the lifeboat went straight under, bows first, with only splintered fragments subsequently rising to the surface. 'B' immediately took over the major role and lined up to drop her lifeboat at 1604 and had the satisfaction of watching the survivors board it without too much difficulty. Darkness was now falling so a message was flashed 'You will be picked up' and the Warwicks returned to base leaving the ditched airmen the relative comfort of a stable, well equipped boat in place of their rubber dinghies. 'T', which had flown out to stand by and assist if necessary maintained a watch in the darkness until at 1956 hours, by the light of flares she'd dropped, her crew saw an RML complete the rescue and save all six men. Mr B. Hall of Sheffield continues the tale:

> I was a member of the crew of RML 515, one of eight boats of the 60th RML Flotilla stationed at HMS *Midge*, Great Yarmouth. We were cruising a few miles outside that port when we received a message that a US bomber had ditched about 100 miles east of Hull, so we opened the throttles on our 'B' class Fairmile and headed out through the sandbanks to reach the area as quickly as possible. It was well dark by the time we neared the position, but guided by aircraft flares we were soon able to see an Airborne Lifeboat crewed by the survivors; and had them aboard our boat within minutes. We took the lifeboat in tow and headed back to Yarmouth as quickly as we could with full credit to the RAF boys for their guidance and help.

The Americans had only been in their dinghies an hour before being found; their fully-loaded bomber on its way to Germany had sunk within ten seconds of hitting the water. (The author is unable to reconcile fully the various locations given in the above.)

1 January   Mosquito MV 248 was away from Banff at 1235 to search for survivors of 'U' 248 over in the direction of Stavanger. At 1447, in position 5754N 0336E (about 110 miles south-west of that port) it was over an Airborne Lifeboat displaying the number '7' which appeared to be empty. A light which could have been a flare was then observed some 200 yards from the lifeboat, but contact was lost in the poor light whilst orbiting. It wasn't until the following day that Mosquito 'J' 248 found the lifeboat momentarily and managed to give an approximate position around which subsequent fruitless searches were made.

2 January   'K' of 280 Squadron took off from Beccles at 0800 hours in company with 'A' which carried an Airborne Lifeboat; with them went an escort of Mustangs. Whilst searching 'K' picked up an automatic homing signal, and at 1100 hours was over an American (?) Airborne Lifeboat containing four men in position 5409N 0634E (50 miles west of Heligoland), with a floating mine keeping them company nearby. 'A' dropped her lifeboat and indicated by visual signal that the survivors should recover petrol from it so they could get their own boat under way again; but they received no reply nor was any apparent action taken. 'K' then dropped a Lindholme as an additional aid. On the 3rd 'X' 280 was over the lifeboat again, this time in position 5406N 0618E, and after being foiled in dummy runs by the kite aerial being flown from the boat dropped another lifeboat at 1425, carrying away the kite aerial in the process. Cloud was down to 700 feet. No attempt was made to reach this new lifeboat, so separate fuel containers were dropped and recovered by the survivors, but the engines of the USAAF boat were still not started, or would not start. Searches were extensive the next day (4th) but it was not until after dark, 2028 precisely, that 'K' found the American boat, still stationary, in position 5414N 0648E. Knowing that RMLs were also searching 'K' sought them out and dropped sea markers every three minutes to guide them to the lifeboat; but failing to make communication contact returned to the lifeboat and dropped flares knowing that these would attract the boats. Only then was VHF contact made and the position of the lifeboat given so that the survivors were picked up later that night. No comment was made about the apparently inexplicable behaviour of the Americans. Attempts to trace this 'drop' on the USAAF microfilm records have met with no success, which is not surprising as the first claimed ERS drop was in April – so it was almost certainly a Mk I or IA.

11 January   On this day 279 Squadron lost one of their crews, shot down in 'B'. When last seen at 1447 in position 5813N 0630E (approximately) by the crew of a Beaufighter orbiting a ditched Mosquito pilot there was an ME 109 in close pursuit. Later another Beaufighter sighted wreckage about 20 miles off the Norwegian coast. The rescuers of 1 January were beyond aid.

12 January   Undaunted by the grief of the previous day 'G' (P/O Duthie) and

'S' (W/O Williamson) of 279 Squadron took off from Fraserburgh to provide A/SR cover for a 617 (Dambusters) and 9 Squadrons' raid on the U-boat pens at Bergen, carrying Tallboy bombs especially developed to penetrate deep into the earth and destroy the foundations of structures. On the return journey the Lancaster piloted by F/O Ian Ross (RAAF) was attacked by FW 190s and forced down in position 5958N 0415E (only 60 miles south of their target). The plane made a perfect 'ditching' in fine weather with good visibility and all the crew managed to get onto the fuselage, to be circled by another Lancaster, piloted by F/O Watts, which sent out distress and position calls before being forced by shortage of fuel to return to base. A third Lancaster piloted by F/O James Castagnola also circled and dropped all possible buoyancy aids, including the crew's own Mae Wests. Escorting Beaufighters of 18 Group also did all they could to assist. Warwick 'G' found the Lancaster at 1600 with the men still on the fuselage and dropped the Airborne Lifeboat to them at 1605, close enough for one of the crewmen to leave the group and swim to it as the aircraft started to sink – an heroic feat in midwinter in those northern waters. Two Lindholmes were dropped as well, to assist any men in the water, but both failed to inflate. The sudden arrival of enemy aircraft forced the two Warwicks to withdraw hurriedly, but not before they had seen a JU 88 strafe the survivors and the lifeboat. Returning later 'S', in an effort to complete the rescue, at 1725 dropped another lifeboat in the darkness at the place where red flares, first seen from a distance, were repeated; quoting a position of 6108N 0205E. Subsequently dropped flares shew the lifeboat with a dinghy nearby, but contact was then lost although the search continued until shortage of fuel forced them to leave. P/O Duthie, of 'G', writes of his sorrow and anger at seeing the JU 88 destroy their good work. No further sighting was made of either men or the boat despite extensive searchings. Two months later a Norwegian fisherman recovered the body of one of the aircrew, F/O Mawbray Elwood, aged 24, from the island of Asnar, in the Arctic Circle.

13 January   Drop to dinghy midway twixt North Shetland and Faeroes, in darkness, probably to enemy aircrew. (Details not available.)

3 February   280 Squadron's 'Z' (F/L Radford) took off from Beccles at 1232 on A/SR Patrol and at 1412 was diverted to 5302N 0325E where a Fortress was reported flying at sea-level. On arrival, at 1421, in position 5301N 0322E (90 miles north-east of Great Yarmouth), 'Z' found a dinghy with two occupants, having been led promptly to the place by two Thunderbolts circling and 'O' of 280 Squadron already dropping smoke floats. As the latter was not carrying a lifeboat 'Z' took over by dropping hers from 700 feet at 1430. As the survivors paddled towards it with the intention of boarding HSL 2631 came over the horizon at a great speed, to take them aboard before they had a chance to sample the lifeboat's facilities. The lifeboat was sunk by gunfire.

The Warwicks were then diverted to 5234N 0315E but could find nothing there; 'Z' commenced a square search and at 1715 came across three dinghies with seven survivors in position 5312N 0412E (30 miles further out). Having already dropped their lifeboat 'Z' could only assist by dropping a set of

21   Flying Fortress survivors in their dinghies February 1945

22   A Mark IA safely down

Lindholme gear, which was recovered, and calling for further assistance. This quickly arrived in the form of a Catalina flying boat, aboard which the wrecked airmen were taken at 1735. Twenty-three USAAF bombers were lost on this day; two were known to have ditched and from them 17 crewmen were saved by various Air/Sea Rescue methods.

10 February   Lt. D. C. Shoemaker of 305 Group USAAF had an Airborne Lifeboat dropped to the two survivors of his aircraft. (Details not traced.)

16 February   Airborne Lifeboat sighted 5523N 0401E (230 miles east of Newcastle) by 'B' 279 but contact lost in patchy dense fog. (Details not traced.)

19 February   First service drop of Mk II from Beccles, believed to be by a plane of 280 Squadron. (Not an operational rescue.)

4 March   From Fraserburgh 'D' 279 (F/O Reilly) took off at 0845 to a reported dinghy sighting in position 5632N 0606E (about 300 miles east of Berwick). The dinghy was eventually sighted in weather which was reported as being 'shocking' and an Airborne Lifeboat dropped 30 yards upwind, at 1100 hours, to three men in battle-dress, who made no attempt to reach it. Two Lindholmes were then dropped very close, one of which failed to open, but again there was no positive response. Meanwhile 'Y' (Sq. Ldr. Burge), which with 'K' and 'E' was also out searching, located a dinghy a few miles to the north-west, with two men in it. A lifeboat was dropped to them by 'Y' at 1417 but one of the parachutes failed to release so the boat blew away beyond reach downwind. Contact with both dinghies was then lost in the storm. 'K' (W/O Williamson) made a sighting, in a break in the weather at 1709, of two empty lifeboats and a dinghy with an apparently lifeless body lying in the bottom. Further searching by 'E' on the 5th could only report the two lifeboats, now 25 miles apart, and two dinghies. Although RAF aircrew wore a battle-dress type of uniform the specific use of the term 'in battle-dress' in 279 Squadron's daily report suggests Army personnel, but what such men would be doing flying in this area could be anybody's guess. Knowledge that the type of aircraft which ditched could have been a B 24 (Liberator) of 467 Bomb Group lost in the vicinity that day doesn't help much, although two men were saved from that ditching.

10 March   In the slightly kinder waters of the Adriatic a Mosquito was forced to ditch about 50 miles west of Pola. Warwick BV 415 (F/L Rawlings) of 293 Squadron took off from Cesenatico at 2135 in the hope of dropping an Airborne Lifeboat to the two survivors by the light of flares provided by a Baltimore and a Boston. Unable either to locate the dinghy or see the expected flares the Warwick was eventually forced to return to base, and landed just before midnight. Take-off the next day was at 1255 to proceed to position 4454N 1232E (east of Ravenna) where a Mosquito was orbiting a man in a dinghy. On arrival at 1327 two smoke floats were dropped to guide in a Walrus, hoping that it could rescue the survivor although he was in an area heavily infested with mines. At 1400 Walrus L 2207 (F/S Bickle) landed outside the minefield and the two W/O AGs, F/S Goldstein and F/S Burnett, tried to paddle their dinghy to the man, but the current was very strong and eventually they had to give up. After a short aerial conference BV 415 dropped her lifeboat very efficiently, close to the Walrus; the two W/Ops paddled their dinghy to her, cleared away the gear, started the engines and proceeded through the moored mines to pick up W/O Chamberlain RE OCTU 56 Squadron, and having done so carefully steered their way back to the Walrus, which had drifted some distance to the north. At 1545 the amphibian was airborne and accompanying Spitfires sank both the dinghies and the lifeboat rather than allow them to fall into enemy hands or cause further pointless searching.

1 April   This operation saw the first service drop of an American A-1 Airborne Lifeboat and much has been written about it. One account, in a letter, apparently by a witness of the 'drop' omits many of the facts and much of the RAF's strenuous efforts quoted in other reports, and contains so much 'Gung-ho' and misrepresentation that it would be amusing were it not such a deadly serious matter. The official report filed by the survivors generally agrees with those of the RAF persc..nel involved and all these sources have been used to compile this shortened version.

'Z' of 280 Squadron (F/L Bower), was airborne from Beccles at 0556 to seek a ditched PBY5 (the RAF called them the Catalina) 15 miles north-east of Borkum with an escort of three Mustangs from 357 Group. Apparently the PBY5, piloted by Lt. Laponas, had taken off from Halesworth on the 30th at 1225 and with an escort of two P 51s of 55 or 56 Group proceeded to a patrol position off the Dutch coast, to find and rescue the pilot of a Mustang. At 1430 'Colgate' (Control) directed them to a new position three miles off Schiermoonikoog where a survivor was seen adrift in a dinghy. The PBY5 was put down on the water despite steep seas but a wave crashed into the starboard engine, breaking an oil pipe, rendering it useless and takeoff impossible. The fighter escort was advised and word duly passed back to 'Colgate'. The Mustang pilot was swept away, never to be seen again. 'Z' found the ditched plane just before 0900 on 1 April and an Airborne Lifeboat was dropped on the hour. The aim was good, for it splashed down about 100 yards from the PBY5, the pilot of which rashly tried to taxi to it on his one usable engine, but rammed and smashed into it with its tail whilst trying to secure it alongside. By now a gale was blowing bringing up a very rough sea and the boat being continuously dashed against the metal hull of the plane, was soon badly damaged, consequently it was not boarded and soon drifted away a total wreck. At 1200 hours enemy fighters, some of the new ME 262 jets, known to the RAF as 'Squirts', shot up the PBY5, severing its tail and wrecking the port wing. As it started to settle in the water the crew, fortunately all uninjured, gathered all the emergency equipment they could and took to three dinghies at 1225, soon to be found by search aircraft.

A second lifeboat was then dropped by 'Y' 280 (F/O Maxwell), but in the fierce wind it landed some distance away. The PBY5 crew eventually reached one of the floating lines, pulled themselves to the lifeboat and boarded, but found it to be half capsized, damaged and sinking, so they went back to the relative safety of their dinghies. 'Y' had set out at 0945 accompanied by a Fortress of 5th Emergency Rescue Squadron USAAF from Halesworth, to stand by the operation and give assistance if required, but had been diverted to the new position of 5348N 0700E, where, at 1315, the PBY5 was found and the lifeboat dropped, but it was unusable (as mentioned above) so a Lindholme was also sent down, again some way off. At 1748 the Fortress, Teamwork 88 (believed to be the famous 'Duchess', formerly 'Donna J 11') piloted by Lt. S. H. Newkirk, made the first operational drop of an American A-1 Airborne Lifeboat.

Here accounts vary. The watching Warwick crew reckoned the wind again deflected the aim so the survivors were lucky to reach the lifeboat at 1605 and transfer to it from their dinghies; the survivors state that one of the rocket lines overshot them. (Both accounts could be correct if 200 yards, the length of the line, constitutes a 'wide'.) By 1620 the survivors managed to get the lifeboat under way at about 5 knots on a course of 207 degrees, indicated by a line of flame floats dropped by 'Y'. Rescue vessels had also been converging on the position in rough water and very poor visibility but were unable to make contact, the aircraft also losing sight of the boat. All this was within sight and under harassing fire from the enemy-held coast.

The downed pilot reported that on 1 April the wind was estimated at 40 knots with very low ceiling and waves up to 20 feet high, only 2 knots headway being made and their position only vaguely known. No aircraft were sighted. The following day the same weather conditions prevailed; it was bitterly cold and everyone and everything was soaking wet, some of the men were worrying about their totally numb feet. Again no planes were seen all day. At 0600 on the 3rd the engines stopped and would not restart.

Inspite of extensive sweeps of the area in diabolic conditions and very poor visibility no trace of the A-1 lifeboat was found by searching planes until 3 April when 'K' 280 picked up an automatic SOS and by homing onto it eventually came up with the lifeboat at 1100 hours, drifting helplessly in position 5409N 0634E, much further to the eastwards than had been expected. 'K' then dropped its own Mark IA Lifeboat (the fourth used in the rescue) as well as containers of spare petrol, and signalled the US crew to use their oars to either get petrol from it, or else transfer to it and get under way. No reply to the signal was received, but the PBY5 men rowed towards the Mark IA, passing through and retrieving two of the floating petrol containers on their way, but were too weak to reach the boat. Even with the new fuel they still could not start their engines, attributing the trouble to salt-water contamination already in their tanks. The sea was still very rough and they were undoubtedly very weary, cold and had all previously been seasick. That evening 'E' 280 dropped a fifth lifeboat to them, but again they were unable to reach it, now being extremely exhausted and suffering from exposure. 'E' also dropped spare petrol, but at a little distance as the kite aerial continuously flown from the American lifeboat prevented direct, correct altitude approach. Later two of these containers were recovered by the lifeboat and another, unsuccessful, attempt made to start their engines.

23   Two Airborne Lifeboat exercises off Great Yarmouth and Gorleston involving local HSLs and Naval RMLs

24   RML 514 (Patrick Troughton) in foreground with an Airborne Lifeboat alongside RML 517 or 519; in the background is HSL 2707 (Hants and Dorset) (68ft) (RAF Museum) (Cardington)

The late Patrick Troughton (actor and second Dr Who), then a RNVR Lieutenant stationed at HMS *Midge*, Great Yarmouth, in a letter to the RAF Museum was able to illustrate another aspect of the same operation. An excerpt is quoted herewith:

A gale of wind blew. A unit of 'Z' RMLs were sent out from Great Yarmouth to find them and pick them up. They were unable to do so because of the adverse sea and weather conditions. They returned to harbour almost out of fuel.

I was sent out as Senior Officer of a unit of 'Z' boats, my own RML 514 and RML 498. We were told a Warwick aircraft rescue plane would try to rendezvous with us and drop flares to guide us to the rubber dinghies containing the US airmen. On our outward journey – during daylight – a rescue Fortress succeeded in finally dropping an Airborne Lifeboat to the stricken crew.

At about midnight I sighted what was either a ship on fire or – I hoped – a flare. It proved to be the latter and we succeeded in making RT contact with the Warwick which was dropping the flares whilst homing in on an automatic transmission from the Airborne Lifeboat – which was adrift off Heligoland.

We arrived on position whilst it was still dark and the Warwick told us the lifeboat was 'Right there'. Owing to the heavy seas and darkness we could not find it. I therefore decided to cut engines and allow the unit to drift down wind and tide until daybreak.

As soon as it was light, on April 4th, we started up and began searching again. Soon flares were sighted, and the lifeboat about 1/4 mile away as it rose up on the heavy waves. RML 498 proceeded to pick up the crew – and we both opened up on the lifeboat to sink her – it being too rough to tow her alongside. Indeed we wanted to get the hell out of it as soon as possible as we were so near the German coast in broad daylight. An added danger was from our own Beaufighters which were patrolling – shooting up everything in sight.

We returned to harbour at Yarmouth with the rescued airmen very late on April 4th; actually the early hours of the 5th.

Rescue aircraft had remained over the survivors all through the night of 3rd/4th, constantly dropping flares to maintain contact, although within 30 to 40 miles of the enemy coast. Surface rescue craft were searching all through the operation in foul weather of gale-force winds and very short seas reported up to 25 feet in height, but could not effect contact in the darkness. At 0840 on the 4th 'K' had made a fresh sighting and managed to home RMLs to the survivors, who had now drifted to within 20 miles of Heligoland. The six airmen were landed at Great Yarmouth early on the 5th after a journey of 200 miles.

The rescue operation had lasted seven days and used almost all the ready resources of Air/Sea rescue in the area, and cost the lives of a Beaufighter crew on the 2nd. It was subsequently learned that the American lifeboat had been motored north-west for only 36 miles before running out of petrol, afterwhich it had broached to and the centreboard snapped off clean at the hull by the violence of the seas; subsequent efforts to start the engines being unsuccessful, probably due to water having reached the magnetos. One American account of this rescue (in film reel 2042 ex Maxwell Air Force Base) is at considerable variance to the Squadron reports, making no mention of the Catalina damaging the first boat and suggesting that all the RAF lifeboats had broken up. A further statement that the engines of their boat 'never stopped for 33 hours until they'd used up every drop of gas', could illustrate the strength of the storm, although the survivors reckoned they had only covered 36 miles. 280 Squadron had used Warwicks 'A', 'K', 'E', 'Z' and 'V' continuously throughout the operation.

A much more generous tribute is in a letter from the rescued crew, sent from the HQ of 5th ERS to the Commanding Officers of RMLs 498 and 514:

> On behalf of my crew and myself, I would like to take this opportunity to express our deepest admiration for the Officers and men who saved our lives in the North Sea on the morning of 4th April 1945.
>
> Due to adverse sea and weather conditions, the courage and determination displayed by the Rescue Launches, along with the rescue aircraft, will long be remembered. We sincerely thank every one of the Officers and men who participated in one of the most daring rescues on record. We remain:- Lt. John Laponas – First Pilot; Lt. Theodore J. Langan – Co-Pilot; Lt. Charles V. Buffington – Navigator; Sgt. William Dotson – Engineer; Sgt. James McMullin – Radar Operator; Sgt. Daniel Hochstatter – Radio Operator.

At the end of April a missive was sent out from HQ of 1st ERS, an excerpt from which is quoted herewith:

'FORWARD'.

All good things must have a beginning. We do not believe that the use of the word 'good' is presumptive, for it is our commitment to save life, not to destroy it, which function in time of war, may seem a paradox.

The purpose of this organisation is to accompany Fighter and Bomber Squadrons, effecting immediate rescue of their crews whose misfortune may lie in being set adrift on the open sea. In so doing we may not only save human life but trained and experienced fliers, who can again be at their battle stations with a minimum loss of time.

Statements made by those actively engaged in Sea Rescue work, paint vivid portraits of human suffering experienced by men adrift on the ocean for many days, whose misery is exceeded only by their touching demonstrations of appreciation at the time of rescue.

The US Emergency Rescue Squadron reports which feature in some of the following paragraphs are compiled from their operational records which are on four reels of microfilm. Regrettably many frames in these are either partially or completely unreadable, and in consequence some of the reports quoted are bereft of detail or content and others may have been missed out completely. Whilst this is very sad from an historical point of view, it is tragic in that the efforts of many gallant men cannot be chronicled with those of their peers.

2 April   Warmer waters again in the Gulf of Venice, where a PBY5 of the American 1st ERS sighted a man in a dinghy about five miles off the Istrian peninsula. 2nd Lt. Ray Veitch (SAAF, seconded to 260 Squadron RAF) flying Red 2 to F/L Brown in a force of ten Mustangs shooting up an enemy 100+ motor transport column, had sent out a 'Mayday' after tangling with Messer-schmitts and running into flak over the Maribot–Graz area – of Austria. A severed pipe caused glycol to spray over his windscreen and the engine of the Mustang to fail after he and Lt. Foster had climbed to 7000 feet and headed for home over the sea. Due to damage he could not get the cockpit canopy open and said later that he had the uncanny feeling of sitting at home in an armchair, telling himself how to get of the plane. Obviously he took his own advice but slammed into the tailplane as he baled out and was severely bruised. During the parachute descent he took off a shoe to throw it down in order to judge the nearness to the surface, but left it rather late and went in with a heavy splash just as it left his hand. Unfortunately the ditching, about four miles west of Orsersa, was in the middle of a nasty-looking minefield, so a rescue Walrus which soon arrived was unable to land safely for a pick-up, although it circled continuously whilst Lt. 'Zingie' Harrison sent out a call for a Warwick with an Airborne Lifeboat. 293 Squadron at Foggia immediately despatched HF 968 (F/O Weaver) at 0945 hours which by 1123, accompanied by a Walrus, a PBY5 and eight escorting fighters, was over the airman in his dinghy in position 4502N 1333E. Ten minutes later the lifeboat had started to float down to a successful landing some 50 yards from the survivor, who paddled to reach and board it without difficulty, although none of the three rocket lines discharged in his direction. Meanwhile a boat, attracted by all the aerial activity, had put out from the shore, but was driven off by machine-gun fire from supporting Mustangs. Once aboard the boat, although with no nautical experience, he found the instructions so easy to follow that he had soon cleared away the lines, shipped the rudder and started the starboard engine. Then he experienced some bother. The Warwick crew had sent a message in the carrier tube 'Steer out to sea, Walrus will pick you up. Mines in the area'. Single-handed he was unable to steer the boat and start the slightly obstinate port engine at the same time. He tried lashing the tiller but found this only partly satisfactory as the starboard engine about a foot outboard from the centreline did not stream its thrust onto the rudder so yawing occured. Ultimately he managed to get both engines running smoothly and following a line of smoke floats dropped by the PBY5 motored clear of the mines to where the flying boat (presumably piloted by Lt. Kaminski, see p. 95) which had initially answered the 'Mayday' – having been back to base and refuelled – was waiting to pick him up. This was the commencement of a story worthy of an entry in the Guinness Book of Records, as we shall see.

3 April   On this day six Warwicks of 280 Squadron, 'A' (F/L Gray), 'K' (F/L Forrest), 'X', 'E', 'Z' and 'V' took off from Beccles in attempts to render aid by dropping smoke floats, spare fuel and stores to an American type Airborne Lifeboat found stationary in position 5406N 0618E. As the boat appeared sound, although the engines were not running, no RAF lifeboat was dropped but rescue launches were given the position and homing commenced to a rendezvous about 270 miles east of Hull, within 70 miles of the hornets' nest of Heligoland, with the completion of the operation the next day witnessed by 'K' and 'E'. As this lifeboat has not been traced on USAAF microfilm it is probably on one of the unreadable frames.

5 April   Back to the Adriatic and the Gulf of Trieste. 2nd Lt. Veitch (SAAF), again flying Red 2 to F/L Brown, had been indulging in a spot of 'train-busting' in Kamnik station and an attack on '100+' road transport on the Nazi supply lines in the Maribot–Graz area when he was not so lucky as he'd been the previous day, during which he'd collected a number of hits by 20mm cannon shells but managed to get the badly damaged aircraft home. This time it was another chunk of flak on the glycol system which caused him to break off the action and, in company with Lt. Nelson, climb to 7000 feet in an endeavour to get clear of the coast and out to sea before the engine seized up. In this he was successful and had glided down to 6000 feet just north of Trieste when the engine died on him. Again he was forced to bale out and after going through the shoe drill successfully made a reasonable splashdown two miles offshore at 0840 hours. After climbing into his diminutive dinghy he settled down to wait for a Walrus to pick him up, but kept paddling seawards the whole time. Lt. Nelson continued to circle until a critical fuel position was reached and he was forced to return to base at Ravenna after driving off with rockets an approaching MTB. Lt. Nelson had been relieved by two Spitfires and Lt. Veitch clearly heard gunfire as they repelled other searching enemy craft.

When a PBY5 of 1 ERS piloted by Lts. Dunn and Kaminski came on the scene it was fired on from the shore and as mines were detected in the area a lifeboat Warwick was requested. A considerable delay was now inevitable as it had to fly all the way from Foggia in the south of Italy. When a red-sailed small craft manned by four men in Italian Navy uniform came into the immediate area it was buzzed to drive it away, but replied with revolver fire and kept searching for the dinghy, so the escort had no alternative but to sink it. To quote Stewart Finney: 'The crew of that Cat. certainly deserved a gong' and in his report he recommended immediate awards to the entire Catalina crew for 'sheer cold-blooded guts'. But he never found out if they were received. Capt. Ruciman of 1 ERS took off from Falconara at 1300 hours to relieve Kaminski and Dunn. At the given position Capt. Ruciman found a man in the Airborne Lifeboat, still in the middle of an extensive minefield. He searched for a clear area onto which to land his PBY5 but could not find one, so remained in the area until almost out of fuel.

By the time the Warwick BV 449, again from 293 Squadron, arrived, with a Walrus, a PBY5 and eight escorting fighters from No. 2 Squadron SAAF, led by the CO Stewart Finney, Lt. Veitch's efforts, aided by the breeze, had brought

25 Flt Lt Jim Forrest and crew (Jim Forrest)

26 The 'smiler' who sailed home three times in a month (Mrs E. Veitch)

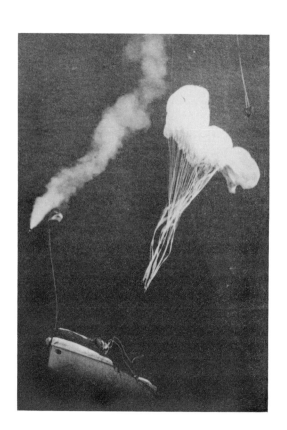

27   Smoke float, pilot and main parachutes just deploying from Mark I

28   'Step the mast and steer for home' (Mark I)

him four miles out and the lifeboat was dropped at 1615 hours. It landed within 50 yards of the survivor who again boarded without difficulty. This renewed activity attracted attention ashore and 40mm shells started dropping randomly over the area. Among the pilots in the air cover was Derrick Whelehan of 112 Squadron, a lifelong friend of Lt. Veitch. Warwick BV 449 piloted by F/O Goldspink, which had taken off from Foggia at 1400 hours, turned for home under heavy anti-aircraft fire from shore batteries, its work done once it had dropped a message 'Steer 210 degrees'. When it was beyond range the shelling switched onto the Airborne Lifeboat which the survivor had just boarded. Whilst he coolly cleared away the drop gear and readied the engines other German or Italian naval craft came out, again intent on capture and hovered outside the shell splash area waiting for the firing to let up. The fighters escorting the Warwick had other ideas and soon drove them away, although Mosquitos, now also in attendance, were forced to sink one vessel. Successive Mosquitos maintained air cover the rest of the day as Lt. Veitch, having the same difficulties as previously in starting the second engine and steering at the same time, headed out to the open sea, unscathed by the shellfire, through the very extensive minefields protecting the Axis ports of Trieste and Pola.

When it was completely dark he stopped both engines in case their noise attracted prowling enemy craft, and after sampling the boat's stores donned one of the protective suits from a locker and managed to get some sleep. At first light the next day (6th) he again got under way and was still steadily motoring clear when located at 0800 hours by a PBY5, piloted by Lts. Kaminski and Dunn which dropped a row of smoke floats to guide the survivor clear of the mines; but his meaning was not grasped, so a note was attached to a small buoy, dropped and duly recovered and the course steered. Mrs Evelyn Veitch sent the author a copy of the note which reads: 'Steer a course out to sea and the Walrus will land and pick you up. We suspect mines in this area.' In a short while Lt. Veitch was in clear area and Lt. Kaminski was able to land his PBY5, pick up the lone boatman and return him to his home base. This was the second time Ray Veitch was hitching a lift with Lt. Kaminski. The greeting was inevitable 'Haven't we met before somewhere?' Lt. Veitch had even kept some of the shell splinters from the near misses as souvenirs.

10 April   The first signs of spring would be showing at Beccles when 'T' 280 (F/L Radford) took off at 1159 to search two locations off the Dutch coast where two Spitfire F 21 pilots of 91 Squadron were in the water. The weather was fine and the escort of Thunderbolts had no difficulty in keeping in touch with their slower charge. The first dinghy was sighted at 1256 in position 5254N 0435E (terribly close to Den Helder) and the lifeboat sent down to him. The man boarded it successfully but was apparently unable to start the engines, especially as shore batteries had opened up and were making things distinctly unpleasant. Meanwhile 'T' had circled around to find the second airman, finally seeing him only a mile or so distant from the dropped lifeboat in position 5256N 0430E but being only able to carry one lifeboat could do no more than send a Lindholme down to him at 1317, which he utilised gratefully. The wind, blowing steadily from the shore, duly carried both the lifeboat and the dinghy clear of the coast and the shellfire whilst 'T' endeavoured to maintain contact with both, as well as to guide an American PBY5 of 5th ERS of Halesworth to the two survivors, and then watched them rescued at 1450 and 1520 respectively.

11 April   'E' 281 crashed near Bally Castle; there were no survivors.

14 April   Roughly 20 miles off the Norwegian coast a dinghy containing six (?) men was reported by the crew of a Beaufighter of 489 Squadron. Accordingly 'G' of 279 Squadron (Sq. Ldr. Levin-Raw) took off from Fraserburgh at 1242 to see what could be found, and achieved a measure of success just after 1500 when a sighting was made in position 5704N 0430E. The lifeboat was dropped at 1539 and although only three of the six parachutes opened the boat landed well only 30 to 40 yards upwind of the dinghy. All seemed fine until it was realised that the release gear had not operated and the boat was rapidly blowing downwind; it seems that the drogue and side rockets did not fire either or else the men in the dinghy would have been able to grasp the floating line as the lifeboat swept past them, soon to be beyond their reach. A Lindholme was dropped at 1612 and a second at 1619. 'V' (F/L Ashby) took off at 1915 to make the long flight to the position 280 miles east of Aberdeen in an attempt to retrieve the situation and in the darkness, at 2127, dropped her lifeboat in response to flares coming up from the surface of the sea. In the later stages of her outward flight there had been trouble with one of the engines and this now appeared to worsen so she turned for home, sure that there was nothing more to be done that night, and was fortunate to limp into her base at 0112 on the 15th. Further searches during that day are mentioned in the Squadron Daily Report, but as there is no continuance of these it appears that a positive outcome transpired.

18 April   'P' (F/L Radford) and 'Y' (W/O Pike) of 280 Squadron took off from Beccles at 0924 for a search patrol along and around the Frisians and on investigating a column of smoke in position 5421N 0504E (approximately 90 miles north-east of Borkum) found seven men in two groups, all in the water, supported by their Mae Wests. 'P' dropped her lifeboat to two men close together, followed a few minutes later by 'Y' whose boat went down to a group of five. All the men appeared too weak to reach the lifeboats, their pathetic struggles apparent to the watchers above; easily reachable inflatable dinghies and more Mae Wests were dropped whilst assistance in the form of a Catalina or a Walrus, with strong escort, was requested. The two planes maintained watch until limit of endurance was reached when they were relieved by 'B'; but at 1708 it was obvious that all the men were dead.

18 April   Meanwhile 'T' (F/O Harvey) had left Beccles at 1401 on search and rescue procedure a little further to the north-west of Borkum and came across a man in the water at 5444N 0457E. Their Airborne Lifeboat was sent down to him at 1529, and as there was no positive reaction from the water it was followed by two Lindholmes, again without any response. The Warwick circled

29   Adrift in an over crowded rubber dinghy

30   Cans of extra petrol splashing down to a Mark II

the position until the arrival of a Catalina, which was only able to pick up three bodies, the tragic remnant of the crew of Halifax 'L' 420. 280 Squadron had nothing to celebrate that night for their long flying hours on the dangerous threshold of Northern Europe. An addition amplifying the rescue attempt is made by the following information from American sources:

> On that day (18 April) First Lt. John A Carroll Jnr took off at 1325 from Halesworth in a PBY5A and circled waiting for an escort. Teamwork 1–4 also took off at 1345 and completed rendezvous at 1435. Two of the fighter escort aborted at 1535. At 1651 two Airborne Lifeboats were found, with two dinghies in the vicinity, plus two men in the sea wearing Mae Wests. An immediate landing was effected and the first man taken aboard at 1605. A second man was recovered at 1607 with considerable difficulty, apparently dead. Artificial respiration was started at once on both men but had to be discontinued at 1614 in order to take in a third man, who had obviously been killed instantly judging from broken legs and head wounds. Artificial respiration was resumed, but later stopped on the second man when it was obvious that full rigor mortis had set in. The first man was still being worked on until the plane landed at which time a competent medical team pronounced him dead.

23 April   Warwick BV 451 of 203 Squadron carried out a search from Blida for a lifeboat dropped on that day in an area five miles north of Algiers. The aircraft was soon recalled as the lifeboat had been found. (? 282 Squadron possibly or an unreadable USAAF drop.)

30 April   Lt. Veitch (SAAF) had been busy again pressing home attacks against enemy transport north of Udine (inland from the Gulf of Trieste) when the engine of his Mustang was hit by flak and commenced losing oil. Once again he managed to reach the sea and after a few horrific moments struggling to free a trapped strap parachuted down into a minefield five miles from Lignano. Others members of his Squadron maintained contact awaiting the arrival of a Warwick with an Airborne Lifeboat, but bad weather had set in making a sighting and a lifeboat drop impossible in the murk and darkness. Contact being lost his comrades returned to base on the last of their fuel. He spent a most uncomfortable night drifting in his dinghy very close to shore. Just after dawn contact was renewed when his Squadron Commander and pilot Brian Ruiter (SAAF) located him and sent for assistance, which arrived firstly in the form of a PBY5 piloted by Major Buchanan. He found it impossible to land safely with any hope of a pick-up so then called on both the RAF and the USAAF for aircraft with lifeboats. The first to arrive on the scene was a B 17G Fortress of the American 1st ERS complete with an A-1 lifeboat, which was promptly and efficiently dropped. The RAF Warwick, BV 449 of 293 Squadron experienced considerable troubles in reaching the casualty so the B 17, piloted by Lt. McMurdio, successfully made their Squadron's first lifeboat drop. The boat was soon boarded although the sea was very rough, but the survivor experienced immense difficulty in starting either of the engines, spending considerable time to-ing and fro-ing between them and the steering gear, which also gave him some difficulty. Eventually he succeeded in getting under way. Again smoke floats were used for guidance and Lt. Veitch was soon clear of the mines, although still experiencing very rough seas. An HSL was requested whilst Major (now) Ruciman and Lt. Kaminski stood by in turn in their PBY5s in case the sea would moderate sufficiently for a pick-up; but the HSL made contact and took him aboard at 1115 on 1 May.

The Warwick, piloted by Australian F/L Rawlings accompanied by Captain Isted of the SAAF, scrambled at 1800 and within 15 minutes found the weather very bad, so had to 'coast crawl' their way north. By 1925 they were experiencing violent electrical storms and seeing numerous waterspouts, but reached the area by 1935 to circle in very poor visibility without locating the dinghy, although encountering heavy, erratic flak from Lignano. In impossible conditions they were forced to return to base.

Lt. Veitch, only 20 years old, came through all his three ditchings and rescues without a scratch. He was awarded an immediate DFC, as well as receiving a despatch from Air Officer Commanding Desert·Air Force in which he was promised the post of 'Honorary Commodore of the Desert Air Force Yacht Club' (should such ever be formed), and established an unbroken 1939–1945 record as the Man Most Rescued by Airborne Lifeboats. The first his parents knew of his escapes was when they read about the three rescues in their Sunday newspaper. What an epic with which to conclude the European wartime exploits.

The Goldfish Club records a member who ditched and was rescued six times in the Great War of 1914–18. Lt. Veitch holds the record for the 1939–45 conflict.

8   The Mark III

Whilst the Mark III had been visualised during the War, as had several other sizes and designs, it did not actually go into production until the early 1950s. The wooden British Airborne Lifeboats shipped to the Middle and Far East at the latter end of the War suffered badly from the climate, so a schedule was drawn up in the late 1940s covering the requirements which the Mark IIIs should meet. Experiments in moulded plywood building had achieved a measure of success, especially in America, but the need was felt that a lifeboat should be totally immune to climatic changes and, if possible, partially resistant to blazing fuel on the surface of the water. Accordingly a light alloy was deemed the best material; this had to be a member of the aluminium range. Before the War the Birmabright Company of Birmingham had successfully developed a salt-water resistant alloy for boatbuilding and its extensive use during the War had only been curtailed by a chronic shortage of, and colossal demand for, that metal for aircraft building. The chosen design, although it appreciated the earlier models, was not from the drawing board of Uffa Fox but the product of a team led by Mr Peter Everard and Mr Carl Butterfield of Saunders Roe, at whose Beaumaris works the prototypes and over 50 production Mark IIIs were built.

The post-War years had brought a tremendous increase in the number of flights, especially civilian, over the sea, covering distances and oceans previously undreamed of for land-based planes. For many forward thinkers the era of the flying boat was drawing to an end. Saunders Roe, long renowned for their flying boats, many with metal hulls, initially built three prototype lifeboats entirely on their own initiative, intending that they should be married up with the Shackleton, just being introduced for maritime reconnaissance. With a designed maximum of ten persons in mind the new lifeboat was 30' 2" overall length, 30' on the waterline, with a moulded beam (maximum) of 7' 1", and a moulded depth of 3' 2", designed to draw only 13" of water. The maximum airborne weight allowed was 4460 pounds. Oars and sails were to be provided, the latter totalling 170 square feet in a fore and main sail Bermuda rig, as supplements to the innovative Vincent HRD inboard engine of 12 bhp at 2940 revs, driving a three-bladed, fixed-pitch propeller of 12 1/2" diameter and 9 1/2" pitch mounted in a tunnel formed centrally in the underside of the hull, within the profile of the lifeboat. More details about this amazing engine, for which the author is indebted to its designer Mr P. E. Irving, are given in Chapter 10.

A metal hull offers more latitude in construction than is possible when using wood, and Saunders Roe approached the task in a novel way. Although the design was completely new it still had to conform to the same basic rules; but

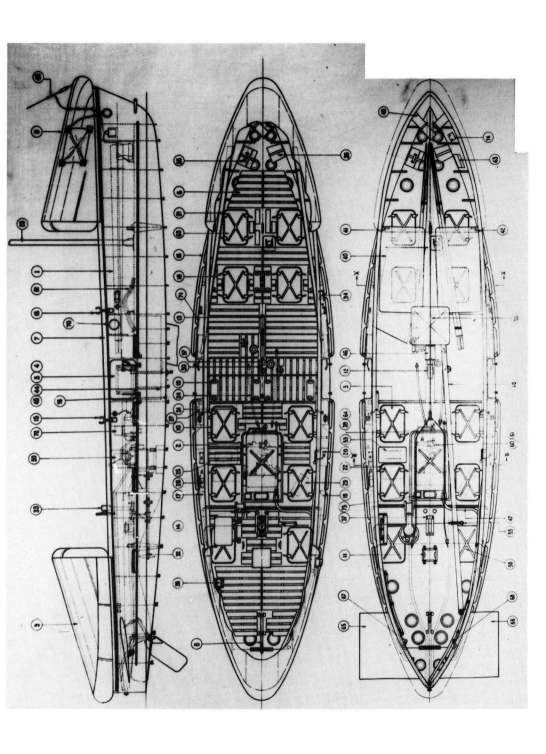

31   General arrangement of the Mark III (Laird (Anglesey) Ltd)

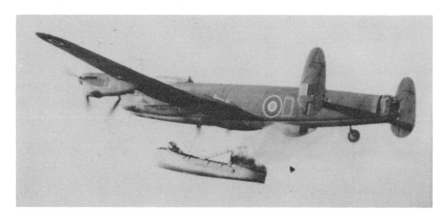

32   Mark IIA dropping clear of its Lancaster

33   Mark III beneath its four parachutes (Saunders Roe ex Laird (Anglesey) Ltd)

as the Shackleton was wider in the fuselage than either the Hudson or the Warwick there was no need to incorporate the pronounced reverse sheer or so much of the tumblehome of the two previous Marks. So the Mark III had a straight gunwale line which allowed more headroom under the inflatable end buoyancy chambers and a greater moulded depth to the hull. For sea-kindliness some tumblehome in the hull was retained as was the canoe type stern to give maximum ground clearance aft, as well as seaworthiness, and the central keelson as the most efficient way of imparting the requisite stiffness for single point suspension. Throughout, the lines were intended to give the best combination of aero and hydrodynamic properties both when air-borne or afloat under power, sail or oars. Once again the gunwales were shaped to hug the fuselage of the carrier plane but a major improvement was in making the rudder retractable, rather than as a separate unit which had to be shipped and secured.

For convenience of manufacture the hull was built in port and starboard halves joined in final assembly at keel, stem, stern and along the twin portions of the keelson, gaps being formed in this at specific places to accommodate the propeller tunnel, the rudder housing, the centreboard slot, bomb hook etc. Each half of the below deck structure was built up on one of the twin sections of the keelson, which extended the entire depth from deck to keel acting as a watertight longitudinal bulkhead. To these were riveted (as aluminium weld-ing was not then economically practicable) 23 frames, at varying spacings, some for watertight bulkheads, others as forming and strengthening mem-bers (or ribs) to all of which the shell plating was riveted. Each portion of the keelson comprised a flat plate reinforced at top and bottom with angles to which the skin and deck plating would be riveted. From the bow to amidships the two portions ran parallel about an inch apart, thus allowing for the centre-board, then opening out to about two feet spacing in way of the propeller tunnel and engine room before coming together to within two inches of each other to form the rudder slot before joining onto each side of the stern post castings.

All the frames were of light alloy sheet rolled into a channel section to give a wide seating for attachment of, and to, other components; mostly these were made up in two sections, one for each side to the centreline, but of three sections in way of the propeller tunnel and engine compartment. The stem was formed of a shaped capping plate fastened to a curved 'V' casting which took the for'ard end of the keelson members, whilst the stern was formed from three separate castings, the two below deck placed with the twin parts of the keelson to form the after end of the rudder slot, the third above deck serving also as anchorage for those below; all securing as well the outer plating, the deck, and the gunwales. Internally the hull was strengthened with bulb angle section stringers which were intercostal between bulkheads, passing through the intermediate frames and being secured to all by riveted angle brackets. One of these stringers served as a deck rising whilst above it an intermediate stringer, broken only at the access door, stiffened the bulwarks below the gunwales formed of inverted channel section members, riveted to the frames, the shell plating, the stem plating and the stern castings. As with the earlier Marks this was cushioned at completion with canvas covered 'Dunlopillo' rubber to act as both buffer and seal to the aircraft.

The sheet alloy shell plating was cut and shaped in convenient lengths to fit the hull before being riveted to the frames etc. at all possible points, with the butt joints brought between frames so that internal butt straps could be riveted to both pieces to ensure strong joints. The thickness of materials above deck was 18 SWG with 16 SWG below, as was the deck also. Thirteen hatches cut in this were all reinforced with coamings, two sides of which rested on intercostal members between the tops of the bulkheads; whilst the other two sides were supported by the top bars of the frames, all of which were cross-tied to the upper edge of the keelson, thus providing additional supports to the deck structure. Realising that with the greater depth inside the bulwarks the centreboard slot would not be able to cope with the amount of water which might come on deck, four scuppers aside were cut through the bulwarks at deck level, each being 12″ long by 3/4″ wide, with rubber flaps attached externally to the upper edges so that water would flow outboard only.

The propeller tunnel formed between frames 17 and 23 reached almost to the deck at its highest point; the frames in its way being shaped to form a rapidly increasing, followed by a slowly decreasing, arch, with the six preformed alloy sheets of the skin plating welded together and riveted to the frames and the 'chines' formed at the lower edges of the keelson members, as well as to other adjacent materials. A rectangular transparent 'window' panel was also built into the tunnel, over the propeller, for inspection and/or clearance if it became fouled. When not under way this section of the tunnel would be above normal waterline.

Because this was an all-metal hull, and because planes were flying at much higher altitudes than previously, special provision had to be made for the watertight compartments to be automatically vented, to prevent damage by pressure and temperature changes during flight. This was by fitting inverted 'U' tubes through the deck; screwed down inspection panels also being fitted in the deck for all the watertight compartments, some of which were for buoyancy only and not served by any of the thirteen hatches.

As with the earlier Marks the entire weight of the fully equipped boat was taken on the bomb hook during flight, and by the sling points during the parachute descent, the keelson again forming the anchor member for these and the winching lug, by which the boat was brought up to the underside of the plane, as well as the towing point bolted through the skin plating to the keelson angles for'ard.

On both the Marks I and II the rudder and steering had presented problems in shipping, retaining, handling and strength, so a vast improvement was made in the Mark III by having the rudder permanently mounted and rigged, but by a single pivot mechanism, retracted into the slot in the keelson during flight, a locking pin engaging into a lug being all that was required to secure the rudder accurately once it was lowered when the lifeboat was afloat. Gone too was the vulnerable familiar tiller for steering, which inexperienced crewmen some-times found difficult to master, being more used to a wheel which turned in the direction one wished to go, instead of the tiller which had the opposite effect. So a column-mounted wheel now took its place, pivoted at its base so that it

34   Building line of Mark III's at Saunders Roe, Beaumaris (Laird (Anglesey) Ltd)

35   Mark III ready for trials at Holyhead (Laird (Anglesey) Ltd)

36   *The aft deck of Mark III (Saunders Roe and RAF Museum)*

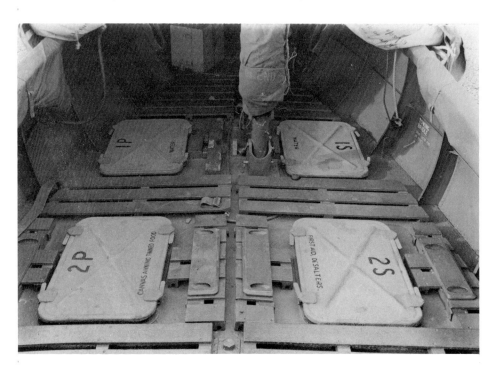

37   *The Mark III foredeck (Laird (Anglesey) Ltd)*

would lie flat with the deck whilst the lifeboat was attached to the aircraft but for use could be raised into a vertical position and locked into place. A simple reduction gearing and shaft was housed at the base of the steering column and from this wires led to the tiller arm at the head of the rudder spindle.

Another very important refinement was the provision of a bilging system to the engine compartment. This was entirely automatic being driven by the engine itself and discharging with the cooling water from the engine. A semi-rotary, hand-held bilge pump was also part of standard equipment so that its suction hose could be used through any of the deck hatches or inspection points; very useful too for washing down if the Skipper was keen on maintaining a really 'tiddley ship'.

On odd occasions it had been found that the parachutes for the previous Marks, whilst developing, had been damaged by catching on the bomb hook and/or the winching lug, so an automatically clearing guard was devised. This was 'tunnel shaped', mounted on light deck rails and operated by the release of a 'bungee' cord so that when the bomb release operated it covered and screened the projections in the few seconds before the parachutes started to develop.

The higher gunwale of the Mark III lifeboats would have been almost impossible for a man to climb over from the sea unaided, even if he were in peak physical condition, so what had begun as access ports on the Mark I, solely for the ground crew to get their hands and arms through for the final connections, now developed into man-sized 'climb aboard' doors, opening outwards and downwards on their hinged lower edges, fitted with a grab handle and a tubular folding ladder clipped to the inner leaf of each door, so that it could be lowered when required. A simple lever-handled bolt, easily accessible from outboard, held the door closed during flight. On the Mark II one set of the bilge keel hand rails had been raised to provide toe holds for men climbing into the boat; these were now further refined by being brought up to just below the scuppers and extended over the entire length of the boat on both sides, the 'hand grips' being fitted on the underside with soft neoprene flaps to prevent water spurting upwards through the gaps as the boat moved through or rolled on the sea.

In the bows, the drogue, rocket and bow line were fitted in five-inch diameter tubes built into the plating on each side of the stem and set at angles of 45 degrees to the centreline of the craft, both being anchored to the deck, initially one having a fairlead hole in its inboard end for the bow line to run through from it stowage after the rocket fired, the other blanked off. After trials this was altered in that the line was stored in a pack on top of the for'ard apron so that it could run out more freely and thus increase the effectiveness of the rocket. Once again the self-righting, turtlebacked canopies were fitted at bow and stern, automatically inflated to a pressure of 1.25 psi but showing improvements in design in that provision was made for side curtains, usually known as 'dodgers', to be laced between them, supported on light stanchions which could be set in the rowlock plates thus enabling the entire sides of the boat to be shielded from the weather and a light canvas awning also rigged above. This was made with a drainage hole at its centre so that it could be used

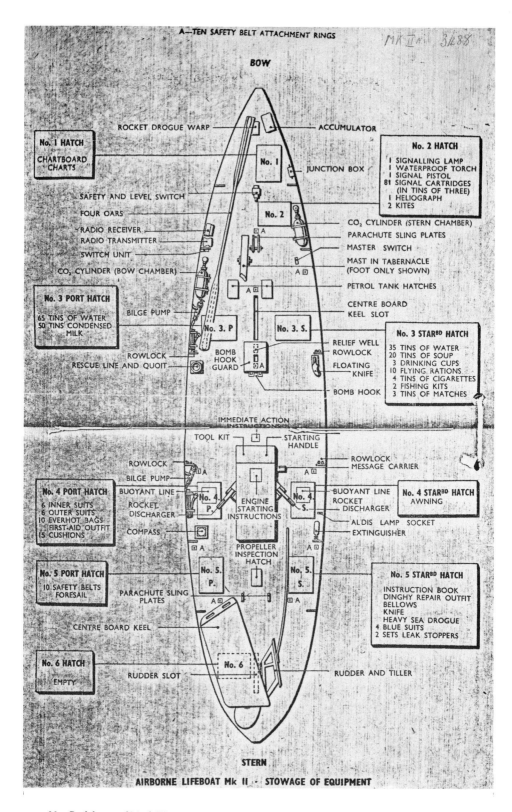

38 Deck layout of Mark III

to catch rainwater, as well as serve as a sun shield in tropical climes. Provision was also made for very bad weather by fitting safety belt attachment points to various above deck frame positions throughout the lifeboat.

Considerable thought had gone into making the mast and rigging easier to erect, both from physical and knowledge points of view. The first improvement was in having the mast permanently fixed into a tabernacle on the deck. The casting for this was mounted just abaft the for'ard parachute sling point, adjacent to the starboard section of the keelson and anchored to it, as well as being surrounded by a stiffened deck structure. A slot, foreside of the tabernacle allowed the heel of the mast to pivot downwards from a mounting pin at deck level, thus requiring much less effort to raise the upper portion from its resting place atop the aft buoyancy chamber. Whilst airborne it rested on the deck on top of the deflated chamber, which, as it filled from the CO_2 bottles during descent, would lift the mast from its recumbent position to an angle of 30 degrees and thus clear of the deck ready for the survivors to climb aboard. When fully erected it would be secured by a drop-nosed pin passing through mating holes in the cheeks of the tabernacle and the mast.

The engine compartment was built between frames 15 and 18 – for'ard and aft – with the two sections of the keelson at each side, giving a space some two feet by four feet. In way of this the bottom of the boat was reinforced by stiffeners at six-inch spacings athwartships and two rows of stringers running fore and aft between the watertight bulkheads at 15 and 18 positions. The engine was mounted on four shock-absorbing brackets, two aside, bolted onto the bases of the twin parts of the keelson, so that most of the machinery was below deck. To accommodate the small amount above that level a six-inch high coaming was bolted to the deck, designed to house, at its after end, behind a transparent panel, the oil pressure warning light, the oil pressure gauge, an engine speed indicator, a fuel pressure indicator, an ammeter, and in a recess on the port side another panel with a combined choke and throttle lever assembly, a gear change lever, and a fuel pump priming control, all non-electrical fittings being connected to the engine by Bowden cables. The entire coaming could be removed if an engine change was required. An easily detachable cover was fitted above the coamings to give access for efficient servicing and maintenance. To reduce noise level and fire hazard the entire compartment was insulated with 'Fibroglass' or 'Isoflex' secured in place by alloy sheeting, perforated on the sides, plain beneath, where there might be a small amount of oil accumulating. From the base of the engine a short Cardan shaft led to a flexible coupling on the propeller shaft which led through a tail shaft bearing and shaft log to the propeller, supported by a skeg where the tunnel reached its apogee.

Special accommodation was built in for the accumulator serving the electrical circuits; this was below deck, between frames 16 and 17 on the port side, the compartment being insulated throughout and served by a ventilated hatch cover. The electrical system was quite complex with sixteen separate pieces of apparatus fed or controlled by the circuits. Plate **39** illustrates this very effectively, except that it fails to show the electrical feed line from the engine generator to the accumulator. Bonding presented no problems as apart

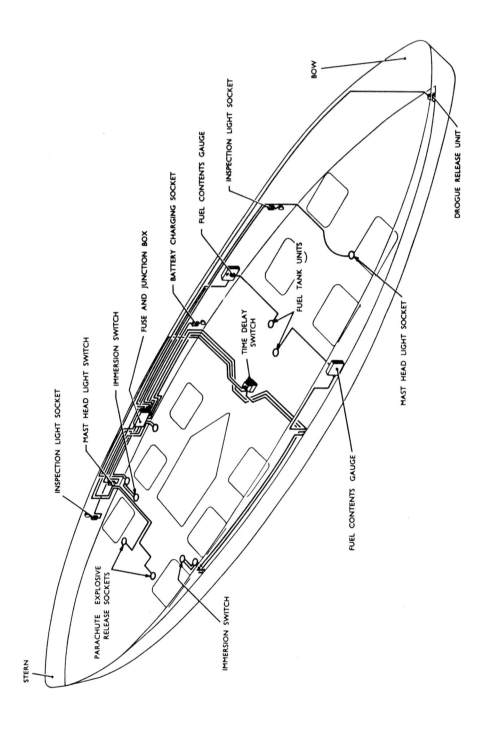

BOW

DROGUE RELEASE UNIT

INSPECTION LIGHT SOCKET

FUEL CONTENTS GAUGE

BATTERY CHARGING SOCKET

FUSE AND JUNCTION BOX

FUEL TANK UNITS

TIME DELAY SWITCH

MAST HEAD LIGHT SOCKET

IMMERSION SWITCH

MAST HEAD LIGHT SWITCH

INSPECTION LIGHT SOCKET

PARACHUTE EXPLOSIVE RELEASE SOCKETS

FUEL CONTENTS GAUGE

IMMERSION SWITCH

STERN

39 *The electrical system of a Mark III (Saunders Roe Ex SAAF) Marks I, IA and IIA also had electrical installations but very basic by comparison*

from the engine, which was connected by two braided copper leads direct to the hull, it was unnecessary as all the main metallic fittings were connected directly to the metal hull, and in consequence differences in potential did not occur. The fuel tank bay, with its twin 65-gallon tanks of high octane petrol shaped to the form of the hull, was situated immediately forward of the engine compartment, and also received special treatment, the vented hatch cover having two holes, one for the fuel filling pipe connection and the other for bilging. The covers to both compartments were normally bolted down. A tank contents gauge was mounted on the deck to port, sheltered by the gunwale and the tumblehome of the bulwarks.

The sail plan, totalling 170 square feet, continued the style of the former lifeboats, but with modifications and improvements. The mast, made of light alloy tube, was secured in the recumbent position by a kicking strap which released itself as the chamber inflated during descent, so that by the time the crew boarded it would be resting on top of the buoyancy canopy all ready to be raised and secured with its drop-nosed locking pin, leaving only the simple rigging of forestay and port and starboard shrouds to be clipped into their respective anchorages by snap-hooks. The foresail halyard, already rove, led over a sheave at the masthead and down to a cleat at the foot of the mast. The sheet for this sail would be already attached to the clew so that its two tails could readily be led aft. The tack led down to a hook-on attachment on top of the for'ard buoyancy chamber, whilst a single row of reef points permitted a reduced sail area if required. The foot of this sail was cut high enough to permit it to be used with the for'ard buoyancy chamber inflated.

The mainsail was hoisted in a similar manner, being secured to the mast by six traveller hoops, the tack fastening by a length of line to a cleat at the foot of the mast and the sheet leading from the tail of a sheave block affixed to the deck, through a single block at the clew, back down through the deck block so that the helmsman had a controllable pull on the sail. Two gaiters were provided to encase the sails and rigging, an inner to contain the mast, sails and running rigging, with the outer covering the inner and the standing rigging. By this sequence the mast could be raised and rigged with the sails still packed away, brailed up to the mast, awaiting use; the gaiters were fastened along their lengths by 'Dutch' lacing, for easy removal or fitting.

In keeping with the advance in design, coupled with the absence of wartime restraints and shortages, the centreboard was formed from two sheets of alloy with shaped channel section members between to give a streamlining; when in use it passed through a rubber insert in the deck which prevented water coming up the slot and was secured in the down position with a locking pin. Stowage lugs on the deck prevented it being a nuisance between times. The stabilising fins too assumed a new profile, now being in aerofoil section, appearing like stubby wings at each quarter; but still, necessarily, discardable when the lifeboat was afloat, by operation of a lever; once this had been released from its securing pin, and withdrawn, the fins dropped away.

For greater comfort and convenience a padded seat for the cox'n was positioned to port, abaft the steering column, between frames 19 and 20; this folded away against the bulwark when not in use. With the high bulwarks rowing would have been almost impossible for a man seated on the deck, which is far from an ideal rowing position anyway, so folding seats of alloy tube and canvas were provided for the oarsmen. These stools were secured in the correct positions by their feet being inserted in holes in the deck duckboards, but could be stowed away beneath the deck when not required, with projections on the duckboards serving as stretchers for the rower's feet; these were hinged so that they could be raised for use, or lowered out of the way when not needed.

It is obvious that the deck presented an uncomfortable, even dangerous, working surface with lugs, hatches and other impedimenta underfoot, so the duckboards mentioned above were fitted between and around the projections to give a safer platform, covering the entire deck apart from the extreme fore and aft sections. Fifteen inflatable air cushions, each measuring 30 by 32 inches, were stowed in a locker below the deck. These could be used singly as seats or collectively as beds and being coloured yellow on one side with blue on the other could be used either to attract attention, or alternatively as camouflage. Blue was retained as the overall paint colour so the lifeboat could merge into the background normally, but yellow recognition aprons marked with the lifeboat's number were supplied to cover the buoyancy chambers so that with the supplement of the yellow side of the cushions the boat would stand out sharply against the background of the sea if it was decided that sighted aircraft were not hostile.

The lifeboats were well and fully equipped with gear and stores – much better than in the wartime days. The floating sideline rockets were retained and even such items as fire extinguishers, a solar still for fresh water and sea-water desalination apparatus were aboard. The radio equipment had been much updated, with separate transmitting and receiving sets to provide two-way communication between the lifeboat and a search aircraft, a surface craft or a shore station in the International Distress Frequency of 500 kc/s. Two alternative aerial systems were provided for the transmitter and receiver, with a radio oscillator which could transmit signals capable of being received on ship or aircraft radar screens as a further method of assisting searchers. The alternative aerials were the familiar rocket-assisted kite and the 'Vee' system used on the Mark IIs in which the forestay is insulated at its foot and becomes part of the apparatus together with another wire leading down to the stern well clear of the leach of the mainsail, the lead in for this being at the bow, just above the drogue rocket box.

An entirely new release gear was incorporated into the sling system from the parachutes, an immersion switch on the hull actuating an explosive hydraulic mechanism, based on a type which had been introduced on a few of the Mark I lifeboats and their Mk II successors. The main parachutes, from which the lifeboat hung 60 degrees bows down, were a pack of four 42-footers beneath an 18-foot retarder 'chute pulled from its pack by a static line as the lifeboat left the aircraft. Once the weight of the boat was taken by the parachutes other static cords attached to them operated release mechanisms on the CO_2 bottles to inflate the for'ard and aft self-righting canopies. At the same time the immersion switches were brought to 'live' state so that once the boat had come

40   SAAF Shackleton with Mark III Lifeboat (Saunders Roe ex Laird (Anglesey) Ltd)

41   Shackleton 2 with Mark III Lifeboat at Farnborough SBAC Air Show in 1953
(AVRO ex Atlanta Industries Ltd Johannesburg)

to the surface after its initial plunge the switches (duplicated) commenced operations to release the parachutes and eject the drogue rocket from its tube in the bows. As an additional aid to survivors trying to reach the lifeboat the carrier Shackleton was equipped with a buoyant contact cord, 440 yards long, equipped with small grapnels, which could be streamed from the plane and dropped at right angles across the 90-yard buoyant drogue line, thus providing a very wide lifeline for men in the water to drift down onto, and thus pull themselves to the lifeboat.

As previously waterproof working suits were provided for ten men, and a couple of special 'Lindholme' sleeping suits, particularly useful for sick or wounded men; and, of course, adequate stores and equipment for a lengthy voyage. A list of the equipment supplied and stowed aboard is given in Appendix I.

The Mark III could not be termed a total triumph as ultimately many were sold off at ridiculous prices for conversion to sailing yachts. No record has been found of the RAF dropping one in a rescue operation, nor when they were phased out. A number were used in trials, with 807 to 824 allocated to various stations (Appendix III), but all had been withdrawn to join those in store by 1956. A Mark III with SAAF number '3' is preserved in the SAAF Museum at Pretoria.

9 Operations from VE Day

26 May   The 'swan song' for 279 Squadron – failure and success. 'V' and 'Z' took off from Thornaby at 1020 following a sighting report about 40 miles off the Suffolk coast town of Southwold. They had to search the area for quite a while before sighting the six survivors of a USAAF B 17 bomber in dinghies at position 5521N 0245E. 'V' (F/L Hayes) dropped her lifeboat at 1215 but was horrified that the parachutes did not open and the boat broke up on impact with the sea. 'Z' (W/Cdr. Cox) which had been searching a way off, now homed on to the position to drop her lifeboat at 1445. To the relief of all, the drop was completely successful and the six men were observed boarding. Surface back-up had already been called for but it was almost two hours later that an HSL came into view and was guided to the lifeboat to take the survivors aboard and the boat in tow.

29 May   In the Pacific the 4th ERS were operating from Iwo Jima. Lt. Leeuven and crew took off in B 17G 365 at 0928 to take station on the course of bombers returning from Japan. Whilst there he was called by a 'Blackjack' with two engines out and a third malfunctioning. A bearing was taken on the casualty and course set to meet it, only to observe it ditching as the 'Dumbo' (365) approached. Survival gear was immediately dropped to the five or six men seen in the water and a rescue submarine on a similar waiting mission was contacted by radio. Unhappily its ETA at the casualty was two hours after 365's limit of endurance was scheduled to be reached. In view of this and the sighting of sharks nearby the Airborne Lifeboat was dropped from 600 feet at 120 mph. It landed within 50 yards of the survivors and was boarded. As no further search is recorded it is assumed the submarine eventually made rescue contact. The Flying Fortress was in the air for 13 hours and 15 minutes on this mission.

3–5 June   279 Squadron moved to Beccles and along with the Tain and Reykjavik detachments transferred to 281 Squadron.

8 June   Walrus L2217 found an empty Airborne Lifeboat at 1950 hours, position and condition not stated, no evidence traced of a recent 'drop'.

13 June   The report of this China Sea operation by the 3rd ERS quotes it as 'probably the most perfect mission ever staged by a "Jukebox" '. Capt. Holt and his crew were alerted to search for the crew of a B 24 which had ditched somewhere between Luzon and Formosa and accordingly took off from Floridablanca at 1030: having conducted a fruitless search until 1730 they headed for home. At 1820, a strong SOS was picked up on the radio, compass bearing 240 degrees. Immediately changing course the big plane homed in on the Gibson Girl transmitter until 1905 when two liferafts were spotted. The survivors fired flares and used their seamarker to assist in pin-pointing their position. The rescue plane circled the rafts and released smoke bombs to obtain the wind-drift before dropping their lifeboat which splashed down 40 feet from the distressed men. One minute later the rocket lines fired off and the men had no difficulty in reaching and boarding the boat. A note was dropped giving position and the course to steer. A few hours later PT boats came alongside and took the survivors aboard. Once again alertness had paid off and the manner in which the downed airmen used their rescue equipment proved what it could do if given the chance.

17 June 'I' and 'Y' of 281 Squadron equipped with Airborne Lifeboats provided air safety cover for a Royal plane flying from Northolt to Long Kesh in Northern Ireland. Their services were happily not required.

1 July Based on Chichi, B 17G 262, of the 4th ERS, piloted by Lt. Wunderling, took up station eight miles south-east of Chichishima Retto to cover a P 51 fighter sweep on that island and then went to the assistance of a pilot who baled out of his burning machine two miles away. Parachuting in full sight of 262 the survivor climbed into his liferaft at 1125, just as the rescue plane passed overhead. Smoke bombs were immediately dropped confirming Lt. Wunderling's opinion that the wind would drive the liferaft into the enemy held beach, the drift being quite rapid in the steady breeze. The Airborne Lifeboat was dropped at 1130 from 900 feet at 105 mph and landed within 20 feet of the fighter pilot, Lt. Campbell, the B 17's navigator being responsible for the excellent aim. The dropping mechanisms functioned perfectly and the downed pilot was in the boat two minutes after it touched down. A patrolling destroyer was notified of the drop, and its position, and replied that it would be on the spot at 1600. The rescue plane maintained contact until the vessel was sighted when it dropped another smoke bomb and flew between the lifeboat and the destroyer until pick-up was achieved. It was noted that even with the parachutes hanging heavily in the water the boat had drifted over a mile in four and an half hours. No effort was observed during this time on the part of the survivor.

20 July In the Pacific a B 17G piloted by Lt. Faulkener took off from Horotai at 0533 to search for a dinghy in 0358 N 07E ? (fix unclear) only to be ordered to return for an Airborne Lifeboat. The second take-off was at 0959 and by 1152 they had dropped their lifeboat to one man in a dinghy exactly in the position previously given. In less than a quarter of an hour the survivor, Lt. Louis Thealeaser, was in the boat. His P 40 had ditched on the 19th, so after floating around for 24 hours he must have been very relieved and pleased to see his rescuers. The B 17 maintained air cover to limit of endurance then returned to base, and Lt. Thealeaser motored the Airborne Lifeboat into port at Middlesburgh Island on the 22nd.

29 July   Playmate 26 of 4 ERS took off from Iwo Jima at 2320 to provide rescue cover for planes operating with the Third Fleet. At 1000 hours the next day it was ordered to seek a lone survivor close in to the beach within sight of Mount Fujiyama; at the time 26 was without a fighter escort. This and subsequent searches were unsuccessful until they were joined by fighters which led them to a man three to four miles off shore in Suruga Wan Bay. After circling to ascertain sea conditions the pilot decided to put down in spite of eight to ten feet swells on a glassy surface. The landing was very bouncy and many rivets in the hull were sprung so that the flying boat took in a considerable amount of water. Despite jettisoning all heavy equipment and reducing fuel level to the absolute minimum they were unable to take off again; the waterlogged hull causing water to be flung into the propellers. After destroying all classified matter the crew abandoned ship and took to the liferafts, their escorts advising Control of their plight and position. By now they were an hour overdue on their schedule for returning to base; within 15 minutes of abandoning the flying boat a B 17G was overhead preparing to drop its A-1 Lifeboat to them. This was successfully accomplished and the survivors were soon aboard and attempting to start the engines. It was an hour and an half later before one would run and in the interval the lifeboat had drifted to within two miles of the enemy held beach. After only half an hour's progress towards open sea the engine stopped and would not restart, so sail was set but with the lie of the wind the only course to be made was parallel with the shore, and the sail made them more obvious. An hour later one engine was got going and a fresh attempt made at an offing. At 1500 a submarine was sighted outside the coastal minefield on an interception course, resulting in the airmen cum mariners being taken aboard the submarine *Peto* at 1730, later, complete with the original casualty, Lt. Brock and crew, transfering to the submarine *Carilan* to be landed at Saipan on 6 August.

10 August   Search was made for Halifax 'M' of 518 Squadron, piloted by Sq. Ldr. Peijus, missing whilst on a long-range meteorological flight from Tiree. 'J', 'L' (W/O Branes) and 'P' (F/L Emck) of 281 Squadron were sent from Limavady to an area around 130 miles west-north-west of Londonderry. The still floating Halifax was found at 1519 by 'F', of the same Squadron, piloted by J. Mansell Smith, and a search started for the missing crew. The sighting of a Very light at 1535 caused 'F' to bring in Warwick 'J' (Sq. Ldr. Loweth) to a dinghy and its occupants who were in position 5618N 1116W, some miles distant from the ditched plane. 'J' first sent down smoke floats and then dropped her lifeboat so that it splashed down within 30 yards of the dinghy but the parachutes failed to release or collapse and the boat was blown rapidly away in the very strong wind. The inability of the survivors to reach the lifeboat, although it was close, would suggest that not only did the release cartridge not fire, neither did the drogue or the side rockets, indicating a failure in the electrical circuit. 'F's pilot, writing from Australia, adds details, and completes the story.

That morning, the 10th, Tiree was very heavily fogged in. . . . our

Warwicks would not take off . . . visibility was five yards only. It was my day off and just after breakfast I was asked if I would take a Halifax and join the search. We Long Range Meteorological Reconnaissance pilots were very highly trained for these special conditions and in my view if, in peacetime – which it was now in Europe – a pilot feels genuinely that a nil visibility take-off is beyond his capability, it is better that he refuses to go rather than risk a probable crash. My crew was rounded up and we agreed to go. Eventually we found 'M' in very different weather to that we'd left on Tiree. Some miles away, below the horizon, the *Jamaica Producer* was ploughing her way home with either the first, or one of the first, cargoes of bananas for Britain for several years. She was contacted and diverted to the survivors and I had the satisfaction of photographing the men being taken aboard. The ship also ran out a derrick and hoisted the lifeboat on deck.

17 August   Warwick BV 363 (F/O Denny) of 284 Squadron was airborne from Istres, inland from Marseilles, to take a lifeboat and drop it to survivors in a dinghy almost 100 miles to the south, but ten minutes after take-off a profuse petrol leak from the port engine forced their return to base. A Fortress was despatched from another base to fulfil the mission. (American details not found.)

19 September   In several of the operational accounts parachute malfunction is recorded with tragic results; here to add a little light relief is the content of a letter from ex-F/L E. H. Daniels (no relation to the author).

> . . . However, when the Lancasters started flying the troops home from Pomigliano and Bari in the late summer of 1945, the powers that be decided to lay on an exercise to show all and sundry that should, by some mischance, a Lancaster have to ditch, the Air/Sea Rescue Service was to hand and ready. It was my good luck/misfortune (?) that they selected 293 to provide the aircraft and boat, and that the CO detailed my crew to do the job. The exercise (codenamed 'Shufti') was laid on at Manfredonia Bay a little to the east of the RAF airfield at Foggia.
>
> A large number of Army personnel from all over southern Italy, together with others from the four RAF Wings and AHQ Italy, were gathered on the beach. Even the AOC Italy was watching from his launch lying offshore. The beach was black with the multitude!!!
>
> As I recall it we flew across from Pomigliano to Foggia for briefing, and thence to the area of the exercise where four or five bods had been sitting in an inflatable dinghy a few hundred yards offshore. My crew had taken great pains to ensure that everything was a great success, especially 'Geordie' (F/S F. G. Young) who as navigator had helped in devising an instrument to act as a 'bomb sight'. We flew in low over the assembled troops and then dropped our smoke marker, and made our dropping run over the target. From that point on it was pure unadulterated chaos – or pantomime.

42   Bombing up a Mark IIA to a Lancaster (It Ain't 'Arf Hot Mum) (J Chartres)

43   Mark III after an exercise drop (Saunders Roe ex B Waterhouse)

On 'Geordie's' signal I dropped the boat which left the aircraft with quite a large 'crack', more like a pistol shot. The first of the six parachutes opened, but the shroud lines got entangled with the manual release of the parachute cluster from the boat; the remaining five chutes, suspended from the sixth, drifted gently on to the beach with the onshore wind. Meanwhile the boat, on an even keel, was plunging seawards towards the men in the dinghy. They were not slow to recognise their danger and all of them leapt overboard seconds before the boat landed – crash landed would be a better description – right alongside the dinghy. If they thought their ordeal was over they were due for a shock. The boat's landing had been so violent that everything except the bare shape of the gunwales went straight to the bottom of the bay, including the CO_2 bottles which were designed to automatically inflate the flotation bags in the boat. In fact they then started to explode, scattering fragments over the men in the water as well as asphyxiating them with CO_2.

As the signal 'Exercise Abandoned' went up from the CO's launch we slunk quietly back to Pomigliano. We were prepared to disembowel the Engineer Officer, whose men had been responsible for the maintenance of the boats and aircraft, etc. but a rather frightening trip back through the Benevento Pass, which we were lucky to get through alive, put that out of our minds.

Several years later I was in the company of a number of RAF officers when one told the story of the drop he had witnessed from the shore. (He had no idea of my involvement.) He then twisted the knife! He quoted one of the Army men, who, watching the parachutes drift on to the shore remarked 'Cor! – bloody marvellous; they don't even get the parachutes wet.'

1 October   7th ERS. On this date an Airborne Lifeboat was dropped by one of the B 17s to a survivor, but before the man could reach the lifeboat a PT boat picked him up. The lifeboat was dropped within 70 yards of the man. One reason for him not reaching the boat was that the sea was large in swells that day and the visibility was not good. (Other details not decipherable.)

1 October   At 1150, 4th ERS at Hana were alerted that Curtiss Commando C 46, No. 345 was overdue from a local engineering flight. After checks on other airfields had been made three B 17 aircraft were scrambled between 1229 and 1334 to search for the missing crew in sea areas adjacent to Okinawa. The four survivors were sighted in liferafts at 1348 by the plane piloted by Lt. Schraeder. The navigator, Lt. Mines, dropped the lifeboat so that it landed within 35 feet of the liferafts and the four men were able to board it easily and proceeded to start the engines. The drop position was radioed to the crash boat base and a craft sent out which picked up the survivors at 1500. A helicopter was also sent out with a medic in case any of the men were injured.

24 October   281 Squadron was disbanded.

December   The 7th ERS to merge with the 6th, and be moved to another base, believed to be Hawaii.

10 December   ERS, stationed in Alaska, reported parachute failures in practice drops of A-1 lifeboats.

1946

5 April   A detachment from 280 Squadron was sent to Reykjavik as cover for Dakotas returning to the United States.

Undated   The 'heyday' of Airborne Lifeboats was over but the occasional operation continued. 'UV' of 294 Squadron (F/O Mackay), with 'U' took off at 1400 hours to search an area around 15 miles south-west of Leghorn for a Spitfire pilot in his dinghy and were helped in finding the man by orbiting aircraft in position 4332N 1004E. The Airborne Lifeboat was dropped successfully except that one parachute either caught up or failed to release. The Warwicks dared not shoot this away until it had blown well clear of the survivor, by which time the lifeboat was too distant for him to reach, so the operation was a failure. Happily a back-up HSL was on its way and this picked up the airman a while later.

4 June   On a flight from Tunis to Castel Benito to repatriate F/O Crawt and collect supplies for Malta, Anson PH 660 experienced engine trouble and was forced to ditch shortly after noon some ten miles off the African coast to the west of Tripoli, the port engine overheating and the starboard seized. The three men aboard got into the dinghy and spent seven or eight hours adrift before being located by a Warwick of 284 Squadron from Malta, which dropped an Airborne Lifeboat to them. It landed well and would have been easily reached had the parachutes detached properly; instead they acted as a sail. The Anson pilot, F/L Victor Avila, very courageously swam after the wayward lifeboat and finally managed to board it, although by then it was well out of sight of the dinghy. The Warwick assisted the ultimate rescue of all three men by dropping smoke floats in a line to indicate the direction towards the dinghy, so after clearing away the tackle and starting the engines Avila was able to motor back to his companions and bring them aboard. F/O Crawt and W/O Bryce must have been very, very relieved to see him return. Once together again they headed for the coast which was reached at nightfall. The ditching position is quoted as 3257N 1258E in a deposition made out on 21 February 1982.

21 June   280 Squadron officially ceased A/SR duties, but until 3 July continued odd operations whilst men and aircraft were available.

1947

25 February   A Tempest aircraft, piloted by F/L Sturgeon of 75 Squadron was forced to ditch about noon, 200 miles east-south-east of Malta, approximately 80 miles off the North African coast, whilst on a flight to Cairo. The cruiser

HMS *Leander* and the destroyer HMS *Virago* were known to be in the area so were requested to carry out a sweep in a search for the pilot. About 1330 he was sighted by a Coastal Command A/SR Dakota from Luqa, which summoned a lifeboat-carrying Lancaster of either 37 or 38 Squadron; which then made the first successful operational drop of a Mark II Lifeboat. The Lancaster's crew watched the survivor board before flying off to locate any surface craft which might be in the vicinity. HMS *Virago* fitted the role perfectly and had picked up the lifeboat and the pilot by 1930 in the evening to hustle the latter below for dry clothing and a tot of something to take the chill out of his bones. On Thursday the 27th both were landed at Malta. A report and pictures of the lifeboat and HMS *Virago* appeared in *The Times* (of Malta) that weekend. The prompt rescue earned congratulations for all concerned from the AOC Malta, and the Air C.-in-C. RAF Mediterranean and Middle East.

The Times of Malta in its issue of 20 April 1948 concluded an article with the words 'Thus Malta shares another role, that of a "Lifeboat Station of the Air".' In the preceding three columns a practice drop of a Mark II Airborne Lifeboat from Lancaster 'F' of 38 Squadron is precisely described under the heading 'Operation Bathtub' with three photographs to add emphasis to the text, and tribute is paid to the entire Air/Sea Rescue organisation. Most regrettably the newspaper's photograph library was later destroyed in a fire.

1948

3 June   The 2nd ERS were still finding business in the Pacific. The pilot of a P 50 built by Grumman was forced to bale out about 15 miles south of Aguni Shima. Within seven minutes of being alerted Lt. Heraty and crew were in the air with B 17G 3518. The ditched man was finally located and the A-1 lifeboat dropped to him; unfortunately it fell short and the hapless man was unable to reach it in his weakened condition. One-man liferafts were dropped until one fell close enough for him to grasp. Meanwhile other facilities had been summoned and the survivor was picked up shortly afterwards.

25 July   A lifeboat was dropped by 3rd ERS operating with the 5th Air Force in the China Sea area. Regrettably details are not readable.

1949

20 January   Still in the Pacific, Flight B of 2nd ERS at Misava was alerted for immediate take-off to render assistance to the pilot of a P 51 reported to have baled out about ten miles east of Wachinobe. The pilot was without the required one-man liferaft but did have a Mae West. Although no sea-marker dye was apparent the man was ultimately located and an A-1 lifeboat was dropped within 300 feet of him. At once a helicopter with a medical officer aboard was despatched to the scene so that he could be lowered to the lifeboat and thus recover the helpless pilot. Before this assistance arrived a Japanese fishing vessel came on the scene and took the lifeboat in tow before picking up the body of the pilot. Medical reports later revealed that the unfortunate man had died within five minutes of entering the water.

23 August   At 2310 hours Rescue Pearl alerted the 2nd ERS unit of a sailboat which had overturned approximately three miles south of the entrance to Pearl Harbor, setting three occupants adrift in the sea. At 2355, a C 46D was airborne to function as a low-level spotter aircraft for the 'Alert' aircraft, Flying Fortress SB 17C, which was airborne at 0029 on the 24th, after the A-1 lifeboat was detached and M-26 type flares mounted. This unit's function in the overall operation was to provide illumination for naval and Coast Guard boats and numerous Air Force crash boats in the immediate vicinity. Seven flares were dropped successfully by the B 17 aircraft and during the period of illumination all three survivors were located and rescued by surface craft. The mission was secured at 0140.

1950

10 April   The only recorded incident where an Airborne Lifeboat was operationally dropped on an inland lake (but remember Lake Erie is about 240 miles long by 90 at its widest).

Four boys were reported at 1900 hours to be adrift in a rubber raft without paddles or life preservers five miles offshore from Cleveland, Ohio. An SB 17 was sent from Lowry in Colorado and was over Lake Erie at 0025 on the 11th, but searched and contacted surface vessels without result. After landing to refuel and pick up additional flares the search was resumed until 0304 when a landing was made at Selfridge for necessary radio maintenance and to change the crew who had been on continuous duty for 16 hours. With a new crew and more flares the search was resumed at 0453, supplemented by an SA 10. By now a frontal system had moved into the area giving low cloud ceiling and gusts up to 57 knots, nevertheless the raft was sighted at 0700 when visibility was less than a mile, interrupted by heavy snow showers. Due to the weather conditions contact was impossible to maintain and smoke markers were ineffective with the snow and spray from 15-foot waves. It was not until 1015 that it was possible to drop the A-1 lifeboat with remarkably good aim in view of the weather conditions; so close in fact that the raft drifted onto it. Regrettably it was too late, there were no signs of life at all. At 1035 a Coast Guard vessel was homed to pick up the raft and the four bodies.

22 June   After escorting 28th Bombardment Squadron's B 29 5370, with two dead engines, into Guam the 2nd ERS received a message from B 29 4041 that it was lost and short of fuel, requesting a heading into Guam. This was immediately given but no further communication was received from the plane. SB 17 5604 was at once despatched to locate the aircraft and at 0335 on the 23rd spotted a bright green flare. The rescue plane stayed in the vicinity until daybreak but did not make any further sightings. As it was obvious by this time that 4041 had ditched, all assisting agencies were contacted and a full scale search instituted. At 1130 hours a MATS R-5D covering its assigned area spotted two liferafts, seven-man size, containing six persons. Then at 1245 three men in Mae Wests were sighted by a B 29 of 514th Weather Reconnaissance Squadron, some 25 miles from the other survivors. An A-1

44   Three stages of an A.3 drop from a B29 Super Fortress (EDO Corp)

lifeboat was successfully dropped to each of the groups by different B 17s at 1300 and 1315 hours. At the first sighting two surface craft, one of which was the minesweeper USS *Munsay*, had been sent out from Guam which located the lifeboats, picking up six men from one and one from the other. On the 24th one body was found in a rubber liferaft and one in a Mae West. Searches for the remaining two crewmen continued fruitlessly until June 27th. It was known that all crew members survived the ditching, none having baled out. This is the last operational use of Airborne Lifeboats found by the author.

1954

Undated   On a Royal flight to the West Indies back-up rescue services were to be provided by Lancasters fitted with Mark II Airborne Lifeboats.

So the operational history of Airborne Lifeboats drew to a fading close. Much ingenuity, energy and expense of lives and material had gone into their brief flowering – a record marred all too often by failure of equipment, especially parachutes and release gear, which negated the efforts of the rescuers and cost the lives of far too many gallant young men. Where the faults lie is not for anyone to conjecture now; we can only give tribute to those who sought to save others, even, sometimes, at the cost of their own lives.

10 The Engines for RAF Marks I–III

At sea you're on a hostile element even in fine weather; there's no hard shoulder to pull onto for a quick repair or to await help in relatively peaceful conditions; instead there's a constant battle against winds, tides, waves and salt air, and there are immeasurably greater obstacles than gradients, road conditions and traffic hazards. The sea does not let up; in fact it seems ever eager to take advantage of a weakness or an adverse situation – and there's a high degree of incompatibility where sea air and water are concerned with small boat engines. So when choosing an engine reliability has to have priority over the conflicting demands of weight, space, fuel consumption, ease of starting, accessibility, centre of gravity etc. With the Airborne Lifeboat all these factors had to be considered when the choice was being made, plus one other for the first two Marks – availability in a wartime situation of shortages of materials and production capacity.

Mark I: The Middy

In operational Airborne Lifeboat usage there was no more than an outside chance that any of the aircrew survivors would know much about marine engines, so simplicity had to rank high alongside reliability; and in a small boat suitability of engine is harder to achieve than in a motor car. So initially Uffa Fox had a problem on his hands. His first prototype appeared to be fitted with Marston Seagull longshaft outboards, very simple and relatively reliable in the context of the times, but the criticism of the boat included the engines. At what stage he considered the 'Middy' is not known, but it is certain he would have met it previously as fitted in yacht tenders and dinghies; and once it came to his mind he would have seen its considerable advantages in low weight, low centre of gravity, ease of installation and maintenance. Its temperamental nature would not have been so obvious. In his books he makes light of the difficulties of obtaining Middy engines for tests and trials, scouring the country for ones to be reconditioned by the manufacturers being the only solution. Once Airborne Lifeboats were accepted for production as Service craft the power units were specially manufactured by the British Motor Boat Manufacturing Company.

The Middy, used only in Marks I and IA, was initially developed by the British Motor Boat Manufacturing Company in 1933 and complete with reverse gear, pivoting head and wheel steering sold for £35, which would be ten to twelve weeks' gross earnings for a boatbuilder. It was based on the standard 'Britannia' outboard with twin cylinders rated at 4 bhp at 3000 rpm, a flywheel magneto and an Amal float feed carburettor. The power 'head' comprising a cylinder head and crankcase assembly was mounted above a circular base plate which was designed to be bolted to the interior planking of the boat, through which a flanged boss protruded to mate up with, and bolt to, a propeller and gear unit fitted from the outside of the hull. A strengthening pad was needed inside and this would also serve as a level platform so that the engine would stand vertical. A circular base-plate was fitted outside the planking to take the heads of the engine holding down bolts and to secure the edges of the cut planks. The actual drive between the power unit and the right-angled gearing for the propeller was by a short shaft which slotted into a drive socket when the lower unit was offered up for the four flange bolts to be affixed.

As the rated output of the Middy was only 4 hp, it was insufficient to give the lifeboat a practical operating speed – which could have been the key to the engine selection decision. To fit a single propeller shaft in the normal manner would necessitate extra structural work and timber in the hull to strengthen the keel and stern where the tail shaft would pass through. It would also involve a large propeller on a vulnerable shaft projecting below the hull, supported only by its skeg. The Hudson aeroplane had been chosen as the carrier because of its sound qualities, reliability and availability, but it had one serious drawback. Whilst on the ground there was not much clearance between the aft end of the fuselage and the tarmac (or grass), which was a contributory reason why Uffa Fox opted for the canoe-shaped stern, and the necessity for this low profile was especially apparent when the Hudson was touching down and the oleo legs telescoped. So the simple solution was to fit twin engines, one on each side of the keelson approximately amidships, with their small propellers protruding through the hull, thus eliminating, at one go, the problem of individual low power, danger of a conventional propeller system being damaged by ground contact, extra work and weight in the after end of the boat and a long shaft which might be distorted by the shock of the boat landing on the water.

On the Airborne Lifeboat it was decided to omit the reverse gear as precise 'alongside' handling would not be required, also the internal wheel steering because there would be no space to accommodate it, thus keeping the engine weight down to a realistic level. With normal outboards turning the engine on its pivot alters the thrust and thus the direction in which the boat goes; with the modified Middy in the lifeboat this could not be done, so a rudder became necessary for use all the time, not just when the lifeboat might be under sail.

To the modern outboard user these little motors might appear of almost 'ark' vintage, so a few more details might not come amiss. The twin cylinders were of the horizontally opposed, two-stroke type, with a bore of 50.5 mm, a 41 mm stroke and a piston displacement of 165 cc. Each engine had a rated power output of 4 bhp at 3000 rpm and a mean marine power output of 3.67 bhp at 2100 rpm. The cylinders were cast in close-grained nickel-iron and the aluminium alloy pistons had normal type deflector heads. The ignition system was of the usual outboard engine type of a flywheel magneto feeding current to the two 18 mm single-point sparking plugs. Lubrication was by the two-stroke method of mixing oil with the petrol in a ratio of one pint of oil to two gallons of fuel (one in sixteen), the lubrication reaching all parts because of the crankcase compression employed for the fuel mixture. The 'petroil' tank, of six-pint

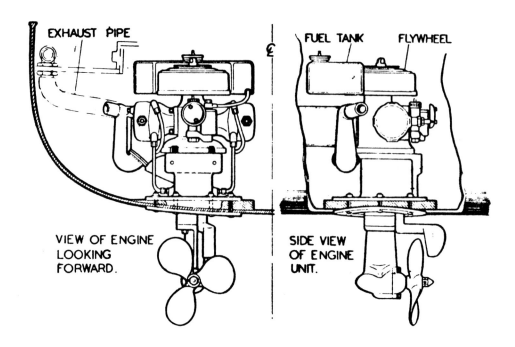

45   The 'Middy', 'Inboard-Outboard' for Marks I and IA

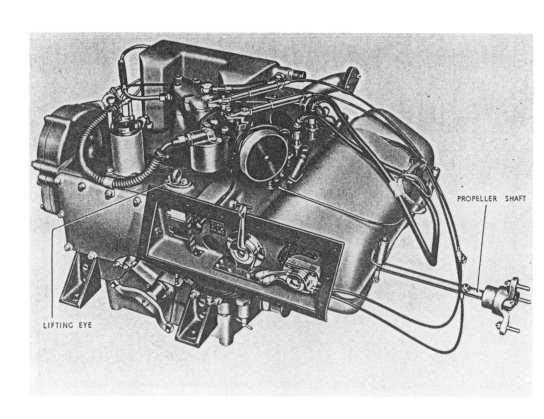

47   The HRD Vincent for Mark IIIs (Laird (Anglesey) Ltd)

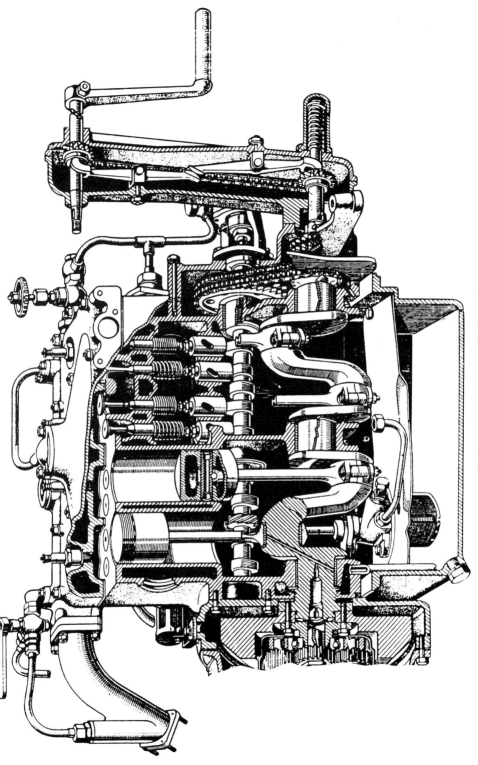

46 The 'Austin' Marine for Mark IIs (Austin Rover)

capacity, was attached to the engine, being saddle-shaped around part of the flywheel magneto. With such a small tank it was essential to watch that the fuel did not run out, principally because the two-stroke engines of the time, for no apparent reason, were often very difficult to restart whilst warm. The tank could be refilled through a vented removable cap in its top, whilst the motor was running, from spare cans of fuel carried in the amidships lockers. These had to be well shaken before pouring to ensure the two constituents were completely mixed. The twin-jet Amal carburettor complete with choke, mounted on the aft side of the engine, was readily accessible for cleaning. A big danger with these, or any other two-stroke engines which were not in daily use, was that the high proportion of oil in the petrol would start to separate out and deposit as an oily gum which could cause clogging of the jets or make the carburettor float stick. As there was no way of disengaging the drive from the propeller the engines had always to be started under load.

For starting a cord was wound around a notched flange on top of the flywheel magneto, given a sharp pull in the hope the engine would fire and then pick up; it seldom happened the first time; the third perhaps. This was quite effective but could be very tiring if repeated attempts were necessary, and for men not feeling or operating at their best it could be totally exhausting, made worse in the lifeboat because the top of the engine was necessarily below deck level so it was impossible to get a straight pull on the cord. The enclosed coiled spring return method had, unfortunately, not been invented. Just above and abaft the blades of the propeller a small, bracket mounted scoop protruded into the slipstream and the ensuing pressure pushed cooling water up to circulate around the cylinder head before being discharged overside on the port quarter, clear of the crew, along with the engine fumes.

The three-bladed manganese bronze propellers were only of 7 1/2″ diameter, each secured to its small horizontal shaft, leading from the double bevel gearing, by a silver steel pin through a hole in the shaft engaging in two slots in the propeller boss, the whole unit being locked on by a securing nut. If the propeller were to be fouled by a rope this pin would shear so that the engine would race, but remain undamaged if quickly shut down.

When under way it was advised that the hatches to the engines should be kept closed, so that shipped water or spray could not put them out of commission, and to prevent any fumes upsetting the crew. To allow each engine to 'breathe' an inverted U breather tube was fitted through the deck, close to the skin planking, literally under the gunwale, thus it was well shielded both from accidental damage and possible flooding. Should any water enter through this breather its position well outboard of the engine ensured that any drip, or flow, would discharge harmlessly into the watertight compartment, whence it could be baled or pumped out.

Whilst of quite low power by modern standards, these engines were very sturdy units and gave the 23-foot craft a speed of 6 knots under reasonable conditions, and the ability to proceed under one engine only should circumstances so dictate. They were quite quiet too, especially with the hatches closed, an admirable quality if the boat were near to an enemy coast or shipping. Some Airborne Lifeboats covered dozens, even hundreds, of miles under their own power.

Mark II: Austin 8 hp Marine

During the war 3500 of these engines were built at the Longbridge Works in Birmingham, of which 150 were reserved for fitting into the Mark II Airborne Lifeboats; the remainder being installed in the lifeboats of merchant ships or in Admiralty Dories. This was, again, a small production engine and therefore not often encountered. Paper comparison of the 23-foot Mark I with its twin 4 hp motors and the 30-foot Mark II at 8 hp might suggest that the latter was underpowered; but this does not appear to have been so in practice. This could lie in two factors, firstly the difference in total cylinder cubic capacities and secondly, because the propeller of the Mark II operated in a tunnel, it could obtain a better grip on the water and produce a less dissipated thrust. Also the two propellers of the Mark I were much nearer the bows of the boat, working in a relatively shallow depth of water and so could have been picking up quite an amount of air from the movement of the boat and surface retention, especially in choppy conditions. The speeds of the two boats are quoted as 6 and 7 mph respectively.

In appearance the Austin Marine resembled, and was undoubtedly an adaptation of, one of their most famous car engines. It was a four-cylinder petrol engine, water-cooled from outside the hull, therefore having no radiator. The sparking plugs were fitted into the top of the removable cylinder head, giving very easy access for cleaning etc. The camshaft, driven by sprocket and chain, operated the side valves, with the crankshaft running in three steel-backed white metalled bearings. Electric current was supplied by a sprocket-driven magneto, type GJ 4/5 being fitted on engines numbered 300 to 960 inclusive, but numbers 961 onwards had type GJ 4 incorporating an impulse starter to ease the chore of handle swinging. This was quite important in the Airborne Lifeboats as the engine was set in a well of watertight bulkheads so the operative had to kneel on the deck and reach down into the confined space to get a full swing, even though the starting handle was raised on a pedestal.

The reduction gear box was of the usual marine type, having two operating positions, the lever forward for going ahead and towards aft for going astern, both from a central neutral position. The gearing reduced the crankshaft speed to a short propeller shaft of 1 1/8″ diameter steel which passed through a watertight stern tube in way of the tunnel planking shaft log to the propeller abaft the supporting skeg. The cooling water was circulated round the engine by a gearwheel pump, having been drawn up through a submerged sea-cock in the planking. From the pump it was delivered to the cylinder block jackets and cylinder head before passing into the exhaust manifold and discharging overside.

The bore of the cylinders was 2.235″ (56.77 mm) and the stroke 3.35″ (88.9 mm), with a total capacity of 900 cc, which made it a very sturdy unit and goes far in explaining the performance figures. Fuel was fed from two self-contained petrol tanks below the fore deck, one each side of the mast fitting, by an AC 'Sphinx' type 'T' fuel pump, thus ensuring a constant feed regardless of the movement of the boat. The plugs were either Champion SK 8 or Lodge SR 900, firing a mixture fed to the cylinders by a Zenith type 24V updraught carburettor incorporating a choke and flame trap, situated on the port side of the installation. Lubrication was from an oil pump mounted in the crankcase sump, which held twelve pints of oil. The right-handed bronze propeller of 15 1/2″ diameter and 13 1/2″ pitch, by Bruntons of Sudbury, was fastened to its taper-ended shaft by a conventional key and secured with a terminal locknut.

To make the engine less liable to the effects of bilge or shipped water it was installed in its own watertight compartment, bounded by bulkheads fore and aft and by the separated portions of the keelson at each side, and it was to these that the feet of the engine were secured on shock absorbent mountings, the whole installation being contained in a heavy flexible rubberised material bag which was closed at the top with a sealing tube; all points at which pipes or shafts entered the bag being individually sealed. This was fine in theory so long as there was adequate ventilation and access was not needed; unhappily it did not work so well in practice so that later the bag was bisected horizontally with the lower portion battened to the sides of the engine casing, the upper portion apparently being discarded.

Because the engine was too tall to be totally housed beneath the deck it had to be enclosed in a casing, the top and sides of which from deck level upwards, were removable for servicing and/or attention. On the forward end of this was mounted the choke and primer controls, and the petrol tap union whilst the after end provided a convenient position for the instrument panel, containing the throttle lever, the magneto switch, the air intake cap and an oil pressure gauge.

A report by the Marine Aircraft Experimental Establishment at Felixstowe in 1946 states that this engine was not very satisfactory for the Airborne Lifeboats; with hindsight it could be that the exigencies of wartime production could be partly to blame for some of its defects, but not all. One item mentions 'a number of defective and corroded parts after only ninety-five hours running, with the oil very sludgy'. The report attributes this to the low running temperature of the engine and a continuous current of damp salty air through the crankcase, due to the provision of a carburettor intake connection to the valve chest and the retention of the normal filler cap breather on the opposite side of the engine. One would assume that at some stage the extra breather was put in so that the fumes would not distress the crew, but leaving the original vent open allowed so much moist air to circulate that the presence of water was discernible in the sump oil.

Other problems were also disclosed: 'the water passages in both the block and head contained a very heavy deposit of slime, sufficient, in some cases, to appreciably reduce the communicating holes between head and block, notably around No. 1 cylinder and the outlet at the top between Nos. 2 & 3.' And so the report goes on: 'Valve stems corroded to the extent that they were difficult to remove'; 'Valve springs broken or 1/8″ short on all loadings'; 'Timing sprocket and teeth corroded and the chain rollers burnished by running completely dry'; 'Starting handle bearings partly seized and the throw out spring rusty as no oil in this part of the crankcase, due to inadequate passageways'; 'Carbon deposit very heavy and of a soft nature as might be expected in an over cooled engine'; 'Spark plug insulation had broken down at the screening sleeves'. The magneto was found to be in good condition although the splash shield was not satisfactory and the two lower gauze vents were blocked with paint. The starting handle grip was criticised as being too small and liable to seize solid.

The report makes very sorry reading indeed. But, design and manufacturing faults apart, it must be appreciated that there are difficulties in providing an engine which would be able to operate successfully in all parts of the world; overcooling may be a good trait in the tropics but deadly in temperate or sub-arctic zones; add humidity and salinity ranges and it is asking rather too much from a standard engine; especially as flight conditions could freeze the sump oil, which would not have time to thaw out before an attempt might be made to start the engine. So, all in all, one can realise why there could be problems with Airborne Lifeboat engines, apart from the inexperience, exhaustion or injuries of the survivors whose need was often desperate.

Mark III: Vincent HRD Engine

The Mark III was conceived originally with the Pacific Ocean 'island hopping' campaign in mind. The lifeboat would need a range of up to 1000 miles at a speed of at least 5–6 knots and be self-supporting for extended periods. The engine specification set limits on weight and size, and emphasised easy starting, radio screening, temperature and humidity adaptability as well as, possibly, being submersible. The prototype finally chosen was the Vincent 500 cc Twin, T5AM/X, based on patents taken out by P. C. Vincent, head of the famous motorcycle company of that name, and especially developed for the Mark III lifeboat by P. E. Irving, to whom, from his Australian home, I am indebted for many of the following details. These are of particular interest for any 'two-stroke' buff to follow.

The engine had two horizontal power cylinders with an induction cylinder mounted between them, the whole block being placed athwartships to drive two hollow, three-throw crankshafts running in pressure lubricated white metalled bearings. The crankshafts were coupled by a roller chain so that the pumping crankpins were in phase and operated a pair of double-acting pistons. The cast iron pumping cylinder had two sets of drilled ports which acted as inlet ports to supply the two outer spaces or the inner spaces between the pistons according to their direction of motion. After the ports closed, the mixture was partially compressed and then delivered to one of the power cylinders when its transfer ports opened: the space between the pumping pistons supplied No. 1 power cylinder, and the two spaces behind them supplied No. 2; the difference in displacement by the presence of the half-inch piston rods was disregarded. The piston rods were sealed against leakage by a combination of piston rings and lipped rubber seals, connecting rod side thrust being taken by integral crossheads. Although no oil was added to the fuel, wear on the cast iron pumping pistons and liner was negligible after hundreds of hours running. The power cylinders also consisted of grey-iron liners with drilled transfer and exhaust ports communicating with scroll chambers in the block. The main exhaust ports were on top of the block and fed into a fully water-cooled silencer. The Amal type 30 HVL marine carburettor was also on top and protected by a water shield containing a small flame trap. Scavenging was, of course, on the uniflow system, and no reliance was placed on exhaust resonance.

To provide asymmetrical timing of the power cylinder ports the exhaust crankshaft had a lead of 24° over the transfer crank, and as can be seen in the table of dimensions, this furnished a blow-down period of 33°, while the exhaust ports closed 14° before the transfers. The transfer ports were angle drilled to provide a small amount of swirl, but the exhausts were drilled radially and chamfered externally to make them self-cleaning. Beside the usual top rings, each piston had one plain ring and one slotted scraper ring in the skirt. The crankshaft coupling chain also ran over a layshaft sprocket giving a forward propeller speed reduction of 2.04 to 1. A five pinion reverse gear was housed in the sump, ahead or astern being engaged by multi-plate clutches running in oil. Starting was either by Rotax direct electric starter or, initially, by a spring assisted lever. All electrical gear, including the BTH type KD2-SS4 magneto, was shielded in itself and then enclosed in a water-tight metal cover. The block and all major castings were of corrosion resistant magnesium-aluminium alloy anodised and sealed with potassium dichromate, and all exposed ferrous parts were either stainless, or cadmium plated.

The block was water-cooled by gear pump, but kept empty when the boat was in flight (thus saving weight and eliminating possible freezing) and the slight delay in the waterjacket being filled by the pump when the engine was started assisted in a rapid warm-up without the danger of cracking which might occur with a cast iron block. It was essential that the engine would accept full throttle and develop good power immediately on starting. As the propeller, designed to run in a tunnel, could only absorb 15 hp before cavitation occurred, the engine was developed to give maximum economy at or below this power, and fuel consumption was reduced to 0.71 pints/bhp/hour at 11 bhp, with only a small increase at 14 bhp. On test this proved sufficiently low to give the lifeboat a still air range of 1020 miles on 50 gallons of fuel at 5.3 knots, well within the specification.

In November 1946 tests were carried out by the Marine Aircraft Experimental Establishment at Felixstowe to ascertain if the Vincent engine would be suitable for fitting in the Mark II Lifeboat in place of the Austin, as well as to 'prove' it for the Mark III. It was not intended that a direct comparison should be drawn between the two engines, but in many respects this would seem inevitable. The MAEE suggested that the Amal type carburettor be replaced by a Zenith for further tests, although not designed to work underwater. It further noted an increase in engine weight of 23 pounds due to modifications and did not consider the range to be more than 600 miles. It noted, also, that the lever type starting was 'tricky' and needed a pull of 75 pounds at an awkward angle on a traverse from horizontal to 45° past vertical. An incomplete 'pullover' could result in a 'kickback' with the chance of a broken wrist for the operative. Survivors might be of light physique, or not be in good enough physical condition, due to injury, cold, fatigue or sea-sickness; to cope with such a task the testers recommended that an electric starter be incorporated in spite of the additional weight and complications of a generator, extra wiring, larger accumulator and cut-out. The fuel pump was found inadequate, not being self-priming even with a perfectly airtight fuel line, if the line were long and ran for most of its length above the tank level. The engine was found to be very noisy and the position of the exhaust caused fumes to blow into the centre of the boat. By fitting a length of 1 1/4″ copper pipe and leading the discharge over the quarter the noise level was reduced, the fumes taken clear and a slightly better engine performance registered. Therefore, this report did provide a firm base on which further development could proceed; illustrating the necessity for a test body with real experience of actual operating conditions as a bridge between manufacturers and users, even though such procedures have often slowed down development to the pace of a 'dodderman'.

It was not until September 1953 that the MAEE actually carried out trials with the Mark III lifeboat and Vincent engine, again at Felixstowe. The end of the War had brought about a run-down in demand for most equipment and with the stocks of Mark IIs coming into service there was no urgency to develop its successor; but the years between were not completely wasted for the 1953 report based on trials with three Mark III boats with differing construction techniques records: 'Top speed 6.6 knots; maximum range with all-up load in calm weather 1100 nautical miles at speeds between 4.7 and 5.2 knots'. Another report in the same month suggested further modifications which would facilitate engine removal and installation, thus reducing maintenance time and labour. The most important of these was in the wiring system. Originally the five wires leading to the engine had to be individually disconnected and reconnected; the suggestion was that these should be brought into a common loom terminating in a breeze plug which could be fitted into a similar socket at the watertight bulkhead. This and other minor points were incorporated into the production engines fitted to the Mark III Airborne Lifeboats designed for the RAF and supplied to the South African Air Force, for Shackletons to carry. One very important item was the installation of a heater in the sump, supplied with current from the carrier plane, to prevent the oil solidifying whilst the lifeboat was in flight.

Summary of engine details Type T5/AM1

Two power and one induction cylinders. Bore 56mm, stroke 50.8mm, capacity 497 cc, compression ratio 7:1. Power 12 bhp at 2940 rpm.
Crankshaft 13.5 bhp at 3080 rpm. Rotation anti-clockwise looking at the face of the output coupling. Idling speed 750 rpm.
Weight (dry) complete with all accessories 264 lb (approx.).
Carburettor: Amal, horizontal, marine type 30 VLH with butterfly strangler.
Flame trap: Amal 88/100.
Fuel pump: Amal type 150.
Ignition: BTH type KD2-SS4 magneto with PJ5 impulse starter.
Sparking plugs: Lodge RS2, fully screened. Gap 0.002 inch.
Fuel: Aviation gasoline 100/130 grade. Tank capacity 130 gallons (Imp.),

consumption 0.8 pints/bhp/hour at 2940 rpm.

Lubrication: Oil, circulated by gear type pump to the main and big-end bearings. Oil type OM 31. Sump capacity 3 1/2 gallons. Pressure 6–10 psi. Temperature (inlet) 50–60 °C. Consumption 0.312 pints/hour. Shaft log lubrication by grease XG 190 or LG 190, by grease cup.

Gears: Reduction ahead 2.04:1; Reduction astern 2.56:1.

Cooling: Sea water through a gear type pump and ejected with exhaust gases.

Starting: (Mechanical) geared impulse. (Electric) 12 volt starter motor, solenoid operated. Rotax N3EY/C 0209 12 volt and N5CP 12 volt respectively.

Generator: Rotax B 1821, 12 volt 50 watt.

Regulator: Rotax F 0403 12 volt.

Immersion Heater: GEC HE37690, 24 volt 500 watt.

Time delay switch: Venner LBDS. 24 volt 2 amp.

Propeller: Three-bladed, fixed-pitch, nickel-aluminium-bronze of 12 1/2 inches diameter, 9 1/2 inches pitch, revolving anti-clockwise looking forward.

Accumulator: Lead acid, type D, 12 volt, 25 amp/hr, or 12 volt 40 amp/hr.

Port timings (measured relative to the transfer crank): ·

Induction port opens	19° before TDC
closes	79° before BDC
Transfer port opens	39° before BDC
closes	39° after BDC
Exhaust port opens	72° before BDC
closes	25° after BDC

Settings: Choke 0.88 inch, Main jet 120–170, By-pass jet 35, Air bleed 7.

Strangler plate: Drilled with 1.3/16 inch hole.

Contact breaker gap: 0.012 inch. Timing as marked on exhaust side flywheel. Mark IGN 1 to be in line with crankcase face (at top of opening) when contact breaker points are just opening for No. 1 cylinder.

11 Other Developments

Wartime Designs

Throughout the War, fertile minds were busy on further developments of Air/Sea Rescue, including the Airborne Lifeboat concept. Indeed, Gp. Capt. Waring was not the only man to put the idea forward. Naturally, there was secrecy about wartime thoughts and schemes so the same, or similar, ideas crop up in various sources from time to time. In the files at the Public Record Office is a letter, dated 2 January 1944, from a Sq. Ldr. Thomas dealing with his idea for a lifeboat to be carried by an aeroplane; although no details are quoted an accompanying illustration gives a reasonable outline of what was in his mind. No further correspondence is filed with the letter so the existing Mark Is of the time and the extent of work already in hand on the Mark II obviously precluded further thought or action on his design. On 2 March the same year G. A. Davey Esq., of 'Goodwood', Kingston Avenue, Staines, writes of his plans for a 'Rescraft', apparently an aircraft-borne boat, but the absence of illustrations, plans or further letters leaves one wondering just what his brainchild could have been; with the tantalising thought that it might have been a 'survival capsule' almost 40 years ahead of those now in use on oil and gas rigs and similar installations. Similarly, early in the War, Mr George Selman, who was Chief Designer with the British Power Boat Company, drew up plans for a 'dropping dinghy' for use with the Hampden bomber; but once again only greater depth of research may reveal details of this.

One of the most outstanding ideas of all came from W/Cdr. Paul Barnard, who was Commanding Officer of 280 Squadron at Bircham Newton, and on reading his letter to Gp. Capt. Waring, dated 14 July 1943, one wonders why further developments and trials of this project were not proceeded with, as here is given the conception of a covered-in lifeboat, now universally accepted.

> Dear Group Captain Waring,
>
> I have an idea for what I consider a bigger and better Airborne Lifeboat which although it would not replace the present one, or have its all round usefulness, would be useful on many occasions and have several advantages lacked by the present type of Airborne Lifeboat.
>
> My idea is to have the Airborne Lifeboat in the form of a Glider cum seaworthy Motorboat, with a crew of 2; a pilot and a Doctor or Sick Bay Attendant, both reasonably skillful yachtsmen.
>
> The Glider would be released in the usual way and glide down but as

the Pilot was making the actual landing Rockets would be released to bring the Glider to a standstill immediately, thus enabling it to land in any sea. As soon as it touched the water the Pilot would jettison the wings by means of a simple lever and the fuselage of the glider, being in the form of a strong motorboat, would, without its wings, (and tail if necessary), be normally seaworthy. It would also be a simple matter to jettison the streamlined top covering of the gilder fuselage if so desired, or else this could be made part of the motor boat hull.

The advantages I consider, are as follows:

(1)   The Glider cum Boat could be much larger, more seaworthy & better equipped than its 'underbelly' counterpart.

(2)   A live, fit crew would be on the spot to pick up aircraft or ship's survivors and render First Aid and navigate the boat.

(3)   The boat would have a range of several hundred miles at a fair speed, be armed and stocked with food, be unsinkable and able to sail efficiently if the worse came to the worse.

The idea is perhaps a little far fetched but I really do think that it would not only be practicable but a most useful adjunct to ASR. I might add that I am only too ready to do any of the tests in the capacity of glider pilot. Perhaps you will consider this idea.

Y/s.

Regrettably the matter does not again figure in the files of Air 20/4709; possibly there were doubts about the practicability of landing 'in any sea' without damage to the craft or its crew, bearing in mind the high incidence of damage to Walrus, Catalina and even Sunderland aircraft when they attempted to pick up survivors in conditions other than might be described as 'fine or calm', but the amazing thing is that just such a craft was visualised by Noel Pemberton Billing who inserted an advertisement in the Royal Aero Club's Year Book of 1914 for a 'Flying Lifeboat', described as 'one which, like some gigantic hymen-opterous insect could shed its wings and tailplane after alighting on the sea, and thereupon leap forward through the waves as a conventional surface craft'. It was a scene which the illustrator depicted with more verve than credibility. Apparently there were no customers.

Uffa Fox also was very active, apart from building some of the Airborne Lifeboats in his Medina Yard at Cowes, feeding ideas for his draughtsmen and women to turn into working drawings for consideration by concerned bodies. No fewer than nine separate designs emanated from this source during the next year or so, each worthy of at least a few lines of description.

(1)   A 24-foot Airborne Lifeboat mentioned in letters but no design traced to date.

(2)   A 16-footer for use by the Fleet Air Arm with a maximum (exterior) beam of 4' 8". In broad principle it followed the Mark I but had only one Middy engine set to port almost amidships. Many of the sections emphasise a very definite tumblehome, necessary to give the boat beam

and freeboard when fitted to a plane (unstated) with a narrow fuselage. It would have been an unpleasant boat in any kind of sea as the deck at the centre drainage slot was only a few inches above the still-water level.

(3) Named RN 1, this 17' 6" design, also for the Fleet Air Arm had a maximum beam of 4' 10" and an even more pronounced tumblehome to give a maximum gunwale width of only 3'. As a blueprint of the lines only is in my possession, marked 'Final Plan'. I believe it is the outcome of previous work on the 17' 9" project mentioned below. All three drawings held are dated 1944. In a series of photographs an Airborne Lifeboat, stated to be 17' 6", is shown attached to a Barracuda, which was designated by its makers, Fairey Aviation Company, as a Torpedo Dive Bomber. An illustration in the company's book shows Barracuda Mk II, MX 613 carrying this lifeboat during 'experiments and demonstrations', but no operational usage has been traced, nor the builders and the number produced. In other photographs it can be seen that in one hull, at least, the drogue and rocket boxes in the bows were square in shape and that the transverse line-throwing rockets, although mounted on the deck, fired through holes in the topsides, and that three parachutes were used for dropping. See Plates **48 and 49**.

(4) At 17' 9" the lines drawing is very similar in design and scantlings to No. 3, and shows a deck arrangement in which there is a dismounted engine stowage hatch abreast of the centreboard slot and an engine operational seating, with clamps, abaft the after parachute sling plates, and thus within easy reach of a man at the tiller. A petrol tank right up in the bows with a pipe leading aft could suggest an outboard engine was contemplated but with a connectable gravity fuel lead to provide a larger initial supply and thus lessen running out and refilling problems. Regrettably no further information is to hand.

(5) Around March 1944 there is mention of a special Airborne Lifeboat designed by Uffa Fox specifically for the use of merchant seamen. The length is not stated but its carrying capacity was estimated as being for 35–50 men. Bearing in mind his opinion that the 30-foot version would accommodate 25 men this must have been a considerably larger hull, although it is mentioned that the boat would have sails only so engine space and weight would be saved. A Ministry of War Transport ship's lifeboat of 26 feet which the author designed in 1940 and put into production the following year was authorised for 40 men on the basis that each person was officially allowed 21 inches of seating space – which actually meant 'living space'.

(6) The 35-foot boat visualised on a blueprint for use by Lancaster and Flying Fortress planes had an estimated speed of 7 knots, a range of 500 miles under power and a capacity for 50 men. The undated set of lines gives no indication of the proposed power unit, sails etc.

(7) This 40-foot size apparently once existed as a blueprint but the author

BARRACUDA MK II
(WITH LIFEBOAT)
MERLIN
JANUARY 1945

48   Barracuda with trial Fleet Air Arm 16' 9" boat (Fleet Air Arm Museum)

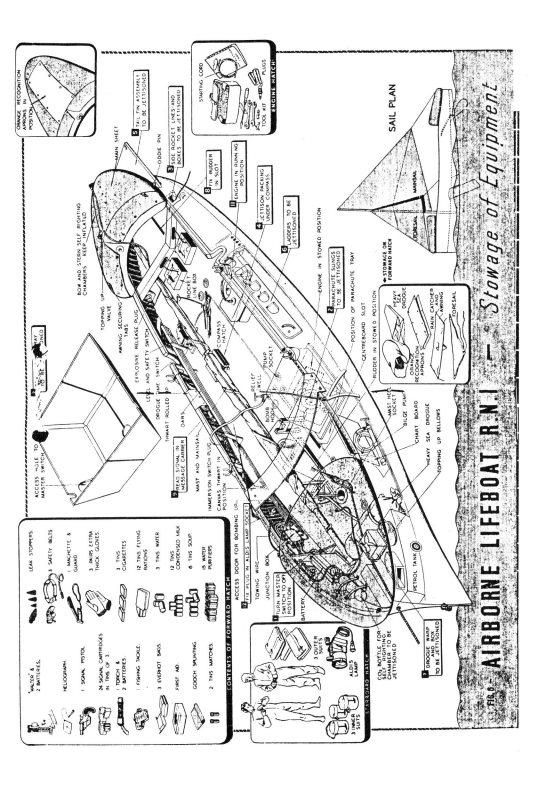

49   *Deck plan and equipment for RN1*

has no copy of this.

(8)   A similar situation exists concerning the 45-foot size lifeboat.

(9)   The 50-foot boat to suit the Lancaster and Lincoln planes is better documented in three blueprints, dated December 1944, which show the sail plan having a vertical gunter and staysail on the foremast and a low profile Bermuda Mizzen, also with a staysail, both trailing sails being fitted with booms. The lines give the impression of a 'stretched' Mark I with the extreme reverse sheer reduced to a straight line as far aft as station 8, though the sections still show an extensive tumblehome. The quoted speed of 10 knots and range of 1000 miles have no indication of engine power or propeller dimensions, or mountings, to assist in assessing their sources; although the quoted capacity of 200 men, if fully filled, would have meant an even more cramped boat then a Ministry of War Transport 26-foot lifeboat. Correspondence infers that at least one trial hull was built at Medina Works, but no construction notes or photographic evidence has been traced.

When the Mark II lifeboat was in the planning stage thought was being given to other designs and the use of other methods of construction than conventional mahogany planking. In furtherance of this, tenders were invited from the boatbuilding industry with only the basic parameters being defined, within which the competitors were asked to submit both design and construction details and costs. Six companies submitted detailed tenders: Aldous Successors of Brightlingsea, The British Power Boat Company of Hythe, The Itchenor Shipyard Ltd, Uffa Fox Ltd, Vosper Ltd and Wates Ltd.

The designs were considered firstly on compliance with requirements of practicality, seaworthiness, strength, weight, construction and air-drag. A summary of the submissions makes interesting reading within today's knowledge, and excerpts from an assessment of late 1943 are quoted herewith:

(3.1) . . . Uffa Fox has submitted two types of construction – the normal timbered and planked of the first Mk II prototype and a moulded plywood hull. The weight of the first design is heavier than the other competitive designs, but this is mature whereas the weights of the other designs would probably exceed the estimates if the boat were constructed. Bearing this in mind the weights are much the same and would possibly run out at 3,000 lbs. The Uffa Fox moulded ply design would run about 2,800 lbs and with lightening of the bulkheads and keel case a lower weight could be achieved – possibly 2,650 lbs.

(4)   The type of hull is similar in all designs – excepting British Power Boats. The latter design has a hull with a fixed keel, two chines, transom stern, and a double skin of straight ply which is divided into watertight compartments. The deck is below the waterline and protection to the crew is given by the deep sides. It is not capable therefore of self emptying. The two inflated chambers forward and aft occupy deck space and do not form a protective cover for the crew. The deep hull is carried up the side of the

aircraft and with the broad flat gunwale makes a very bad junction for good aerodynamic performance. The fixed keel and chines are also undesirable for the same reason. . . . this design . . . does not meet the requirements and there is some doubt as to its self-righting properties.

(4.1) Wates' design is also eliminated with its chines and flat plywood construction. The flat bottom and large unsupported areas are a very bad feature. No details beyond a drawing of the hull are available. . . . there does not appear to be room for the parachute packs. The end of the tunnel fouls the suspension lug which has no visible means of support. . . . this design is very crude and has little to recommend it.

(4.2) Vosper's design is very clean and well conceived but advice should be sought on the best shape of the bulwarks for fairing into the aircraft. Some tumblehome amidships seems desirable, but this should be kept to a minimum for good seaworthiness.

A small amount of reinforcement . . . to parachute attachments, the double keelsons are a good feature. . . . the moulded skin gives a strong structure. . . . This design has much to recommend it.

(4.3) Uffa Fox's first design is well known . . . It is heavy but the weight could be reduced. The central keelcase runs over most of the length and serves many purposes . . . It has the disadvantage of throwing the engine and propeller to one side with the result that a heavy and constant effort on the helm is required to maintain a course. The tunnel is also more likely to be ventilated as the boat moves in a seaway . . .

(4.3.1) The attachment of the planking to the keel has proved to be a great weakness in this construction, although it could be improved by additional weight of structure. A considerable saving in weight could be achieved by reducing the skin thickness to 3/8″ and also the thickness of the bulkheads and keelcase.

(4.4) The alternative design of a moulded plywood hull is a better proposal. This is moulded in five sections with glued scarphed joints on four bulkheads. It is intended to dispense with stringers and timbers . . . The hull can reasonably be reduced to 3/8″ thickness . . . but the minimum acceptable thickness can only be found by tests and this would be worthwhile. Technical approval of the proposed joints should be given before construction . . .

This design . . . is very attractive, but the disadvantage of the offset engine is considerable.

(4.5) Aldous Successors design is much the same in form and construction as Uffa Fox's first but the engine and propeller are in the centre of the hull with a fore and aft bulkhead on each side. Double diagonal planking is proposed, but the planking would be more efficient if one layer was laid fore to aft. . . .

The tunnel is just aft of amidships and has sweeping curves which reduce the depth of hull and affect its strength seriously. The fairing of the tunnel may allow the step to ventilate because of the small immersion of the side of the tunnel. . . . and a complete redesign of the tunnel would be necessary to bring the hull up to the strength by deepening the longitudinal bulkheads.

In view of the inherent weakness of this type it is not recommended.

(4.6) The Itchenor Shipyard design is also similar to that of Uffa Fox. The skin is double diagonal 3mm ply with close spaced stringers and two widely spaced fore and aft bulkheads. . . . The use of plywood planks riveted together is not a good feature and must result in a weaker structure. . . . One good feature is that the planks are carried continuously over the keel. [Drop tests had shown this to be the weakest point in Mark I construction.] The engine is in the centre amidships with a long shaft to the propeller which is housed in a recess in the bottom of the hull. . . . a trap door closes the gap in the hull when the propeller is dropped. This appears an unnecessary complication which may lead to difficulties in service.

(5) In all the designs, excepting British Power Boats', the bottom of the afterbody is comparatively flat. This is to prevent the boat from squatting when sailing at maximum speed. The flat bottom is bad for the alighting condition and may call for additional strengthening. It is suggested that an arbitrary minimum angle of 5 degrees between the bottom transverse sections and the horizontal should be specified. All prototype hulls should be dropped several times at a rate of descent 5ft/sec. in excess of that given by the parachutes . . .

(7) Vosper's design and Uffa Fox's moulded plywood design are considered the most promising for development, bearing in mind the criticisms mentioned.

The design eventually produced, attributed to Uffa Fox, embraced the better features from some of the above, and also included some of the panel's suggestions. It was round-bilged, of treble skin construction (which none of the tenders had envisaged) with conventional timbering and bulkheads. The engine was situated amidships and a compromise on Fox's; Itchenor's and Vosper's dual and single longitudinal bulkheads theories were achieved with the use of a tunnelled propeller; but one wonders now why the moulded plywood construction was not followed. Were the materials not available in the War-oriented economy? Or were our techniques so lamentably far behind the Americans already busy on their 'Flying Dutchman'?

Although production of the Mark II commenced on the Uffa Fox design with conventional treble skin planking, Vosper had been given the go ahead on 20 April 1944 for a trial and test hull in moulded plywood, carried out on 15 October. Memo 266A, on which the date is indecipherable, reports on this as follows:

This craft, which was ordered after inspection of tenders to the Mark II design from various marine craft contractors, has now been written off on parachuting trails.

From trials already carried out it would appear that this craft compares favourably with the standard Mark II design from the point of view of handling at sea. Drop trials from a crane have shown the hull to be as satisfactory as the Merron moulded for the Mark II boat. Wind tunnel and flight trials demonstrate that its behaviour in the air and on release from the aircraft can be satisfactory. One parachute trial was carried out from a Warwick aircraft and the boat on this occasion functioned to our satisfaction.

The whole layout of this design is very clean and the boat is approximately 150 lbs lighter than that of the standard Mark II.

The hull construction was in the form of inner and outer diagonal plywood skins, scarfed and glued with synthetic resin cement to an inner obeche core. The contractor obtaining glueing pressure by use of steel straps tightened down over the assembly. This method is not perfectly satisfactory as it is not possible to ensure 100% adhesion of surfaces, and one 6″ square section of outer skin came adrift on the crane dropping trials. We are satisfied that improved methods will enable the contractor to secure improved and satisfactory glueing.

The detail parts of the craft are, unavoidably, not interchangeable with those on the standard Mark II craft on which development was not completed when the Vosper design was drafted.

It is our intention that should any further specifications for lifeboats be issued, Vosper Ltd. are to be given . . . (no more on file).

Mention in the foregoing memo of Merron Ltd brings in the last of the Mark II experimental hulls. Minutes of a meeting on 18 April 1944 show discussion on the hull form and its method of construction in moulded plywood, and the materials to be used, including a statement that Uffa Fox would supply drawings of the sections of the hull at every six inches throughout its length, and allows him only ten days to produce the first batch and 28 days for the whole set.

The next mention of this is in a 'loose minute' of 23 February 1945 which draws attention to problems with the Airborne Lifeboats shipped out to India, shrinkage and warping of materials being the principal failings, leading to extensive leaking. Even constant spraying with water did not arrest trouble with the lifeboats in the Middle East as it encouraged plank warping and edge lifting. Although crated, the Mark Is arriving in India were in terrible condition after their several months of voyaging, and it was not expected that the Mark IIs would be any better. The minute goes on to say:

[Assistant Director Research & Development – Survival] has, however, two alternative methods [of construction] which are being pursued.

(1)   Moulded plywood (Merron Ltd) whose first hull was commenced in June 1944 but has not been completed owing to lack of priorities. The American airborne lifeboat is being built by this method.

(2)   Plywood sandwich construction (Vosper). The prototype already completed and ready for its first test drop.

The minute closes by stating that when satisfactory trials are completed a small number of such boats will be built for despatch to the Far East for operational use so that they can be assessed for tropical suitability.

Harking back to personal experiences, the author was asked during the summer of 1943 to visit a furniture maker in Bow (London) who was attempting to fabricate dinghies for the RAF by building up laminations of veneers. Apparently 'boat' knowledge and advice were all that was required and on a subsequent visit, prior to dropping tests, a very serviceable hull appeared to have been constructed; being drafted to Norfolk at the end of the year brought my involvement to an abrupt end. The question is, was this the beginning of the Merron boatbuilding venture?

The end of the Merron boat came on Friday 6 July 1945 when on a trial drop the main parachutes failed to release from the packs and the boat came down on the retarder parachute only, with disastrous results. This report, however, considers the hull method to be sound and speaks of ten hulls being taken off conventional production schedules for the 150 Mark IIs and replaced by Merrons; five to be suitable for Lancasters and five for Warwicks.

Eleven days after the Merron prototype loss a 'loose minute' considers the moulded hull construction only 80% satisfactory and speaks of the 'Alclad' metal hull as offering 100% satisfaction, although, apparently, the unknown writer had reservations. No further reference to the Alclad has been traced; it was to be several years before Saunders Roe produced their alloy boat, the Mark III, the subject of Chapter 8.

The Mark II was still providing food for thought as well as teething troubles. These were mainly with workmanship, badly placed or unsuitable fittings and starting and servicing the engine. The principal thinking was on improved equipment and stores for the survivor crew, but there was a proposal afoot that a coxwain should be dropped with the lifeboat. On far too many occasions the crews of Hudsons or Warwicks had watched helplessly as weakened men had tried to reach or clamber aboard their lifesaver, and had finally drifted away to solitary deaths; a manoeuvrable boat with a man aboard could have saved many of these unfortunates, as well as increased the survival chances of those who had managed to get aboard and then experienced difficulties. The following points were considered.

The position of the cox'n in the boat would be governed by the centre of gravity and the presence of existing fittings and equipment. A suitable place might be amidships in a recess in the deck to one side of the keelson. He could be in a semi-recumbent position, facing forward, but would need to get into the lifeboat from the aircraft to gain his parachuting station just before the drop. He would need to be equipped with a manually released harness, which would not only hold him in the boat no matter at whatever angle it might hang, but would also have to restrain him in all directions against splashdown shock. As a safety precaution an immersion switch release should also be provided. During initial drop and at the time the boat settled on the water there would be vigorous movements of the wire sling strops attaching the boat to the parachutes; these could be very dangerous, even lethal, so a strong guard would need to be fitted for the man's protection; also voice communication with the aircraft crew would be vital right up to the moment of release.

Ultimately test drops were made with a dummy secured in a cockpit set amidships in the boat. In every case the boffins decided that the dummy cox'n was dead with horrific injuries by the time the side rockets fired; so the end of the Far East war brought a conclusion of the trials, probably to the great relief of sundry potential coxwains.

During the War research and development was widely shared with our Allies, which is probably why the Germans perfected their Asdic and Radar so rapidly after the fall of France; even our highly advanced aero-engine details were freely handed to the Americans, enabling their manufacturers to turn out 'Rolls Royce' aero-engines for our fighter planes, etc. The same applied to the Airborne Lifeboats. Initially the USAAF was quite happy for the RAF and RN to carry out A/SR services around Britain, but as the war in the Far East developed they became aware of their own increasing need for similar equipment and organisation, so US airmen were seconded to RAF A/SR Squadrons to acquire the British know-how. As early as 31 August 1943 Major General J. K. Crain of the London Munitions Assignment Board had correspondence with the Director of Aircraft Safety about shipping a Mark I to America. Confirmation of this is given in a letter of 31 December 1943 from the DAS, the third paragraph of which reads:

> With regard to the Airborne Lifeboat, Wing Commander Bicknell of the Deputy Directorate of Air/Sea Rescue, at the request of the Air Technical Section, ETOUSA, proceeded in company with Lt. Col. Munsell to the U.S.A. with an Airborne Lifeboat Mark IA, and a quantity of spares, for dropping trials from American aircraft. These trials were completed successfully and the boat was left with the Emergency Rescue Branch at Wright Field. May it be stated whether the presence of this boat in Wright Field will meet your requirements or whether it is your desire for another boat to be earmarked for your needs.

It is apparent from documents that during 1943 and early 1944 several more boats were shipped aboard, to the USA, Canada, Australia, New Zealand and India for local trials and development as well as for use and demonstration at overseas Air Training Schools, in addition to operational service boats and aircraft being forwarded to Middle East, Iceland, and India Commands. Only the Americans appear to have embraced the idea to the extent of developing Airborne Lifeboats for their own particular wartime needs; probably most of the other countries were too hard-pressed in other fields to give the requisite time and resources to an individual project which already seemed well covered by the RAF.

Approximately 130 B 17G bombers (Flying Fortresses) were converted by the USAAF to carry their new A-1 lifeboats, being renumbered B 17 H and TB 17H. These almost deserve an entire chapter to themselves but must be dealt with rather more briefly here. Document 158240 on microfilm from Maxwell Air Force Base commences by giving tribute to the British design for its innovative soundness before going on to explain the American need for larger boats to meet their longer Far East operational flights, larger aircraft and larger crew numbers. Their actual development programme did not start until November 1943, with blueprints of the Mark A-1 being given to the Higgins

Boat Company, who expressed a desire to design and build an entirely new type of boat, using plywood laminations, and promising delivery of the hull within 20 days of their plans being approved. A few days later another set of blueprints was handed to Western Plastics Incorporated who intimated it would take them 30 days to produce their first plastic hull to a new design, their product being made by stretching cotton cloth over a former and spraying it with ethyl cellulose, and from then on building up a hull in layers. The manufacturers claimed this process, known as 'Chemold', produced a cheap, remarkably strong, light and durable shell.

The Mark IA brought to Wright Field in November 1943 was twice dropped successfully from a B 17 before a modified Mark IA was fitted to a Fortress for two successful test drops from Eglin Field. The first was from 700 feet at 125 mph and the 'survivors' were in the boat within two minutes. These two tests were the basis on which the boffins of the Higgins Boat Company, the USAAF and Ratsey & Lapthorn (sailmakers) founded their plans for a larger Airborne Lifeboat to be known as the A-1, the RAF Mark I schedule of seven passengers being insufficient for the planes in use over the Pacific Ocean.

The first boat designed by Higgins was torpedo' shaped and quickly discarded as being unseaworthy. Two further models by them, based on the British Mark II design, met the same fate for the same reason; then an experimental 18-footer met a shattering end after a disastrous flight in which everything went wrong and the boat was totally destroyed. Despite these troubles the final A-1 specification was drawn up in a relatively short time. The lifeboat was to be 30 feet in length, the weight not to exceed 3300 lb all up including parachutes etc., and have a range of 1500 miles.

Meanwhile Western Plastics had also been busy, but their models did not prove satisfactory, being 25% heavier than a plywood one of the same strength, resulting in the conclusive end to their participation when in drop tests the impact of landing on the water broke the inside woodwork loose from the moulded hull. Another company, Wills and Roberts Plastics Manufacturing Corporation, brought forward an idea for a boat to be dropped without parachutes on the 'skip bombing' principle; but it was concluded that whilst it would work well on calm water any wave movement at all would result in a premature nose dive or similar disaster.

The first A-1 drop tests were made during February 1944, with concluding ones in April, using fully equipped boats, with seaworthiness adequately proved in 30 mph winds and 20-foot high seas, and using both sails and motors. Note the celerity with which this project was pursued in contrast to the years of frustration and delay it had taken to get the Mark I into the air. At some stage the length of the boat was reduced from 30 to 27 feet, the final specification calling for a maximum beam of 7', a moulded depth of 3' 6" and a draught, with centreboard down, of 4' 6". The effective range was to be 1500 miles at an approximate average coverage of 100 miles per day. The weight remained at 3300 lb. It is interesting in studying the illustrations to see that the boat is not canoe-sterned as were the RAF ones but had reverted to a transom style very similar to the discarded first Uffa Fox design. Could it be that the RAF style was better for the short turbulent seas around Britain whilst the transom style was more suitable for the less broken water of the Pacific? The fact that the American A-1 used off Heligoland in April/May of 1945 experienced trouble to the extent of two men being swept overboard (and recovered) and the centreboard broken, might give credence to this possibility.

A Directive of 26 May 1944 stated a requirement of 600 lifeboats, recommending one-source procurement, and 'Immediate Action' priority in view of the urgent need for its lifesaving capabilities. The contract went to Higgins, although it was later reduced to 300 boats. By October only 20 boats had been delivered, earning frowns from USAAF HQ as 15 were urgently needed by the end of November, and substantial quantities from then on. Perhaps Higgins also had problems in obtaining the requisite high-quality materials; anyway the rebuke appeared to have some effect for 75 boats were ready in December, but held up for lack of the self-righting chambers, which were styled, fitted and operated on lines similar to those of the RAF lifeboats.

Further operational trials had given a speed of 8 mph using both engines and 5 mph with only one. The final product, later to be known affectionately as 'The Flying Dutchman', was built by laminations of prime birch and mahogany veneer laid criss-cross over a mould, being totally impregnated with glue during the process. A heavy rubber-type material cover, shaped to the outer lines of the hull, was then fitted over the glued wood and the whole subjected to pressure by air extraction and heat, resulting in a moulded shell six-tenths of an inch thick. This method also allowed increased build-up of material where required for extra strength and permitted equal-strength securing of internal woodwork to the shell.

Much of the equipment stowed on deck and in some of the 20 watertight compartment lockers was standard US Army or Navy issue and was all packed in vinyl bags to protect it from wet or damp. The final parachute technique evolved was to use three standard 48-foot cargo canopies, pulled open by static line attached to the aircraft. It had been found that severe oscillation occurred when a single canopy only was used. Recommended dropping height was 1500 feet at an air speed of 120 mph when directly over the survivors. The slings were attached to the boat at two points and allowed a 50 degrees bow-down angle of sea impact. Comparison of the A-1 illustrations with Mark Is shows many similarities in thinking and planning, clearly illustrating the design's parentage.

The twin engines, of 5 hp each, were manufactured by the Wisconsin Motor Corporation of Milwaukee; initially these had manual starting but were later changed to automatic. They appear to be based on the same principles of operation and installation as the 'Middy', but this is not confirmed. The two sails, in a low profile Bermuda rig on a 20-foot mast, totalled 145 square feet.

All did not go completely smoothly in the Flying Dutchman's development for a report of a test in August 1944 reveals that on a release at 3000 feet the boat dropped 1500 feet in free fall before the parachutes decided to develop to check the potentially disastrous descent. When examined the boat was found to be holed in two places but was still able to make base under its own power. As a result the hull thickness was increased by two laminations and the parachute packing taken over by the Parachute Branch of the Personal

Equipment Laboratory. It would seem that 'gremlins' were also operative on the other side of the Atlantic. Capacity was finally rated as 12 men.

The A-1 did not represent the full extent of American Airborne Lifeboat development for there were also later produced a large number of 18-foot boats, with a 6-foot beam, known as the 'Navy AR8', to the BuAer specification. These were for carrying on Catalina flying boats (PBY5A), either singly under the starboard wing, or one under each wing. Of laminated plywood construction, with a single-cylinder, four-cycle, air-cooled engine of 5 hp and an all-up weight of 1400 lb. It was dropped from 450 feet at 95 to 100 knots indicated air speed on no less than eight standard 24-foot parachutes, specially packed in two four-chute packs, to be opened by static lines, the rate of descent being about 25 feet per second. The boat's range is quoted as 250 miles at 5+ knots, sails also being provided. The listed capacity of eight men comfortably and ten cramped is illuminating.

Post-War Development

The British Mark III, which featured in Chapter 8, was one of two post-War Airborne Lifeboat projects, the other being the American A-3 (referred to in initial discussions as the A-2), also built of aluminium alloy, by the EDO Corporation of New York, to a 1949 specification for carrying by the B 29 bomber (Super Fortress).

The overall length of the A-2 was originally stated as 30' 9/16" with maximum beam 6' 3 1/4", maximum depth (bottom of skeg to gunwale) 3' 11", weight (empty) 2133 lb, weight (as attached to plane) 2736 lb, and a capacity of 15 men. The preamble to the specification states:

> The hull shall be of semi-monocoque structure using longitudinal and transverse structural members covered and connected to the skin.
>
> There shall be ten watertight transverse bulkheads, which together with the keelson and engine compartment sister keelsons shall provide twenty watertight compartments. Each of these below the deck to be provided with openings and access plates; except that for the engine, which shall be provided with a suitable hatch cover.

Monocoque is an assembly, usually of metal, in which the covering or skin absorbs a large part of the stresses when in use.

Once again a centreline keelson was incorporated for a backbone strength member, ending as in the Mark II, at the for'ard engine compartment bulkhead, the strength factor continuing aft by similar twin members each side of the engine. Sister keelsons is the picturesque terms used; with through stringers providing a fixing for the outboard edge of the deck as well as stiffening to the sides above the bilge. Gunwales shaped to fit the contour of the carrier plane gave mating surfaces and rigidity to the topsides. Lateral strength and skin resistance to impact was imparted by stiffeners, which we might term 'frames', running from the gunwales to the deck and thence to the keel or sister keelsons, which were similarly linked. The hull was assembled on conventional 'boat' lines rather than the 'twin' system used by Saunders Roe, and a very different type of hull was used, the long lead in bow more reminiscent of a sailing yacht than a motor boat.

The inboard engine could not be contained below the deck so its hatch was bounded by coamings atop which a quick opening watertight cover gave protection to the four-cylinder, four-cycle, Redwing petrol engine, fitted with the luxury of an electric starter. This power unit driving a 1″ monel shaft to a 14″ diameter, 16″ pitch, Columbian Ailsa Craig propeller was scheduled to give a speed of 8 knots, under still water conditions. The electrical systems were fed from a 6V storage battery constantly recharged by the engine when running.

Looking at the photographs of the boat in flight one is struck that the leading end of the craft carries an 'underwater' bulge. This is the fairing around and over the propeller and the rudder, for the boat is being carried stern first. In Plate **50** an A-3 is being dropped from a Super Fortress, on a single 100-foot parachute, which would not start to open until well clear of the plane. Both the propeller fairing and the stabilising fins were mechanically detachable when the boat was on the water, by which time the self-righting buoyancy chambers would have inflated. An easily attachable canopy could be erected between the inflated ends to give shelter from the tropical sun, and like the RAF Mark IIIs, this could also be used to collect rain-water.

A total of 100 of these A-3 lifeboats were built, their recognition marking being A-3 501 and upwards. Whether any of the A-3 boats saved any lives has not yet been ascertained, nor when the last of the American Airborne Lifeboats was withdrawn from service.

At, or soon after, the end of the European War a number of aeroplanes were passed by the RAF to the French to form the nucleus of their new Air Arm and Naval Air Arm, among them some squadrons of Lancasters, a few of which were adapted for Mark II Airborne Lifeboats for Air/Sea Rescue work. Five lifeboats were sold from RAF stores. The author has been unable to trace what happened to them.

The Australians also took a post-War interest in the lifeboats. Air Staff Operational Requirement No. OR/Misc. 4 states: 'The Air staff require an airborne lifeboat for fitment to Lincoln aircraft for search and rescue', and a further minute of 3/5/48 requests advice as to the most suitable type available. Considerable correspondence ensued. A minute of 30/11/48 includes: 'The Air Staff consider the provision of an Airborne Lifeboat to meet Operational Requirement No OR/SUR.2 a matter of urgency'.

By 2 October 1950 a Mark IIA had been received from England and fitted to Lincoln A73-47 at Fishermen's Bend before allocation to Aircraft Research and Development Unit. On 22 November it would seem that the Mark II boat did not match up to local conditions, nor did the continuous delay in completing trials find much favour. A local contractor was being called upon to totally re-rig the lifeboat with new spars, redesigned sails etc. and to carry out modifications to the rudder, so that sea trials were only completed by 31 January 1951, with flying and dropping tests still to come. A minute of 10 April 1952 estimates 12 lifeboats would be required, 3 for No. 10 Squadron, 3 for No. 82 Wing, 2 for R/S East Sale and 4 for reserve; suggesting that one Lincoln

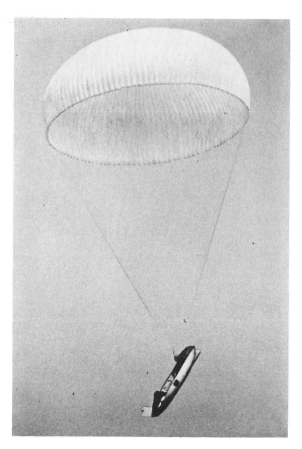

*50   A3 lifeboat
on trial drop
(EDO Corp)*

51   A.3 under way (note tail planes not jettisoned) (EDO Corp)

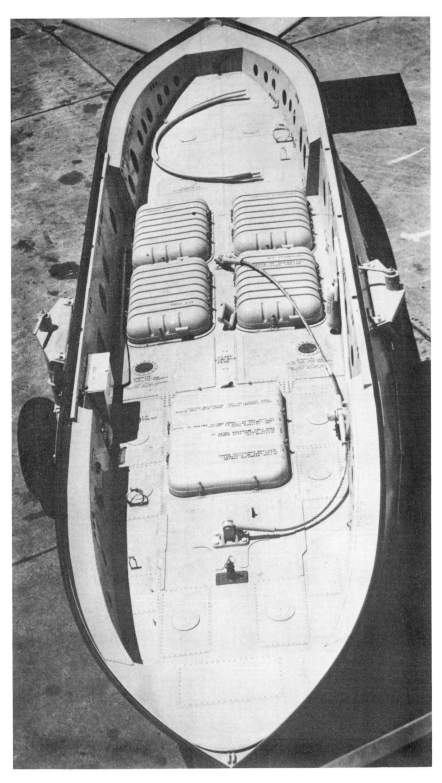

52   The tidy deck layout of the A.3 (EDO Corp)

should be continuously available at Darwin, Townsville, Amberley and East Sale bases. In a further note on 27 April DRM is requested to prepare a specification and initiate supply action for these boats to be built.

By 8 October 1952 the project was still not under way and part of a memo of that date reads:

> (a) The proposal on this file for the purchase of 12 air-borne life boats are in response to an Air Staff requirement.
>
> (b) Notwithstanding this, I feel that in view of our very limited funds available for new equipment we should postpone the purchase in favour of more pressing requirements.
>
> (c) I suggest, therefore, that the project be reviewed in twelve months time.

So much for urgency.

The Australians evidently considered also the Mark III option, for Lincoln aircraft, as a Saunders Roe quote exists dated 16/7/53 for 13 lifeboats, at £12,980 each, plus sufficient cradles, trolleys, lifting slings, parachute clusters etc. and a supply of spares, totalling £15,040 each ex-works. This did not compare favourably with the Mark II, however.

In August 1953 a report noted that it would cost not less than £1000 to make the Mark II serviceable and that the work would be beyond the capacity of the RAAF and would have to be by civilian contract; 'as all funds (Marine Craft) are fully committed it will be necessary for separate arrangements for finance to be made'. The Director of Armament advised on 21 August a long list of equipment, much of which was not available, which would be required, thus further escalating costs and delay. By 28 August the entire matter is summed up by D.Ops. who requests a decision as to whether the Mark IIA should be repaired for service for search and rescue purposes during the impending Royal visit and used in any future emergency, or whether it should be placed on the disposal list. One wonders, in retrospect, just how this boat had been treated during its short life; the Defect List reads thus:

1 Planking. Fracture of planking running from chine to keel No. 3 frame, port hand.
2 Fracture of planking from chine to keel at No. 4 frame, port hand.
3 Fracture of planking from chine to keel at No. 5 frame, port hand.
4 In addition to the above fractures five additional smaller planking fractures have been copper plated on the port hand of the craft.
5 A 3″ × 2″ hole has been punctured in the planking on the starboard hand, approximately 12″ from the stern.
6 Four small planking fractures have been copper plated on the underwater sections of the starboard side of the craft.
7 Handrail. The handrail on the underwater section of the port hand of the hull is broken and will require renewal.
8 Mast. Mast has been broken and will have to be renewed.
9 Inflation bags & covers. Fore and aft inflation bag covers will have to

be renewed and the rubber inflation bags now fitted are questionable and may have to be replaced.

10   Canvas dodgers. Port & starboard canvas dodgers to be renewed.

Conclusion. To ensure the craft is made structurally sound, it will be necessary that all existing planking be replaced.

As the timbers (ribs) are only 3/8″ × 1/2″ (?) the removal and renewal of all old fastenings and planking would greatly reduce the strength of these members. It is therefore considered that all the timbers should be renewed.

It is not possible to satisfactorily examine the craft in its present assembled state, and it is considered that evidence of further damage will be revealed when the craft is stripped. This damage may not be extensive but at present it is impossible to assess. As the engine has not been inhibited since the craft was last dropped it will now be necessary that it be completely stripped, cleaned, re-assembled and checked.

Whilst there is only reference of dropping trials in inspected files the sea trials are well documented. It would appear that on receipt the Mark II did not meet with full approval for after initial tests authority was given for it to be completely re-rigged with Gunter mainsail, including a boom. There is a long list of suggested improvements that indicate that the initial idea of the very simplest arrangement for the unskilled sailor, albeit not the most efficient, was being departed from, although the report stresses the simplicity of the new Gunter. This was fitted and tried out on 14 December 1950, apparently very successfully, although the mainsail area was later reduced by 40 sq. ft. as it 'exceeded safe limitations for a lifeboat, particularly when handled by inexperienced crews'. After modifications further trials were made under sail alone with a crew of four in a Force 8 breeze, gusting up to Force 11. 'Driven hard on every leg the craft gave a very creditable performance'. She would point up to within three points of the wind and log speeds up to 8 knots even whilst dragging a dead propeller.

During trials under power the next report speaks highly of the lifeboat's performance, except for a tendency when running before a swell to roll and bury her lee shoulder, permitting the windward quarter to lift so that an intake of air into the propeller tunnel could occur, causing the engine to race. A mysterious item appears here as it continues 'and its obvious design is detrimental to the flow of water entering the tunnel, as the leading edge is vertical'. Neither the author's memory nor blueprints in his possession give any indication of any vertical edge, there being a smooth streamlined curve from the keel to the interior of the tunnel; where the tunnel joins the chines is almost vertical at the apex – could there have been a misreading on this point? F/L Moody, in charge of the trials, suggested a water scoop to ensure an adequate flow. He also suggested that the area of the rudder be increased to reduce yawing and the use of a drogue when running before heavy seas. Under power alone the lifeboat registered 7 knots.

On 2 September 1953 the Australian involvement in airborne lifeboats came to an end by direction of the DCAS, apart from an enquiry about the new A-4 designed by the Douglas Aircraft Corporation in California. The prototype of this was described in an article in *Popular Mechanics* of September 1951:

> In a 'packed' state it resembled a 21″ torpedo, designed so that it could be fired from a normal torpedo tube of a submarine or surface vessel or dropped from a land based aircraft or a seaplane. Made of aluminium the 21 feet long cylinder when released from a rescue plane, at any altitude between 75 and 9000 ft. was retarded in its fall by a 12 ft. parachute and initially plunged into the water, which released the parachute; positive buoyancy bringing it to the surface whereupon the upper cylinder plates were jettisoned by the CO_2 inflation of the main part of the hull, which then erupted into an inflated lifeboat. The aluminium canister, containing the Crossley four cylinder 25 h.p. engine, the reduction gear box and propeller unit, the battery, the auto pilot, the radio & 50 gallon fuel tank, then became the keel. From the aircraft the pilot was able to control the lifeboat by radio signals, opening the fuel valve, starting the engine and then guiding it by remote control until it would be alongside survivors in the water, or a dinghy; at which point he stops the engines so that they can board. Once aboard they could turn a switch to release the lifeboat from aircraft control and hand inflate the self righting tubes which had lain dormant above the self inflating body sections before proceeding to get under way and head for home by themselves, aided by an automatic pilot, two way radio, adequate food and water supplies and petrol for a 300 mile voyage. A similar procedure would be followed if the A.4 were to be launched from the torpedo tube of a submarine or a destroyer. The high bow and stern chambers would make the craft dry when motoring at up to 7 knots, and a zip on canopy could also totally enclose the craft; its 'soft' construction also reducing crew fatigue normally engendered by hammering a rigid hulled boat into a head sea. In some weathers it could be a mite too lively.

This lifeboat did not go into production; two prototypes only were made, and a letter of 10 November 1953 advises that 'this Lifeboat has been neither tested nor evaluated by the USAF and the contract is being terminated owing to the withdrawal of the operational requirement'. Apparently the helicopter lobby won.

In the late 1950s the South African Air Force purchased a number of Shackletons for maritime reconnassance and with them three Mark III lifeboats for long range rescue operations. The initial trial drop, when the planes and boats were first received, was completely successful. In 1958, 1959 and 1960 practice runs for releasing a lifeboat were carried out about twice each month. On 6 September 1960 the second practice drop of a Mark III was made over Langebaan Lagoon, from Shackleton 1723, with Commandant Robbs as the Commander. Not one of the parachutes opened fully and the boat was destroyed on impact. After 1960 the SAAF use of Airborne Lifeboats was abandoned; the helicopter had taken over.

This was the end of the Airborne Lifeboat active service story. Now they can

53   McDonnell Douglas A.4 ashore prior to trials (McDonnell Douglas)

54   McDonnell Douglas A.4 trials (McDonnell Douglas)

only be found in museums, sometimes in sad conditions, bereft of engines and equipment; if any reader should know the whereabouts of any such items the author would be most gratified to know so that the information can be passed on to the RAF Museum at Hendon, the Imperial War Museum at Duxford or the Lifeboat Museum at Bristol, or to one of the many former American base museums in this country.

Although not a lifeboat development, Mr Ken Hunter, Registrar of the RAF Museum, recently brought the 'Skylark' Airborne Boom Patrol Boat to my notice, designed for the Lancaster bomber, to be carried within the bomb bay but with the bay doors open. The plan was for the boat to be loaded with high explosive and dropped unmanned within range of an enemy harbour, or vessel. One or two 'frogmen' would be dropped, also by parachute, so that they could swim to the craft, board it and start the engines for a high speed dash towards the target; at an opportune moment the crew would set the helm and drop overboard leaving the boat to go on alone, hopefully to destroy the harbour or vessel's defensive screen. When the *Tirpitz* was holed up in its Norwegian fiord a craft such as this could have greatly assisted the torpedo aircraft and midget submarines which attacked it.

A Vosper project, the boat length is given as 16 feet with a Gray 'Fireball' Model Six 140 power unit running at 4000 rpm, speed unknown. From the illustrations it appears to be a conventionally designed high speed launch, fully decked, with a very pronounced crop; a forward well and a steering/control position for one man right against the transom, Available photostats are very poor but the interior appears to be clear hull space to amidships giving way to a large engine compartment, then the aft well. Some of the scantlings give clues to the construction: bottom – mahogany, inner skin 3/16", outer 5/16", topsides – mahogany, inner skin 1/8", outer 1/4"; decking – birch plywood 3/32". There follow watertight bulkheads, timbers, frames, transom and girders. A slight clue to the interior is that 'Upholstery is to be kept clean and occasionally rubbed over with furniture cream or white polish'.

Mounted on a wheeled trolley for ease of handling it was lifted into the bomb bay by four sling plates on the frame in which the boat rested; attachment to the parachutes was by a four-legged sling. It would appear that the frame held the boat in the aircraft but dropped free of it on the release from the aircraft's bomb hook. There is no suggestion of armament. If any reader has further knowledge of this craft it would be of interest to the author.

The Goldfish Club

Airborne Lifeboats live on in the memories of many aircrew all over the world and especially in those of members of the Goldfish Club, whose badge is shown on the frontispiece to this book. This unique 'band of brothers' is much less well known than the Caterpillar Club and is now closely associated with the Air Sea Rescue/Marine Craft Section Club. The small rectangular black cloth badge is embroidered with a winged goldfish flying over two symbolic blue waves representing the sea, gold emphasising the value of life, and the winged fish a symbol of the embracing of the two elements. A second rescue originally entitled the receiver to a 'bar', in the form of a third blue wave, but this was later abandoned as qualifiers with up to six additional bars became members.

The Club was founded in November 1942 by Charles A. Robertson who was chief of the design office of P. B. Cow & Co. Ltd, at that time one of the largest manufacturers in the world of Air/Sea Rescue equipment. He was also responsible for the Ministry of Aircraft Production Air/Sea Rescue Drawing Office, which was the issuing authority for production drawings used by factories in the United Kingdom and Empire and, in some cases, the USA.

Due to his involvement in rescue equipment he was frequently in contact with aircrew who had survived the ordeal of 'ditching' and as a result of hearing their stories he was able to improve the range and design of lifesaving gear, and also conceived the idea of an exclusive Club. Members must belong to an Allied Air Force and have been saved by using a 'Mae West' or an emergency dinghy. With the financial backing of P. B. Cow the Club was formed, each member receiving a heat-sealed waterproof membership card and a badge. During the War fine wire for badge use was prohibited, so the early badges were embroidered by hand with silk onto black cloth cut from evening dress suits sent in by the public in response to an appeal by William Hickey of the *Daily Express*. In January 1943 Wynford Vaughan Thomas, famous for his wartime dispatches, interviewed the founder and two members who had ditched on their first operational flight. This BBC broadcast followed by an article in *The Aeroplane* on 26 March written by its editor, laid the foundations of the Club and applications began to flood in, even from POW camps, although in these cases cards and badges were usually sent to relatives for safe keeping.

Because it was not, nor is, an official badge, RAF aircrew wore it sewn beneath a lapel or the flap of the left-hand breast pocket, whilst FAA men had it stitched to their 'Mae Wests'. This reticence was favoured by most servicemen as they would not wish to be accused of the deadly sin of 'line-shooting'. A happy few could also disclose a Caterpillar Club badge as well, if pressed.

At the end of the War membership stood at around 9000, as being saved by sundry marine craft (including Airborne Lifeboats) was by then the requisite qualification. It was intended that granting of further membership should cease, but as applications continued to come in during the ensuing months it was obvious that the spirit of the club was still very much alive. When Charles Robertson left P. B. Cow in 1947 to set up his own business he continued the administration of the Club at his own expense. The first Reunion Dinner was held in May 1951 and such was its success that it was decided to reorganise the Club on a permanent basis, with a management committee selected in March 1953. A regular newsletter is still circulated to members, although the strength has now dropped to below 1000; but there is still a trickle of new members, about 15 each year, mainly from the RAF, RNAS, RN, Commonwealth Air Forces and Navies, the United States Forces and European Air Forces. Helicopter crews make up the bulk of new entrants and civilian aircrew are now also eligible within the ditching rule. A few extra Honorary Members have been nominated and approved, among them Uffa Fox.

Appendix I: General Information

MARK I

Carrier: Hudson for Mark I and Warwick for Mark IA
Capacity: 7 persons
Endurance: 7 days
Length overall: 23′ 2″
Length inside planks: 23′ 0″
Waterline length: 22′ 0″
Draught: 9″
Maximum beam: 5′ 5″
Maximum moulded depth: 2′ 6″
Displacement: 0.5 tons
Construction: double skin mahogany, protruding propellers
Total permissible 'all up' weight: 1700 lb
Engines: a pair of BPC 'Middy' (Britannia) 4 hp two-stroke, petrol and oil
    mixture
Top speed: 6 knots

MARK II

Carrier: Warwick for Mark II and Lancaster for Mark IIA
Capacity: 10 persons
Endurance: 7 days
Length overall: 30′ 2″
Length of interior: 29′ 10″
Waterline length: 30′ 0″
Draught: 11″
Maximum beam: 6′ 0″
Maximum moulded depth: 2′ 10″
Displacement: 0.75 tons
Construction: treble skin mahogany, tunnelled propeller
Weights: hull 1775 lb, engine and fuel 494 lb, buoyancy gear 192 lb, electrical
    gear 46 lb, marine equipment 48 lb, signals 131 lb, rations 180 lb, comforts
    107 lb, navigation equipment 16 lb, parachute gear (complete) 502 lb
Total permissible 'all up' weight: 3492 lb
Engine: 4 cylinder Austin Marine 8 hp (900 cc), petrol

Top speed: 7 knots

MARK III

Carrier: Shackleton
Capacity: 10 persons
Endurance: 14 days
Length overall: 32' 0"
Length of interior: 31' 6"
Waterline length: 30' 0"
Draught: 1' 1"
Maximum beam: 7' 1"
Maximum moulded depth: 3' 2"
Construction: aluminium alloy throughout, tunnelled propeller
Total permissible 'all up' weight: 4460 lb
Engine: 2 cylinder Vincent HRD Marine T5/AM two-stroke, petrol
Top speed: 6.6 knots

EQUIPMENT AND STORES

It is impossible to state accurately the equipment and stores aboard the Mark I and II throughout the whole period of their usage as the items could vary. Always there had to be a constant search for better equipment, so changes were made; summertime stores would not necessarily be the same as those supplied in winter, nor Iceland-based boats carry the same as those in the Azores, so these lists are quoted as comprehensive.

Marks I and II

1 Radio set (Gibson Girl) type T 1333, hand-cranked to transmit distress signals on different frequencies automatically, or the set known as 'Walter'
1 Receiving set R 1345 or R 1545, with GB batteries
1 Lightweight Very pistol (1") and Red Star cartridges
2 Waterproof star distress signals
Spare torch batteries
1 Waterproof torch, Mark II
1 Aldis signalling lamp, 308A
Smoke floats
First Aid outfit
6 Waterproof outer suits with warm inner suits
6 Working protective suits, blue
Rescue line and quoit
Massage oil
Everhot bags
Tinned water (Mark II – 100)
Cans condensed milk (Mark II – 50)

Tinned chocolate
Malted milk tablets
Tinned emergency rations
Cigarettes and matches
Self-heating soup (Mark II – 20)
Recognition aprons
Bigsworth chart board and charts from drop area to home ports
Repair equipment and tools
Top-up bellows
Leak stoppers
Water purifiers
Fluorescin blocks
Spare fuel
Fishing tackle
Floating sheath knife
Heavy sea drogue
Bilge pump
Heliograph 4″
Compass
Desalting apparatus (Mark II)
3 Drinking cups
Kite aerial
1 Patent taffrail log
1 Signalling lamp type 'B'
1 Transmitter SCR578A
1 Jack knife
1 Extinguisher MB No. 5
Spare lubricating oil
Safety belts

RN 1

'Walter' set and two batteries
Heliograph
Signal pistol and 24 cartridges in tins of 3
Torch and 2 batteries
1 Fishing tackle
3 Everhot bags
First Aid kit
Gooch splinting
3 Tins water
Leak stoppers
3 Safety belts
1 Machete and guard
3 Pairs extra thick gloves
3 Tins cigarettes and 2 tins matches
6 Tins self-heating soup

55 Arming the 'side line' rockets of a Mark IA

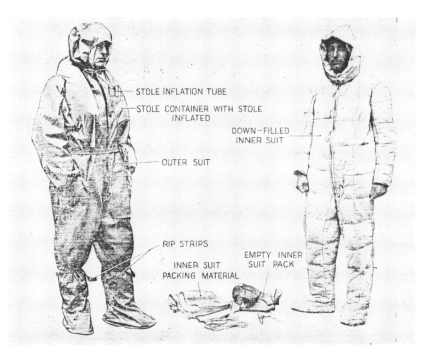

56 RAF survival suits

12 Tins condensed milk
15 Water purifiers
Spare sparking plugs
Tool kit
Heavy sea drogue
Compass
3 Outer and 3 inner suits
Aldis lamp
Rain-catcher awning
Recognition aprons
Charts and Bigsworth chart board

Mark III

Receiver R 1545
Buoyancy cushions
Transmitter with hand generator BC 778A
Rocket assisted kite aerial
Radio oscillator
Awning rain-catcher
2 Lindholme sleeping suits
10 Waterproof working suits
1 Patent taffrail log
60 Distress signals Mk 13
Heliograph
2 Waterproof torches
Aldis lamp
Bigsworth chart board and charts
Compass
Food container
Clasp knife and buoyant knife
Fire extinguisher
Flourescin Blocks
Drinking cups
Everhot bags
Fishing kits
Rescue line and quoit
First Aid kit
Safety belts
112 Tins drinking water
Desalting apparatus
Solar sea-water still
50 Tins condensed milk
20 Tins self-heating soup
20 Tins emergency flying rations
Smoke Floats
Cigarettes and matches

Leak stoppers
Topping-up bellows
Repair outfit

USAAF A-1

1 Emergency radio transmitter
8 Hat headnets
2 Fishing kits
24 Packs sea dye marker
3 Jack knives
16 Tins drinking water
80 Ration tablets
2 First Aid kits
4 Plastic bags, water stowage
1 Set navigation charts
4 Red Pyro. signal kits
1 Fishing spear
1 Corner radar reflector
16 Water desalting kits
8 White woolen blankets
8 Special winter work gloves
12 Pairs winter socks
2 Sponges
2 Signalling mirrors
2 Paulin, signal instruction
2 Magnetic compasses
2 Sunburn ointment
1 Bubble circle sextant
24 Distress smoke signals
8 Exposure suits
1 Navigational ruler
4 Drinking cups
1 Life raft signalling equipment
1 Heaving quoit with line
1 Rain-catcher
1 Bucket
1 Bilge pump
1 Log book
1 Waterproof chart case and charts
1 Abandon ship kit
1 Sail repair kit
1 Can opener
1 Inflation pump
1 Clock
1 Fire extinguisher
Matches in waterproof container

4 Air mattresses
2 Floating knives
2 Waterproof flashlights
2 Units human blood plasma
2 Engine salt-water stills
6 Bars salt-water soap
12 Pairs underwear, drawers
24 Undershirts
24 Hats
2 Pairs rubber boots
2 Wrist compasses
3 Cartons chewing gum
20 Cans cigarettes
100 Cans hard biscuit
200 Cans soup
60 Tins of breakfasts (2 in each)
60 Boxes suppers (2 in each)

Some of the foregoing could be alternatives. The victualling was reckoned to be sufficient for twelve men for five weeks. Soup was to be heated on the cylinder head of the engine, which also served as the heat source for a still to produce two gallons of fresh water for every gallon of fuel used.

RAF SQUADRONS WITH AIRBORNE LIFEBOATS

37 with MR 3 Lancasters and Mk IIA lifeboats September 1947. Reformed at Ein Shemar (Palestine); to Luqa (Malta) initially, with detachments at Gibraltar, Trucial Oman and Durban; then to Khormaksar (Aden), with detachment at Majunga (Madagascar). Disbanded September 1967.

38 at Foggia and Falconara (Italy) July 1945 with Warwick ASR Is and Mk IA lifeboats, then in July 1946 with GR 3 Lancasters and Mk IIA Lifeboats at Ein Shemar (Palestine). Squadron moved to Luqa (Malta) 27 March 1948 joining up with 37. A Mark II lifeboat was successfully dropped off Malta in a public demonstration in 1952.

179 with Warwick V and Mk IA lifeboats at St Eval in November 1944 as successor to 282 Squadron; Lancaster ASR 3 in February 1946 until September 1946 when absorbed into 210 Squadron.

203 at St Eval in 1947, then to Leuchars later that year before taking Mk IIA lifeboat Lancasters at Topcliffe in August 1952.

210 The remnants of 280 and 179 reformed into this Squadron at St Eval, on 1 June 1946 with eight Lancasters MR 3 and Mk IIA lifeboats. There are no reports of lifeboat drops except a trial on 31 August 1946 in which all the rockets and the parachute release fired in mid air as the boat dropped from the plane. The lifeboat broke up on impact with the sea. With MR 2

Shackletons until disbanded November 1971.

240 was moved from St Eval to Ballykelly in June 1952 flying Shackletons; one, or some, of which were equipped with Mark III Airborne Lifeboats; these were used in trials only, there being no operational usage recorded.

251 was reformed at Reykjavik (Iceland) in August 1944 as a Meteorological Squadron, but having three Warwick Is with Mk IAs. No confirmed lifeboat operational drops.

269 operated on a modest scale with Mk I Lifeboats on Hudson IIIAs from Lagen (Azores) from March 1944 after equipping and training at Davidstow Moor. In October of the same year they received replacement Warwick Is with Mk IA lifeboats.

276 from November 1943 operated with Mk IA lifeboats on Warwick Is from Harrowbeer; Perranporth, Portreath and Warmwell – April to September 1944; then Portreath, with a detachment at Querqueville (France) – September 1944; Querqueville det. Portreath – September 1944; Amiens–Glisy (France) det. Portreath – September 1944; St Denis–Westrem (France) det. Portreath – September to October 1944; St Croix det. Ursel – October to December 1944; Knocke le Zoute – December 1944 to June 1945; Andrews Field June to August 1945; Kjevik (Norway) det. Sola; Vaernes; Gardemoen (Norway) and finally to Dunsfold to disband on 15 November 1945.

277 on A/SR work moved with their Warwick Is and Mk IA lifeboats around various eastern and southern counties' airfields such as Stapleford Tawney det. Hawkinge, Martlesham Heath and Shoreham – December 1942; Gravesend det. Hawkinge, Martlesham Heath and Shoreham – December 1942 to April 1944; Shoreham det. Hawkinge, Hurn and Warmwell – April to October 1944; Hawkinge det. Portreath – October 1944 to disbanding on 15 February 1945.

278 started at Matlaske in October 1941 from No. 3 A/SR Flt. and operated in that role from there with Warwick Is and Mk IA lifeboats until August 1943, before moving to Coltishall, det. North Coates, Woolsington, Acklington, Hutton Cranswick, Ayr, Drem, Castleton, Peterhead and Sumburgh from April 1942 to April 1944; Bradwell Bay det. Martlesham Heath and Hornchurch – April 1944 to February 1945; Thorney Island det. Hawkinge, Beccles and Exeter – February to October 1945 before disbanding at Thorney Island on 14 October.

279 was equipped with Hudson III's, Vs and VIs when formed at Bircham Newton in November 1941, with detachments at Reykjavik (Iceland) and St Eval having the first Airborne Lifeboats (Mk Is) on their Hudsons early in 1943 before moving to Thornaby; det. Banff, Wick, Fraserburgh, Tain and Reykjavik to re-equip with Warwick Is and Mk IA lifeboats in October 1944 and staying there until September 1945; then Beccles with Lancaster ASR 3 with Mk IIA lifeboats until disbanding there on 10 March 1946 by renumbering as 38 Squadron (see above).

280 From Thorney Island, where they formed in December 1941, they moved to Detling and Langham before arriving at Bircham Newton to convert to Warwick Is in Ocotber 1943 and from then on dropped their Mk IA lifeboats all around the British Isles. At Thornaby late October 1943 then to Strubby May to September 1944; Langham until the following month, then to Beccles until November 1945; then back to Langham for three weeks before settling at Thornaby at the end of November 1945; all the while maintaining detachments at almost every station at which they'd served plus Aldergrove, Tain, Lagen, St Eval, Tiree, Reykjavik and Lossiemouth before disbanding at Thornaby on 21 June 1946.

281 was reformed from Fighter Command with Hudsons and Warwick Is and Mk IA Airborne Lifeboats at Thornaby on 11 November 1943, staying there until February 1944, and from then on operated mainly off the western shores being based at Tiree February 1944 to February 1945; Mullaghmore February to March 1945, where they received Warwick VIs; then to Limavady det. Tiree March to August 1945; Ballykelly det. Tiree August to 24 October 1945 when the Squadron was disbanded. There had also been detachments to Valley, Wick, Great Orton, Leuchars, Dallachy, Banff and Iceland.

282 did not get Warwick Is with Mk IA lifeboats until September 1944 although they'd reformed at Davidstow Moor in February of that year. They stayed there until Spetember then moved to St Eval with detachments at St Mawgan, Great Orton and Exeter before disbanding on 9 July 1945.

283 was formed at La Sebala in Tunis in February 1943 with 4 Walruses and seemed singularly unlucky with the Mk IA lifeboats they dropped after receiving them for their newly acquired Warwick Is in May 1944. Their base names sound like a Mediterranean tour: Algiers, Maison Blanche, Tingley, La Sebala, Palermo, Ajaccio, Borgo and Hal Far; with detachments at Castel Benito, Blida, Kalamaki/Hassani and Saki; where they disbanded on 31 March 1946. Whilst operating from Malta they were reported to be doing sterling work, even whilst on A/SR, by forcing U-boats to 'keep their heads down'.

284 from its birth at Gravesend and working up at Martlesham Heath in 1943 to disbandment at Pomigliano in Italy on 21 September 1945, the Squadron saw a host of strange places; Cassibile, Hal Far, Lentini East, Scansano, Gioia del Colle, Brindisi, Alghero, where they received Warwick Is with lifeboats, Bone, Elmas, Ramatuelle and Pomigliano, but gave their lifeboats little usage, fortunately. Whilst in North Africa they were much inconvenienced by theft by the local populace of lifeboat and aircraft gear from their open camp.

292 Formed at Jessore 1944. Warwicks were late in arriving so new A/SR Service did not initially get under way. They flew as far as Basra with the lifeboats but, it is believed, the boats were abandoned there and written off though some did join the Squadron later. In tropical service the planes did not come up to expectations; the ground crews had problems with the engines and some undesirable handling characteristics combined with a fabric that would not stand up to tropical conditions gave the long-suffering ground crews hours of work; and most of the Warwicks were unserviceable most of the time. No lifeboat drops are recorded, nor mention of lifeboats being carried.

293 was another Squadron which endured the conditions of North Africa and Italy; at Blida where they received their lifeboat-carrying Warwick Is in November 1943 before moving to Bone in November until March 1944; over the sea to Pomigliano for the next twelve months; Foggia until June 1945, then back to Pomigliano until disbanding on 5 April 1946. At varying times there were detachments operating from Pisa, Rosignano, Rivalto, Cesenatico, Udine, Netuno, Tarquinia and Formigliano; but they didn't get many chances to use their lifeboats.

294 has a very similar story even though they spread their wings as far afield as the Persian Gulf; visiting such far away places as Berka (Cyrenaica) for two months until October 1943, then on to Amriya South, with detachments at various places in Libya, Cyprus and Palestine until March 1944. With detachments as above and in Greece they were at Edku when they took over Warwick Is with Mk IA lifeboats, staying until June 1945. They then moved further east to Basrah, with detachments in the Persian Gulf and the Arabian Sea at Sharjah, Masirah and Muharraq; finally being disbanded at Basrah on 8 April 1946.

OPERATIONAL AIRBORNE LIFEBOAT MISSIONS

Aircrews of planes featured in Chapters 3, 4, 6, 7 and 9 are all RAF unless bracketed (Aus) Australian; (Can) Canadian; (NZ) New Zealand; (SA) South African; (USA) American; (Cz) Czechoslovakian. Regrettably it has not proved possible to trace the names of aircrew of some of the lifeboat-carrying aeroplanes.

1943

May	5	279	'W'	F/S Mogridge; F/S MacGregor; F/S Rusby; F/S Kidd.
			'D'	F/L Firchew; F/O Scott; P/O Field; W/O Burns.
			'Y'	F/O Wilson; F/O Hender; Sgt. Nicholls; Sgt. Cullen.
June	16	279	'F'	F/O Sherwood; P/O April; F/S Saunders; Sgt. Groome.
July	15	279	'W'	F/O Wilson; F/O Hender; Sgt. Nicholls; Sgt. Cullen.
	26	279	'W'	W/C Corry; F/L Gibson; F/O Webdell; Sgt. Melatini.
	26	279	'O'	F/O Pedersen; F/O Stephenson;

				F/S Brown; F/S Pegg.
			'U'	F/L Fitchew; F/O Scott; P/O Field; W/O Burns.
	28	279	'W'	F/S Palmer; F/S Brawn; Sgt. Bullough (Can); Sgt. Windsor (Can).
			'G'	F/O Myatt; F/O Case; F/S Smith; Sgt. Paterson.
	31	279	'R'	P/O Watts; F/S Willis; F/S Shaw; F/S Johnson.
			'O'	F/O Wilson; F/O Hender; F/O Peters; Sgt. Cullen.
			'G'	F/O Myatt; F/O Case; F/S Smith; Sgt. Paterson.
August	1	279	'N'	F/O Pedersen; F/O Stephenson; F/S Brown; F/S Pegg.
	22	279	'R'	F/S Bedford; F/S MacFarlane; Sgt. Cooke; Sgt. Danson. (All Aus)
			'F'	F/O Clark; F/S Frost; Sgt. Every; F/S Rood.
	24	279	'R'	As 22nd – shot down – no survivors.
			'H'	F/L Fitchew; F/O Scott; P/O Burns; P/O Field.
Sept	4	279	'W'	W/O Passlow; F/O Whitten; F/S Miles; F/S Clifford.
	6	279	'W'	F/O Clark; F/O O'Gorman; Sgt. Every; W/O McFadden.
Nov	24	280	'J'	F/S Chesher; F/O Charles; Sgt. Cann; F/S Stewart (NZ); F/S Prior; F/S Donley; F/S Williams.

1944

January	6	279	'N'	F/O Gaze; F/S Robertson; F/S Eadie; F/S George (All Aus).
	8	280	'E'	F/L Chesher; F/O Charles; Sgt. Cann; F/L Willaims (NZ); F/S Stewart (NZ); F/S Prior; F/S Donley.
	28	280	'C'	F/O Williamson; F/O Lewis; P/O James; F/O Dryden; F/S Heywood; W/O Winter.
March	9	279	'J'	F/O Bedford; F/O McFarlane; Sgt. Cooke; F/S Danson. (All Aus)
			'B'	F/O Wilson (Aus); F/O Case; P/O Knight; F/S Cullen.
	11	293	?	Not recorded.
April	8	280	'E'	F/L Chesher; F/O Charles; Sgt. Cann; F/L Williams (NZ); F/S Stewart (NZ); F/S Prior; F/S Donley.
	11	281	'P'	F/S Corney; F/S Greenslade;

				W/O Black (Can); Sgt. Drinkwater; Sgt. Curtis; Sgt. Allen (Can).
	24	281	'U'	P/O Duthie; Sgt. Wilde; Sgt. Moxham; Sgt. Arbery; Sgt. Moncaster; F/S Eaton; W/O Halfry.
	27	282	'Q'	Lt. Vallieres (USA); F/O Lamond; F/O Hooper; F/S Davies.
	27	280	'G'	F/O Williamson; F/O Lewis; P/O James; F/O Dryden; F/S Heywood; F/S Sergeant; W/O Winter.
	29	279	'F'	F/O Brown; F/S McLeish (Aus); W/O Jonassen (Can); W/O Lussier (Can).
May	20	279	'K'	F/O Reade (Can); F/O Clarke (Can); F/O Stapleton (Can); F/L O'Gorman; P/O Clifford; W/O Galloway; P/O Ashcroft; F/L Kenny.
June	2	276		F/O Virgo and unnamed crew.
	6	282	'R'	W/O King; F/S Gostin; Sgt. Sloan; F/S Evans; F/S Shorrock; F/S Stevenson.
	7	276	BV531	F/O Rushton and unnamed crew.
	7	276	HF940	F/O Gamper; F/S Neale; F/O Campbell (RAAF); F/S Emden; F/S Laing; F/S Hunter.
	8	282	'D'	F/O Wise; W/O McBeth; W/O Goodman; F/S Taylor.
	13	281	'U'	P/O Duthie; Sgt. Wilde; Sgt. Moxham; Sgt. Arbery; Sgt. Moncaster; F/S Eaton; W/O Halfry.
	14	282	'G'	F/O Mathieson; Sgt. Edwards; F/S Duschke (Aus); W/O Guest; F/S MacKenzie; F/S George.
	20	280	'L'	W/O Delgazio (Can); P/O Hodge (NZ); W/O Horne; W/O Bennett (Can); P/O Crane; W/O Whitehead.
	21	279	'Q'	W/O Palmer; P/O Brown; P/O Bullough (Can); W/O Windsor (Can).
			'U'	F/L Welpby; W/O Mouland; F/S Burrows; F/S Grant.
			'K'	F/O Carmichael (Can); W/O Simes (NZ); P/O Haynes; F/O Grout.
			'Z'	F/S Hill; W/O Wiseman; F/O Badmer; F/O Straw.
			'D'	F/L Ashby; F/O Stevens; F/O Smith (Can); W/O Bien (Can).
			'B'	P/O Curtis; F/L Mearns; W/O Ager; W/O Cullen (Can).
	29	279	'H'	F/O Carmichael (Can); W/O Simes (NZ);

				P/O Haynes; F/O Grout.
			'W'	F/O Myatt; F/L Case; W/O Macklin; W/O Galloway.
July		280	'Y'	F/O Wallace; F/O Easterbrook; F/S Black; F/OMacDonald; P/O Cross; W/O Newton.
			'J'	F/L Schaffer (Cz); P/O Boyles; W/O Lecky; W/O Benn; F/S Jones; F/O Parker.
	11	280	'E'	W/C McIntosh; F/L Butt; F/O Buck; F/L Richmond; F/O Day; F/S Speller.
			'Q'	F/O Thomson; F/O Walters; F/S Clarke; F/S Seaford; P/O Wildman; W/O Tripp; W/O Trust.
	12	280	'E'	W/C McIntosh; F/L Butt; F/O Buck; F/O Day; F/L Richmond; F/S Speller.
	21	278	'J'	W/O McVeigh (NZ); W/O Summer (Aus); F/S Hallett; F/S Bushall; F/S Duthie; Sgt. Morley.
	23	283	'B'	S/L Crampton; F/O Bain; F/L Gunson; F/O Feast; F/O Lowrie; W/O Nicholls; W/O Dickson.
	24	278	BV475	F/O Whiteley; F/O Heggs; Sgt. Saunders; Sgt. Needham; F/O Weston.
	26	269	'V'	F/O Smith (Can); F/S Carrington; P/O Allen (Can); W/O Cartwright (Can).
	31	282	'H'	F/L Gwynn; F/S Romer; F/O Abbey; F/O Roberts; Sgt. Spencer; W/O Clayton.
August	5	280	'J'	F/L Schaffer (Cz); P/O Boyles; W/O Lecky; W/O Benn; F/S Jones; F/O Parker.
			'M'	F/O Ayres; P/O Hodge (NZ); F/O Smart; P/O Silverside; F/S Taylor; P/O Smith.
	15	280	'Z'	S/L Easton; W/O V. Wolfe; F/S Askew; F/S Reeves; W/O Callaghan; W/O Hart.
			'K'	P/O Hagg; P/O Moore; F/S D. Wolfe; F/S Gregory; P/O Richardson; W/O Benn.
	24	293	'B'	F/L James; F/O Birrell; F/O Wyllis; W/O Belcher (NZ); F/S Boness; Sgt. Todd.
	27	279	'L'	P/O Curtis; P/O Whittaker; W/O Ager; F/S Pearson.
			'E'	F/L Ashby; F/O Stevens; F/O Smith (Can); W/O Bien (Can).
			'H'	P/O Gaze; F/S Robertson; W/O Eade; W/O George. (All Aus)
Sept.	8	280	'O'	F/O Chesher; F/S Plumridge; P/O Richardson; F/S Millar; P/O Crook.
			'L'	F/L Proctor; F/O Duggan; P/O Every; Sgt. Bramble; F/S Butcher; Sgt. Hill.
	13	282	'N'	F/L Gwynn; F/O Abbey; F/S Romer;

				P/O Roberts; Sgt. Spencer; W/O Clayton.
			'D'	S/L Burge; F/S Williams; F/S Lintott; Sgt. Eddy; Sgt. Maynard; F/O Urquhart.
	13	280	'F'	F/O Robins; P/O Wooden; P/O Robertson; F/O Prout; P/O Tourell (NZ); W/O McKeon (Aus).
	14	280	'F'	F/O Harvey; F/O Ridley; P/O Odkin; T/S Dakin (USA); P/O Turner; F/O Lewery.
	20	293	'J'	F/O Goldspink; F/O Foster; Sgt. Tuck; Sgt. Burch; W/O Dolan (Aus); W/O Sharpe (Aus); Sgt. Downey.
			'D'	F/O Cornwall (NZ); W/O Waugh; W/O De Pencier; W/O Renwick; F/S Rose; Sgt. Hawes; F/S Burford.
	25	281	'P'	F/O Murray (Can); F/O Bartholemew (Aus); F/S Evans; W/O Mansfield; F/S Russell; F/S Alton.
October	3	279	'U'	F/L Goff; F/O Cook; W/O Carrett; W/O Mc.Fadden.
	6	278	968	F/O Mc; Williams; Cowley;Martin. Dozee, Benn.
			528	F/O Garden; Geddes; Ranken; Beneke; Evans; Johnston.
	6	280	'Y'	F/O Pull; F/O Dawson; W/O White (Can); W/O Norlen (Can); F/S Mole; W/O Hendry (Can).
	7	280	'A'	P/O Hagg; F/S D. Wolfe; F/S Gregory; P/O Richardson; W/O Benn.
			'E'	F/O Harvey; F/L Ridley; F/L Webb; P/O Hodkin; Sgt. Pigden; F/O Lewery.
	8	280	'L'	F/O Chesher; F/S Jones; P/O Williams (NZ); W/O Donley; F/S Gregory; W/O Edwards.
			'F'	F/O Harvey; F/L Ridley; F/L Webb; P/O Hodkin; Sgt. Pigden; F/O Lewery.
			'A'	F/O Rhodes (NZ); F/O Sullivan (Aus); P/O Newton; F/O Nicholson (Aus); P/O Cunningham; W/O McCombie.
			'Z'	P/O Pull; F/O Dawson; W/O Winter (Can); F/S Mole; W/O Norlen (Can); W/O Henry (Can).
	9	280	'C'	P/O Hagg; F/S D. Wolfe; F/S Gregory; W/O Benn; P/O Richardson.
			'G'	F/O Mason; Sgt. Cracknell; Sgt. Cox; Sgt. Algar; Sgt. Finch.
			'O or D'	F/L Thomson; P/O Boyles; P/O Wildman; Sgt. Close; Sgt. Jarrett; P/O Warner.

Nov	17	281	'Q'	F/O Jenner; F/L Hyde (Aus); F/O Temple; F/S Roberts; F/S Dixon (Can); W/O Moffett.
			'H'	W/O Bolton, W/O Haig; F/S Stinson; Sgt. MacFarlane; F/S Rannochan; W/O Richards.
December	9	279	'G'	Lt. Shanks (USA); F/L Perelman; F/S Wood; Gilyard; F/S Austin; F/S Pole.
	16	279	'P'	S/L Levin-Raw; F/L Banks; F/S Flaherty; Sgt. Venn; F/S Bond; W/O Campbell.
			'F'	F/O Reilly; F/S Goldstone; Sgt. Mabey; Sgt. Hendra; W/O Cooper; W/O Marvin.
	24	281	'D'	W/O Stevens; F/S Nicholls; P/O Rendall; F/S Morrison; F/S Balcombe; W/O Bartlett.
	31	279	'B'	P/O Grimston; P/O Luck; F/S Boram; F/S Foley; F/L Smith; F/S Prior.
			'G'	P/O Duthie; F/S Arbery; F/S Wilde; F/S Moxham; F/S Moncaster; Sgt. Eaton.

1945

Jan	1	280	'A'	F/O Wyatt; F/O Jamieson; W/O Gray; P/O Bird; W/O Henderson; W/O Edwards.
			'B'	F/L Gray; F/S Williamson; P/O Silver; Sgt. Smith; F/S Miller; Sgt. Aynsley.
	12	279	'G'	P/O Duthie; F/S Arbery; F/S Wilde; F/S Moxham; F/S Moncaster; Sgt. Eaton.
			'S'	W/O Williamson; P/O Redman; Sgt. Adams; W/O Wilson; F/S Freed; Sgt. Clipperton.
February	3	280	'Z'	F/L Radford; F/O Tod; F/O Wilson; F/O Reid; F/O Cochrane; F/S Bristow; F/S Robinson.
			'D'	F/L Gray; F/S Williamson; F/O Silver; F/S Miller; Sgt. Smith; Sgt. Aynsley; F/L Mitchell.
March	4	279	'K'	W/O Williamson; F/O Cornall; Sgt. Adams; W/O Wilson; W/O Freed; W/O Clipperton.
			'Y'	S/L Burge; W/O Williams; F/S Maynard; F/S Eddy; F/S Robinson; F/O Withecombe.
			'D'	F/O Reilly; F/S Goldstone; Sgt. Mabey; Sgt. Hendra; W/O Cooper; W/O Marvin.
	10	293	BV415	F/L Rawlings (Aus); P/O Holborn; W/O Marsh; P/O Stembridge; F/S Brown (Can); F/S Burch; F/S Warmsley.
	11	Walrus	L 2207	F/S Bickle; F/S Goldstein; F/S Burnett.
	31	280	'Z'	F/L Bower; F/S Zimmer; F/O Blaker; F/O Lofting; F/O Bell; F/O Stevenson.

			'Y'	F/O Maxwell; F/L Butt; F/L Nicholson; W/O Barnes; W/O Platts; F/S Keeley.
April	2	293	HF948	F/O Weaver; P/O Browne (Can); W/O Marsh; F/S Wood; F/S Phillips.
	3		'K'	F/L Forrest; F/O Milburn; P/O Younger; P/O Lintott; P/O Owen; W/O Sheeky.
			'A'	F/L Gray; F/S Williamson; P/O Silver; F/S Millar; Sgt. Smith; T/S Dakin (USA); F/L Mitchell.
	5	293	BV449	F/O Goldspink; F/L Foster; P/O Thorpe; Sharpe; Sgt. Tucker; Sgt. Dowd.
	6		PBY 5	Lt. Kaminski; Lt. Dunn; and others. (All USA)
	10	280	'T'	F/L Radford; F/O Wilson; F/O Reid; F/O Tod; F/S Bristow; F/S Robinson.
	14	279	'G'	S/L Levin-Raw; F/L Banks; W/O Flaherty; W/O Venn; F/S Bold; P/O Campbell.
			'V'	F/L Ashby; F/L Stevens; F/O Ellyat; P/O Bien (Can); F/S Wylie; W/O Fulton.
	18	280	'P'	F/L Radford; F/O Tod; F/O Wilson; F/O Reid; F/S Bristow; F/S Robinson.
			'Y'	W/O Pike; F/S Williamson; W/O Hoff; F/S Spark; F/S Keeley; F/S Crossley; W/O Little.
	18	280	'T'	F/O Harvey; F/L Ridley; F/O Waller; T/S Dakin (USA); F/O Silver; F/O Lewery.
	30	293	BV449	F/L Rawlings (Aus); P/O Hogan; Capt. Isted (SAAF); P/O Stembridge; P/O Gabb; F/S Chambers.
May	26	279	'V'	F/L Hayes; F/L Monk; F/S Beith; F/S Day; F/S Benjamin; F/O Midworth.
			'Z'	W/C Cox; F/L Ellis; F/L Denniss; F/L Quas; F/L Pennycuick; F/L Vardy.
July	30	4 ERS	B 17G	2nd Lt. Morgan; 1st Lt. McCabe; 1st Lt. Kelly; Cpt. Mead; Sgt. Yeaman; Cpls. Rogerson, Rusnak and Tjapkes. (All USA)
August	10	281	'J'	S/L Loweth; W/O Galbraith; P/O Evett; W/O Milne; W/O McFatrick; F/O Gillham.
			'L'	W/O Barnes; F/S Hall; Sgt. Smythe-Parke; F/S Dunstall; Sgt. Batson; W/O Sterritt.
			'P'	F/L Emck; P/O Murray; F/O Jackson; W/O Armitage; W/O Hewitt; F/S Hunter.
	17	284	BV363	F/O Denny; F/O McLeary; F/O Osbourn; F/S Hemmings; Sgt. Nott.
Sept	19	293	BV430	F/O Daniels; Sgt. Young; Sgt. Alabaster; Sgt. Harper; Sgt. Hensen; W/O Bate.

1946

Undated 294 U447 F/O Mackay (Can); W/O Prescott (Aus);
W/O Laidlaw (Can); W/O McCrae;
F/S Young; Sgt. Dennison; W/O Tighe.

AIRBORNE LIFEBOAT BUILDERS

Recorded quantities total 598 British Marks I, IA, II and IIA built for wartime operations and 54–60 Mark IIIs post-War, with an indeterminate number of US models, several reaching hundreds.

Uffa Fox, Medina Yard, Cowes, Isle of Wight. 142 (?+). A 1–9; B 1–9; C 1–9; AJ 6–9; AK 1–9; AL 1–9; AM 1–9; AN 1–9; AO 1–9; AP 1–9; AQ 1–5; CD 2–9; CE 1–9; CF 3–9; CG 2–9; CH 1–8; CJ 1–7.

Woodnutt, St Helens, Isle of Wight. 86 (?+). D 1–9; E 1–9; F 1–9; G 1–5; AC 6–9; AD 1–9; AE 1–9; AF 1–9; AG 1–9; AH 1–9; AJ 1–5.

Sycamore Brentford Ltd, Brentford. 56 (?+). G 6–9; H 1–9; J 1–2; CJ 9; CK 1–3; CK 5–9; AQ 6–9; AR 1–9; AS 1–9; AT 1–9; AU 1.

Ranelagh Ltd, Morden Road, Merton. 64 Mark I. J 3–9; K 1–9; L 1–9; M 1–9; N 1–9; O 1–9; P 1–9; Q 1–3.

Herbert Woods, Potter Heigham, Norfolk. 110 (?+). Q 4–9; R 1–9; S 1–9; T 1–9; U 1–9; V 1–9; W 1–9; X 1–4; CP 5–8; CQ 1–7; CR 1–9; CS 1–8; CT 1–9; CU 1–9.

Aldous Successors, Brightlingsea, Essex. 46 (?+). X 5–9; Y 1–9; Z 1–9; AA 1–9; AB 1–9; AC 1–5.

Taylor Woodrow Ltd, Ruislip Road, Southall, Middlesex. 47 (?+). AU 2–9; AV 1–9; AW 1–9; AX 1–5; CM 2–9; CN 1–7; CO 1.

Brooke Marine Ltd, Lowestoft, Suffolk. 17 Mark I. AU 1; BA 9; BB 1–9; BC 1–6.

Sadd & Sons Ltd, Maldon, Essex. 30 Marks I, IA, II and IIA. AX 6–9; AY 1–9; AZ 1–9; BA 1–8.

Saunders Roe Ltd, Beaumaris, Isle of Anglesey. 54 Mark III. Numbered 803 upwards.

Merron Ltd. Trial hull built, 10 more ordered; no trace of delivery so assume cancelled at end of War.

Vosper Ltd, Trial hull built; CD 1. No trace of further production.

Higgins Boat Company, New Orleans, USA. 300 A-1 ordered; not known how many actually built.

Edo Corporation, College Point, New York. 100 A-3 built.

Not known (probably Higgins Boat Company). Unspecified number of AR8 for use with PBY5SA.

Brooke Yachts International Ltd of Lowestoft (successors to Brooke Marine Ltd) kindly sent page BY c 661 from the Yard Building Register which contains the following information:

1943. Nov. 25. Ministry of Aircraft Production, C. 42a, Harrogate, Yorks.
Contract Ref. MC 682/D/C 42a; 25th. Nov. 1943; Acceptance 6th.
September 1944. Subject to Variation Clauses. Quoted @ £648. each =
Total max. of Contract £10081. Final Accepted Price each £593. 17
(Seventeen) Airborne Lifeboats – Mark IA. All as per M.A.P. Drawings
and Specifications Ref. DIS 63 Issue No. 10. Complete with Special
Fittings and Equipment, all as Sub-Contracts List 25/11/43: giving
Drawing Numbers and Quantities. ? Electrical Sub-contract included in the
main price – YES. Wiring only by The Lowestoft Electrical Company Ltd.
@ £3. per boat.

> Value for Insurance Purposes say £800 per boat.
> Delivery by Rail, L.N.E. Ry. Advise Movements Control R.A.F.,
> Cambridge when completed.
> If packing cases required for any separate of Equipment this is to be
Extra to Contract. Contract completed 9th. October 1944.

LIFEBOAT AILMENTS

This short paragraph in one of the A/SR manuals throws some light on the
possible 'joys' of a voyage in a lifeboat, seasickness being dealt with in an
earlier paragraph.

> General; Dry mouth; Parched lips and cracked skin, salt water boils;
> Inflammation of the eyes; Fever; Vomiting; Constipation – crew should
> not be surprised at this as bowel action cannot be expected when little or
> no food has been consumed. No treatment necessary or advisable.
> Difficulty of urination – some difficulty in passing urine and bladder may
> feel uncomfortably full, urination may be assisted by dangling hands in the
> sea; the amount passed will be small and may appear thick and dark. Only
> to be expected and no cause for alarm as little fluid is being taken in. The
> best way to urinate in the lifeboat is to kneel on deck amidships so the
> water passed can drain away via the relief well. Swollen legs; Frostbite;
> Immersion foot.

PARACHUTES

All the parachutes used with the wartime Airborne Lifeboats were designed
and developed by the GQ Parachute Company of Godalming, Surrey; who also
made most of those used; but some for the Mark II lifeboat were supplied by
Walmer Manufacturing Company Ltd, Chapel Street Works, Manchester to
the GQ design.

This company was started by Sir Raymond Quilter, grandson of Sir
Cuthbert Quilter, a Victorian financier, who although born in London came of
an old Suffolk family. He built picturesque Bawdsey Manor on the Suffolk
coast and established an 8000-acre private benevolent kingdom within part
of the area known locally as 'The Sanderlings'. When death duties and

economic changes forced the break-up of the estate the Manor was bought in 1936 by the Government for the development of radar by Sir Robert Watson-Watt. Sir Raymond was a very dynamic and courageous man with a deep interest in aeroplanes and parachutes. At an early age he was thrilling visitors at nearby Felixstowe by making parachute jumps over the seafront, just for fun – an experience which he put to very good account and thus contributed to saving hundreds of lives.

GQ designed and produced 'load dropping parachutes' up to 96 feet in diameter; but these were not overly successful as there was much oscillation of the load, leading to damage at touchdown. Basically 64 feet diameter was the largest practical size used. For the Mark I Airborne Lifeboat the company recommended three 32-foot size, and the first drop was with these canopies, using the static line system for opening, but this was found to damage the aircraft. A different method was devised. It began with a GQ vane-type spring-loaded pilot parachute being streamed and pulling out a 12-foot retarder parachute made with two cloths of different porosities. This opened immediately and controlled the opening behaviour and stability of the three main canopies, which were pulled out by the weight of the falling lifeboat. The vane-type parachute was developed by GQ from the original idea of James Evans and later taken up firstly by the British and then by the American authorities.

The parachutes for the Marks I and IA had a stores reference 15B/84; each had 32 gores and was made from camouflaged material, the three being positively connected to each other where the peripheries contacted.

For the much heavier Mark II lifeboat a cluster of four parachutes was used initially, each being 60 feet in diameter, but as there was a delay in deliveries early in 1945 a quantity of 42-foot size were repacked into clusters of four so that work with the Lifeboats could be continued. There does not appear to have been any adverse reaction to the use of these smaller parachutes, and exactly the same format and technique was used for the Mark III; but with both this and the Mark II the practice of fastening the peripheries where they contacted each other was discontinued. Several photographs exist of lifeboat 'drops' using six parachutes, but so far as can be ascertained these were taken during trials or tests.

Strangely Great Yarmouth, the major port for returning Airborne Lifeboats, was also home to Grouts Silk Mills, one of the principal suppliers of parachute materials, although severe bombing later restricted much of their output.

The self-inflating buoyancy chambers at bow and stern of all the lifeboats were designed and manufactured by the RFD Company, the principal member of a large international group specialising in aircraft and maritime safety equipment of which GQ Parachutes is a member. The initials of the group names are those of Mr R. F. Dagnall who founded the company at Hersham, near Walton on Thames in 1920 by making rubberised pneumatic Flotation Bags for Short Brothers to fit into aeroplanes they were making for the Royal Navy. Today the initials are more widely interpreted as standing for 'Rescue From Disaster', a highly appropriate term for this book.

DROP PROCEDURES

The dropping procedure originally evolved for the Mark I lifeboats was very simple and arrived at mainly by trial and error. It was initially to circle the target to assess sea, and, more importantly, wind conditions, the latter by dropping floating smoke signals, observation of which would give indications of direction and strength. They would also assist in pin-pointing the drop zone so that new approaches could be made from the best height and direction. The ideal height for the parachutes to function without unnecessary float down time, which might lead to target inaccuracy, was determined at 700 feet with an air speed of 110 knots flying into the wind in calm and moderate conditions. Release of the lifeboat would be when directly above the survivors; thus it would be up to the bomb aimer to guide his pilot in on the approach run as only he would be able to see directly beneath the aircraft and it would be the bomb aimer's finger which would be on the release button. The released lifeboat's forward airspeed would be opposed by the wind speed until the parachutes opened and then these would carry the boat downwind so that on 'splash down' the survivors would drift down to the boat held almost stationary by the drogue which fired from the bow tube by an incline switch whilst the boat was descending, but only when a 30 degree bow down angle was achieved through the different lengths of the two wire slings between the parachutes and the boat. Simultaneously the CO_2 cylinders would be automatically opened to inflate the turtlebacked canopies over the bows and the stern; then when the stem of the boat knifed down into the sea the inflating canopies would already be well on the way to bringing it to the surface the correct way up. Also on 'splashdown' an immersion switch situated on the underside of the hull would operate the parachute release to prevent the boat being dragged downwind; normally the parachutes would be expected to deflate and collapse but it was essential they should be released as soon as possible. This same immersion switch caused two rockets to fire broadside, each carrying out 150 yards of buoyant orange coloured lines giving survivors means of pulling themselves to the lifeboat. A similar technique was used for the Mark II but wind speed variations could upset the splashdown point so the Mark IA bombsight was used later on.

Certain specific duties were necessary to ready the lifeboat for voyaging and these were set out in 'Instructions For A Ditched Crew' printed on waterproof paper: 'Clear parachutes from boat. Haul aboard orange side lines. Remove compass packing. Haul in drogue Line. Ship rudder [this was stowed flat on the deck of Marks I and II]. Start engines. Watch aircraft for Aldis Lámp signals. Inspect message carrier. Destroy aircraft dinghy. Ship drop keel. Inflate bow & stern chambers (if not already so). Display recognition aprons. Keep contact with escort or search aircraft by night. Master switch [this brought the boat's battery-powered electrical equipment into circuit]. Inspect stowage compartments'.

Other pages dealt with: Stowage of equipment; Erection of mast and rigging; Use of drogue; Engine operating hints; Use of radio; Technique of sailing; Use of chart; Leadership; Behaviour; Allocation of duties; Clothing; Rations; First Aid and treatment of shock and various ailments.

Appendix II: Extracts from Coastal Command Report No. 404

SUMMARY OCTOBER 1954

1   The question has arisen as to the real value of the Airborne Lifeboat in saving lives. In peacetime its use has been negligible so this investigation has been confined to incidents that occurred to aircraft operating from Gt Britain and crashing into the sea during the last two years of the war. The incidents have been classified according to the areas where they occurred i.e. in areas where enemy activity was liable to affect rescue operations and areas within and outside 60 miles from our own coasts not affected by enemy activity.

2   The Airborne Lifeboat was dropped on 68 occasions in the course of 52 rescues operations. In only about half of these cases were the aircrew able to board the lifeboat successfully. Half the failures were due to mechanical troubles and the others due to it being dropped too far away from the aircrew. During the period under review about 2400 aircraft were lost over the sea, thus the lifeboat was used in only about 2% of the incidents.

3   In addition to the incidents in which lifeboats were dropped a further 873 incidents have been examined in which survivors had been sighted either on the ditched aircraft, in dinghies or in the water. The majority of these incidents were within 60 miles of our coast and in none of these latter cases does it appear that the use of the lifeboat would have turned the few cases of failure, 2%, into success. Similarly in the 13 cases close to our shores in which the lifeboat was dropped it would appear that its use did not affect the issue.

4   Close to the enemy coast and at distances greater than 60 miles from our own the answer is not so clear cut. On a generous assessment there were 21 occasions in the former area and 8 in the latter when lifeboats were or might have been valuable. This is at the rate of slightly over one case a month and in the majority of these the object was to prevent aircrew falling into enemy hands.

5   Amphibious aircraft, mainly Walruses, were used in four times as many successful rescues as lifeboats. They were particularly valuable off enemy shores. It is doubtful if the helicopter could fulfil this latter role and in view of the present lack of amphibious aircraft there might be more occasions in a future war in which lifeboats are required.

THE USE OF THE AIRBORNE LIFEBOAT IN WAR

Introduction:

1   Owing to the high cost of the Airborne Lifeboat organisation the question has arisen as to its real value in saving life. In peacetime its actual use has been negligible, hence investigation is confined to incidents that occurred during the war. The proportion of successful air-sea rescue incidents and also the proportion of aircrew that came down into the sea and were saved was only about one-third. Apart from the occasions when aircraft crashed straight into the sea, giving no chance to the crew, the main reason for the poor success of the air-sea rescue operations was a lack of knowledge of when and where the incident occurred. Thus a decision for or against the airborne lifeboat still leaves the main problem of air-sea rescue unresolved.

Method:

2   This analysis is confined to incidents around Great Britain and deals only with those cases in which live aircrew were sighted either on the ditched aircraft, in dinghies or swimming in the water. All such cases were examined whether or not the airborne lifeboat was used. The period covered is from May 1943, during which month the first lifeboat was dropped, to the end of the war. An incident has been deemed successful if one or more of the aircrew has been picked up alive. The information has been taken from the Air Ministry Weekly Reports of Air-Sea Rescue Operations.

3   The incidents have been classified according to the locations where they occured:

a)   Areas where enemy activity was liable to effect rescue operations. The actual distance offshore varied from some 20 miles in the Channel to about 100 miles off Germany and Denmark. The area was varied as the advance through Northern France and Low Countries progressed.

b)   Areas within 60 miles of our own coast, not included in (a).

c)   Areas beyond 60 miles of our own coast, not included in (a).

4   During the period under consideration there were a total of 925 incidents for which a reasonable amount of data was available. Airborne Lifeboats were dropped in 52 of these incidents. During the invasion period special air-sea rescue arrangements were made in the Channel and the details of many of the incidents that occurred were less well recorded. These have been excluded. The analysis has been divided into the two main sections i.e. whether the lifeboat was used or not.

Incidents in which Airborne Lifeboats were used:

5   Sixty-eight lifeboats were dropped during the course of rescue operations in the 52 incidents mentioned above. The success of the drops was as follows:

Occasions ABL dropped successfully	36	53%
Occasions parachutes failed	10	15%
Occasions with other mechanical failures	7	10%
Occasions crews failed to reach ABL	15	22%

6   Thus in only about half the drops were the aircrew able to board the lifeboat; half the failures being due to mechanical failures, and half due to the lifeboat being dropped too far away for the aircrew to reach it.

7   The following table summarises the successes and failures in the different areas. In addition an attempt has been made to assess for each incident whether the use of the lifeboat was really necessary. This is inevitably a matter of opinion but the bias, if anything, has been to give the lifeboat the benefit of any doubt. In the cases where the crews were able to board the lifeboat the general criterion has been the length of time they were in the lifeboat prior to being rescued by other surface craft compared with the time they were in the dinghies. All the cases in which the crews had been in the lifeboat more than six hours have been counted as occasions in which the lifeboat was necessary.

Table II

Location	Incident type	No.	Boarded	U/S	Crew failed to reach	ABL necessary
Near	Successful	22	18	0	4	14
enemy	Failure	9	2	4	3	7
coast						
Over 60 miles	Successful	6	4	1	1	3
offshore	Failure	2	0	2	0	2
Within 60	Successful	12	9	2	1	0
miles own	Failure	1	0	0	1	0
coast						
Totals		52	33	9	10	26

Note:- In the two cases of failure near the enemy coast in which the ABL was boarded, the crews were probably rescued by the enemy. This also probably applied in two other cases of failure.

8   It can be seen that the general pattern of incidents depended very largely on the location. Near the enemy coast and also at distances over 60 miles of our own coast there were only about 25% failures. Within 60 miles of our own coast there was only one failure in 13 and in this case the one possible survivor clung to the lifeboat 15 minutes and was unable to board it.

9   Again, the location of the incident affects whether the lifeboat was necessary or not. In no case within 60 miles of our coast did it appear that the dropping of the lifeboat affected the success or otherwise of rescuing the crews.

In about two-thirds of the other cases the lifeboat probably contributed to saving the crews or might have done so if the lifeboat had been successfully dropped.

Incidents in which airborne lifeboats were not used:
10   The following Table summarises the successes and failures in the different areas. In addition the number of cases is listed in which amphibious aircraft, mainly Walruses, landed and contributed to saving the crews.

Table III

Location	Total	Failures	%	Aircraft	%
Near enemy coast	126	19	15	55	44
Over 60 miles from own coast	62	9	15	8	13
Within 60 miles of own coast	685	12	2	96	14
Totals	873	40		159	

11   It can be seen above that the failure rate is much lower for incidents near our shores than in other areas. This is to be expected. The reasons for the failures to make successful rescues is examined below in greater detail.

Table IV

Near enemy coasts:

Too near enemy coasts, International Broadcast made	7
Picked up by enemy or probably drifted ashore	4
Failed to re-find after original sighting	4
Crews in sea, dinghies dropped to them, but unable to board	4
	19

Table V

Over 60 miles from our coast:

Dinghy sighted but failed to re-find	3
Dinghy sighted by search aircraft, after original sighting, but subsequently lost	3
Survivors failed to get into dinghies	2
Probably picked up by Spanish fishing vessels	1
	9

Table VI

Within 60 miles of our coast:	
Crews seen swimming (no dinghies)	7
Dinghy sighted but lost due to bad weather	3
When picked up dinghy pilot had died	1
Alleged sighting of dinghy but Walrus soon after only saw wreckage	1
	12

Note:- 11 out of these 12 incidents were concerned with crews of fighter type aircraft.

12   It can be seen from Table IV that there was no occasion of the 19 failures off the enemy coast when the dropping of lifeboats would have turned failure into success. Similar results also apply to the failure incidents within 60 miles of our coast (Table VI). In the case of the incidents over 60 miles from our coast there were three occasions when the search aircraft, if carrying lifeboats, might have turned failure into success. In making this assessment the assumption has been made that the first sighting might be made by any type of aircraft and that the aircraft carrying the lifeboat would have to be specially sent or diverted to the sighting.

13   It is apparent from Table III that amphibious aircraft were of very considerable value in making successful rescues, particularly off enemy coasts when they were used in 44% of the incidents. In many of these cases the aircraft, having landed and taken aboard the survivors, was unable to take off. This was sometimes due to bad weather and sometimes due to too heavy a load. On these occasions the rescue was effected normally by transferring the survivors to surface craft homed to the incident. Amphibious aircraft took part in four times as many successful incidents as airborne lifeboats.

14   Some of the crews spent considerable periods in their dinghies before being rescued. Records are not very complete on this point but there is evidence of 20 cases of crews spending more than 2 days in their dinghies, and five cases of successful rescues after five days. Thus the criterion adopted in para. 7 for the occasions when an airborne lifeboat would have been of value of only six hours in the lifeboat is a generous one.

Discussions and Conclusions:

15   It is quite clear from the above analysis that there is no case for an airborne lifeboat in rescue operations within 60 miles of our own coast. Here, the few failures, when live crew had been sighted, were mainly due to the crews being found swimming in the water. In these cases success can only be achieved if the first aircraft spotting the incident is able to drop some type of reliable flotation gear; a dinghy is better in this respect than a lifeboat. Many successful rescues were achieved by this method.

16   Close to the enemy shores and at distances greater than 60 miles from our own, the answer is not so clear cut. On a generous assessment there were, over the two-year period, 21 cases in the former area and 8 in the latter where lifeboats were or might have been of value. This is at the rate of slightly over one case a month.

17   Airborne lifeboats were also occasionally used in the Mediterranean and one type of incident is worth remarking on. A pilot in the course of one month three times ditched his aircraft in mined areas where Catalinas and surface craft were unable to penetrate. On each occasion he was rescued with the aid of an airborne lifeboat.

18   It would appear therefore that in wartime there is a slight case for the airborne lifeboat, particularly for rescuing aircrews that come down close to enemy shores. Hence the main reason is to prevent the crews falling into enemy hands rather than the saving of life. Many more crews were, however, rescued in such areas by means of amphibious aircraft. Unfortunately there are no such aircraft now in the British forces and it is questionable whether the helicopter will be able to take over completely this particular role of the amphibian. There might be occasions, therefore, in a future war when the airborne lifeboat would be the only practical means of preventing ditched aircrew falling into enemy hands.

19   In considering the whole question of the merits or otherwise of the airborne lifeboat it must be remembered that in the period covered by this analysis approximately 2400 aircraft were lost over the sea. In only slightly over 1% of these cases would the airborne lifeboat have been of value with the then existing methods of locating crashed aircraft. Further the lifeboat was only dropped successfully in about half the occasions it was used.

AUTHOR'S NOTE

Whilst this report appears to examine closely the operational usage of Airborne Lifeboats and purports to tell the truth, is it the whole truth, for it examines and judges the efficiency of Airborne Lifeboats solely with the British Isles as the centre of operations, and whilst mentioning the Mediterranean and quoting the three rescues of the same pilot within 30 days, does not take into account the tremendous difference the inclusion of a total analysis would have made to the percentages and thus the drawn conclusions. It also overlooks the fact that at the time the RAF was a world-wide organisation and that its planes were as liable to ditch overseas as in home waters; nor does it mention the high number of cases where the fault was not with the Airborne Lifeboat in principle but with equipment failures which could only be due to poor maintenance or inefficiency by ground crew. Further, it is not stated if the 2400 aircraft lost over the sea were all within the same physical area as covered by the report.

57 Author with two pairs of oars made for the Mark I at RAF Museum Hendon (S B Daniels)

In Chapter 3 of this book 14 rescue operations are listed with 15 lifeboats dropped; Chapter 4 lists 21 operations using 22 lifeboats; Chapter 6 has 27 operations with 33 lifeboats dropped; Chapter 7 recounts 17 operations with 22 lifeboats dropped; Chapter 9 lists 18 operations with 20 lifeboats parachuted down, the majority of which were American in the Pacific war zone. These figures total 97 operations using 112 lifeboats; some rescue operations needed two lifeboats because survivors had drifted apart but in some other cases the first lifeboat drop was unsuccessful for one reason or another. Admittedly four of the RAF operations occurred after the European war had ended and were thus outside Report 404's terms of reference and the area from which its figures were drawn; but a life saved is a life saved whether there's a war on or not. The fact that only 52 operations using 68 lifeboats were considered by the report means that almost half were excluded from the calculations. It is felt that greater emphasis should have been put upon the tragedy of the high percentage of equipment, installation or maintenance failure. An overall analysis based on the operations in this book presents a rather different picture.

97 Rescue operations
98 RAF lifeboats and 15 USAAF lifeboats were dropped (113)
61 Lifeboats were successfully boarded by at least one man
36 Lifeboats were not boarded, many through equipment failure leading to damage. In some instances the lifeboat was beyond the reach of survivors, in others it was dropped as a forlorn hope just in case one of the apparently dead men was still alive
3 Boarded but boats useless
12 Lifeboat drops have unknown results, because of darkness, adverse weather conditions or the intrusion of hostile aircraft

From analysis of the figures of known results it can be calculated that nearly 63% of drops were successful; and even if all the unknown results were failures there is a success rate of almost 56%. There would appear to be very little substantial difference in the rate of equipment or parachute failure in the RAF or USAAF. The number of aircrew rescued is not known as accounts do differ, as we have seen in the operational chapters, but is probably between 200 and 300.

The incidents quoted are all fully substantiated by RAF or USAAF records and take no account of cases where lifeboats were reported but no squadron or aircraft report has been traced to authenticate an actual drop near or on that date in that locality. The 14 USAAF rescue missions with 15 Lifeboats used have been traced from examination of Emergency Rescue Squadrons' microfilm and were they to be more readable there is no doubt that several more interesting rescues and attempts would come to light. Although only three US operations are in the European war zone, there are references in RAF records which lead one to believe that there was a wider use of US lifeboats than has been traced.

Furthermore, Report 404 states the criterion for a successful lifeboat drop to be at least one life saved, but the qualification of at least six hours in a lifeboat suggests that the compilers of the report had never had to spend agonising hours in, or hanging onto, a rubber dinghy in North Sea conditions and completely overlooks the painful fact that occupancy of a lifeboat extends survival time indefinitely compared with a dinghy. There were cases where a lifeboat was successfully dropped and boarded but support surface craft could either not find or reach the boat before enemy action, stress of weather, wounds or hypothermia overcame the crew; this could suggest a weakness in communications rather than in the principle of an Airborne Lifeboat, as in these instances the drop should be assessed as successful although it was nullified by later events. The report also points out that amphibious aircraft were concerned in many more rescues than airborne lifeboats and also states that there were none of these aircraft now on RAF strength. Curious! One wonders why not.

58   Mark I Airborne Lifeboat converted to racing yacht 'Swan' on the Norfolk 'Suffolk Broads

Appendix III: What Happened to the Airborne Lifeboats

What happened to the lifeboats after the War? Certainly many had been lost or destroyed in the course of deployment, others just dropped out of sight; one was even concerned in a court case when it was allegedly found where it should not have been, but many found happy days as recreational craft for the Royal Air Force Sailing Association (RAFSA), the Royal Navy and ultimately private individuals. For example, Mr Cecil Cubitt of Addlestone, Surrey writes:

> I raced 'Swan' very successfully at Oulton Broad from about 1951 until about 1968. My father bought the converted boat from a Dr Johnson at Costessey. The boat was rigged by Leslie Landamore at Wroxham and he raced it on Wroxham Broad until it was sold to my father. Leslie did very well with it 'wiping up' the [racing] punts there. I had no racing experience when I started to sail it [and took it] to Oulton Broad where there was quite a fleet of 'nondescripts' racing together on handicap. They started me on a handicap of 12% and as I improved this was whittled down until I sailed on 'scratch' on level terms with International Stars and a Flying Dutchman and other very fast 'nondescripts'. I won a number of club trophies with it particularly in the late fifties when I was also achieving some success with the Merlin/Rocket fleet.
>
> We had added a trapeze, sliding seat and spinnaker to it. The centreplate was made of Duralumin for lightness and strength. I had quite a reputation for sailing it in virtually any weather. The hull planed at quite a high speed with a good blow on a broad reach. I sold it after I moved to Surrey and the last I heard some years ago was that a parson owned it and it had been seen at Broom's Boatyard at Brundall.

His letter also speaks of his friend and crew, Mr Brian Turner, who did his National Service in RAF Air/Sea Rescue and was amazed to find a fleet of these converteds being sailed in an RAF Club either at Plymouth or Portsmouth around 1953. A further letter states:

> The stern was canoe style – presumably the original . . . The watertight bulkheads were cut, initially to provide locker space for cruising and later to avoid dry rot particularly in the stern section. The decking which presumably had been installed by Dr Johnson was replaced after about ten years and the side decks changed to a roll-in curved style (as per the older Merlin/Rockets) making it much more comfortable to race – the original

flat side decks had a quarter-inch coaming on the inner edge which cut into the back of the legs when hanging out on the toe straps!

The hull was 23 feet long. The mast was deck-stepped and 28 feet long. I do not know the sail area but it could be worked out . . . I guess the luff of the mainsail would be about 26 feet, the foot about 11 feet, giving a nominal area of about 150 sq.ft. The jib is a bit more difficult and indeed after the slide was taken a new, larger jib (almost a Genoa but cut higher on the foot) replaced the one shown. Swan suffered from weather helm (i.e. was inclined to luff into the wind) and the larger jib was supposed to counteract it. A huge second-hand spinnaker was added in the late fifties: the only measurement I know was the length of the spinnaker pole, which was 10 feet. Fortunately the mast had sliding backstays to give it aft support.

The list which follows is nowhere near complete but is quoted from known evidence: it may help a present or past owner to learn a little of his boat's history. The builder's number was carved into the stempost. ACSEA is Air Command South East Asia; MEDME is Mediterranean/Middle East; Reduced to Produce means broken up for usable parts.

Builder's Number	Re-number	Builder	Fate
Marks I and II (total 545)			
A 1	4062	Uffa Fox	Allocated to Thornaby. Disposal to Admiralty 23 September 1949
A 3		Uffa Fox	Believed 279 Sq. drop 23 August 1943
A 4	4068	Uffa Fox	RAFSA 3 July 1950. Believed 279 Sq. drop 31 July 1943
A 5	4069	Uffa Fox	RAFSA 3 July 1950. Believed 279 Sq. drop 26 July 1943
A 6		Uffa Fox	Sent to New Zealand
A 7	4070	Uffa Fox	Returned to Mount Batten from New Zealand; then to RAFSA 3 July 1950. Believed 279 Sq. drop 28 July 1943
A 8		Uffa Fox	Allocated to 279 Squadron
A 9		Uffa Fox	Believed 279 Sq. drop 15 July 1943
B 1		Uffa Fox	Allocated to 279 Squadron
B 2		Uffa Fox	Believed 279 Sq. drop 1 August 1943
B 3		Uffa Fox	Used as Experimental Craft
B 4		Uffa Fox	Allocated to Bircham Newton
B 5	4081	Uffa Fox	Allocated to 280 Squadron. Deleted from Records 18 October 1947
B 6		Uffa Fox	Allocated to 280 Squadron
B 8	4082	Uffa Fox	Allocated to 280 Squadron. Disposed to Admiralty 10 September 1947
B 9	4083	Uffa Fox	Allocated to 280 Squadron. RAFSA 3 July 1950

C 1	4084	Uffa Fox	Allocated to 280 Squadron. Reduced to Salvage 2 May 1949
C 2		Uffa Fox	Allocated to 280 Squadron
C 3		Uffa Fox	Allocated to 280 Squadron
C 4		Uffa Fox	Allocated to 280 Squadron, Wick. Retained in Shetland for Instruction Purposes
C 7	4196	Uffa Fox	Allocated to Thornaby, also MEDME
C 8	4085	Uffa Fox	Allocated to 283 Squadron. RAFSA 3 July 1950
C 9		Uffa Fox	Prototype Mark IB
D 5		Woodnutt	To 84 Maintenance Unit
D 6	4071	Woodnutt	RAFSA 3 July 1950
D 7		Woodnutt	Allocated to 279 Squadron
E 2	4072	Woodnutt	Allocated to ASR School. RAFSA 3 July 1950
E 3		Woodnutt	Believed 279 Sq. drop 13 May 1943
E 4		Woodnutt	Believed 279 Sq. drop 24 August 1943. Written Off 13 December 1949
E 5	4056	Woodnutt	Allocated to Thornaby and St Eval. RAFSA 3 July 1950
E 6		Woodnutt	Believed 279 Sq. drop 26 July 1943
E 7		Woodnutt	Allocated to 280 Squadron
E 8		Woodnutt	Believed 279 Sq. drop 6 September 1943
F 1		Woodnutt	Allocated originally to 280 Squadron. Believed 279 Sq. drop 4 September 1943. Disposal to Admiralty 4 March 1948
F 2		Woodnutt	Allocated to 280 Squadron
F 3		Woodnutt	Allocated to 280 and 283 Squadrons
F 4	4088	Woodnutt	Believed 279 Sq. drop 23 August 1943. Disposal to Admiralty 27 October 1947
F 5	4089	Woodnutt	RAFSA 17 July 1950
F 6		Woodnutt	
F 7		Woodnutt	Allocated to 283 Squadron
F 8		Woodnutt	In Middle East 1945
F 9	4197	Woodnutt	Allocated to 283 Squadron
G 1	4198	Woodnutt	Allocated to 283 Squadron. Reduced to Produce December 1949
G 2	4199	Woodnutt	Allocated to 294 Squadron MEDME. Sold to RAF Sailing Club Nicosia 12 May 1950
G 3		Woodnutt	Allocated to 294 Squadron
G 4	4200	Woodnutt	Allocated to 294 Squadron. Sold by BSDM March 1949

G 5	4201	WoodnutAllocated to 294 Squadron. Sold to RAF Nicosia Sailing Club 12 May 1950
G 6		SycamoreAllocated to 280 Squadron
G 7		SycamoreAllocated to 280 Squadron
G 9	4090	SycamoreAllocated to 280 Squadron. RAFSA 3 July 1950
H 1	4091	SycamoreAllocated to Bircham Newton. RAFSA 4 July 1950
H 4	4204	SycamoreAllocated to 294 Squadron
H 5		SycamoreAllocated to 284 Squadron
H 7	4203	SycamoreAllocated to 284 Squadron. RAF Boat Club Fayid 12 May 1950
H 8	4204	SycamoreAllocated to MEDME
H 9		SycamoreTo 351 Maintenance Unit
J 1	4205	SycamoreAllocated to MEDME. To Command Sailing Club Aden 12 May 1950
J 4	4406	RanelaghDisposal to Admiralty 6 September 1949
J 5		RanelaghAllocated to Thornaby
J 6	4092	RanelaghAllocated to Bradwell Bay. Disposal to Admiralty 10 April 1948
J 8	4093	RanelaghAllocated to Bradwell Bay. RAFSA 3 July 1950
J 9	4066	RanelaghAllocated to Thornaby. Disposal to Admiralty 6 September 1949
K 2		RanelaghAllocated to Thornaby
K 3	4094	RanelaghAllocated to Davidstow Moor and Thorney Island. Disposal to Admiralty 23 August 1949
K 4	4095	RanelaghAllocated to Thornaby. RAFSA 3 July 1950
K 5	4244	RanelaghAllocated to ACSEA
K 6	4206	RanelaghAllocated to MEDME
K 7	4207	RanelaghAllocated to MEDME
K 8	4208	RanelaghAllocated to MEDME
K 9	4209	RanelaghAllocated to MEDME. RAF Sailing Club Kabrit
L 1		RanelaghAllocated to Middle East
L 2		RanelaghAllocated to Middle East
L 3		RanelaghAllocated to Thornaby
L 4	4096	RanelaghAllocated to Thornaby. Reduced to Salvage 19 December 1949
L 5		RanelaghAllocated to Thornaby
L 7		RanelaghAllocated to Thornaby
L 8	4270	RanelaghAllocated to Thornaby. RAFSA Calshot Club
L 9	4210	RanelaghAllocated to MEDME. Last known at

			Maison Blanche 1946
M 1	4211	Ranelagh	Allocated to MEDME
M 3	4067	Ranelagh	Allocated to Thornaby. Written off 6 September 1949
M 4	4045	Ranelagh	Allocated to Thornaby and Leuchars. RAFSA 3 July 1950
M 5		Ranelagh	Allocated to Thornaby
M 6	4051	Ranelagh	Allocated to Thornaby. Disposal to Admiralty 8 April 1948
M 7		Ranelagh	Allocated to Thornaby
M 8	4097	Ranelagh	Allocated to Thornaby. Disposal to Admiralty 11 February 1948
M 9	4098	Ranelagh	Allocated to Thornaby. Disposal to Admiralty 10 September 1947
N 1		Ranelagh	Dropped by 280 Squadron 18 April 1945
N 2	4089	Ranelagh	Disposal to Admiralty 19 December 1947
N 3		Ranelagh	To Store
N 4		Ranelagh	To Store
N 5		Ranelagh	Allocated to ACSEA
N 6	4245	Ranelagh	Allocated to ACSEA
N 7		Ranelagh	
N 8	4212	Ranelagh	Allocated to MEDME. Reduced to Produce December 1949
N 9	4213	Ranelagh	Allocated to MEDME
O 1		Ranelagh	Allocated to RNNAS St Merryn
O 2		Ranelagh	Allocated to RNAS Ronaldsway
O 3		Ranelagh	Allocated to RNAS Crail
O 4		Ranelagh	Allocated to RNAS Arbroath
O 5		Ranelagh	Allocated to Lagens (Azores)
O 6	4100	Ranelagh	Written off
O 7		Ranelagh	Allocated to Mona (Anglesey)
O 8	4101	Ranelagh	Allocated to Kingston Bagpuize. RAFSA 3 July 1950
O 9		Ranelagh	Allocated to Castle Kennedy
P 1		Ranelagh	Allocated to Barrow in Furness
P 2		Ranelagh	Allocated to RNAS Llangenneck
P 3		Ranelagh	Allocated to RNAS Llangenneck
P 4		Ranelagh	Allocated to RNAS Llangenneck
P 5	4214	Ranelagh	Allocated to MEDME
P 6	4215	Ranelagh	Allocated to MEDME
P 7	4216	Ranelagh	Allocated to MEDME. RAF Kabrit Sailing Club 12 May 1950
P 8	4102	Ranelagh	Allocated to MEDME. Disposal to Admiralty 16 February 1951
P 9		Ranelagh	Allocated to Thornaby

Q 1	4103	Ranelagh	Allocated to Thornaby. RAFSA 3 July 1950
Q 2	4104	Ranelagh	Allocated to Thornaby. Reduced to Produce 3 October 1950
Q 3	4105	Ranelagh	Allocated to Thornaby. RAFSA 4 July 1950
Q 4	4217	H. Woods	Allocated to MEDME
Q 5	4218	H. Woods	Allocated to Middle East
Q 6		H. Woods	Allocated to Middle East
Q 7		H. Woods	Allocated to Middle East
Q 8	4219	H. Woods	Allocated to Middle East
Q 9	4220	H. Woods	Allocated to Middle East
R 1	4106	H. Woods	Allocated to Davidstow Moor. RAFSA 3 July 1950
R 2		H. Woods	Allocated to Davidstow Moor
R 3	4107	H. Woods	Allocated to Davidstow Moor. Reduced to Salvage 27 February 1950
R 4	4108	H. Woods	Allocated to Davidstow Moor and Thornaby. Reduced to Salvage 8 October 1949
R 5		H. Woods	Allocated to ACSEA
R 6		H. Woods	
R 8	4109	H. Woods	Allocated to Bradwell Bay. RAFSA 3 July 1950
R 9	4110	H. Woods	Allocated to Portreath. Disposal to Admiralty 10 November 1949
S 1	4041	H. Woods	Allocated to Portreath and Thornaby. Disposal to Admiralty 8 April 1948
S 4		H. Woods	Allocated to Davidstow Moor
S 5	4111	H. Woods	Allocated to Thornaby. Lost on River Trent 1948. Written Off 23 April 1949
S 6		H. Woods	Allocated to Thornaby
S 7	4221	H. Woods	Allocated to MEDME
S 8	4222	H. Woods	Allocated to Middle East
S 9	4112	H. Woods	Allocated to MEDME. At Maison Blanche 1946. RAFSA 3 July 1950
T 1	4113	H. Woods	Allocated to Thornaby. Written off 26 September 1949
T 2	4114	H. Woods	Allocated to Thornaby and Iceland. RAFSA 3 July 1950
T 3	4155	H. Woods	Allocated to Thornaby. Disposal to Admiralty 28 April 1949
T 4		H. Woods	At Maison Blanche 1946
T 5	4115	H. Woods	North West Africa. Disposal to Admiralty 28 April 1949
T 6		H. Woods	Allocated to ACSEA
T 7	4246	H. Woods	Allocated to ACSEA

T 8	4280	H. Woods	Allocated to ACSEA
T 9		H. Woods	Allocated to Thornaby
U 1	4116	H. Woods	Allocated to Thornaby and St Eval, RAFSA 3 July 1950
U 2	4281	H. Woods	Allocated to India
U 3	4247	H. Woods	Allocated to ACSEA
U 4	4223	H. Woods	Allocated to Middle East. RAF Nicosia Sailing Club 12 May 1950
U 5		H. Woods	Allocated to The Azores
U 6		H. Woods	Allocated to Thornaby
U 7		H. Woods	Allocated to Thornaby
U 9	4117	H. Woods	Allocated to Thornaby. Disposed in Hamburg
V 1	4050	H. Woods	Allocated to Thornaby and Pembroke Dock. RAFSA 3 July 1950
V 2		H. Woods	Allocated to Thornaby
V 3		H. Woods	Allocated to The Azores
V 4	4248	H. Woods	Allocated to India. Written Off January 1949
V 5		H. Woods	Allocated to Thornaby. Dropped at Gibralter
V 6		H. Woods	Allocated to Thornaby
V 7	4052	H. Woods	Allocated to Thornaby. Disposal to Admiralty 8 April 1948
V 8	4034	H. Woods	Allocated to Thornaby. RAFSA 3 July 1950
V 9	4118	H. Woods	Allocated to Thornaby. Disposal to Admiralty 17 September 1947
W 1	4119	H. Woods	Allocated to Thornaby. Deleted from Records 25 December 1947
W 2	4120	H. Woods	Allocated to Thornaby. RAFSA 3 July 1950
W 3		H. Woods	Allocated to Thornaby
W 4		H. Woods	Allocated to Thornaby
W 5	4121	H. Woods	Allocated to Thornaby. Disposal 1947
W 6	4122	H. Woods	Allocated to Thornaby. Disposal to Admiralty 10 September 1947
W 7		H. Woods	Allocated to Thornaby
W 8	4123	H. Woods	Allocated to MAEE Felixstowe and damaged beyond repair in Drop Trial. Deleted from Records 14 June 1947
W 9	4124	H. Woods	Allocated to MAEE Felixstowe. RAFSA 3 July 1950
X 1	4125	H. Woods	Deleted from Records 15 December 1947
X 2	4126	H. Woods	Disposal to Admiralty 17 September 1947

X 3	4127	H. Woods	RAFSA 3 July 1950
X 4	4128	H. Woods	To Flying Training Command. RAFSA 3 July 1950
X 5	4224	Aldous	Allocated to Middle East
X 6	4035	Aldous	RAFSA 3 July 1950
X 7	4225	Aldous	Allocated to Middle East
X 8		Aldous	Allocated to Davidstow Moor
X 9	4129	Aldous	Allocated to Thornaby. Disposal to Admiralty 3 June 1948
Y 1		Aldous	Allocated to Portreath
Y 2	4130	Aldous	Allocated to Portreath. Disposal to Admiralty 10 September 1947
Y 3	4271	Aldous	RAFSA Hawarden Club 3 July 1950
Y 4	4054	Aldous	Allocated to St Eval and Pembroke Dock. RAFSA 3 July 1950
Y 5		Aldous	Allocated to India (ACSEA)
Y 6		Aldous	Allocated to India (ACSEA)
Y 7	4249	Aldous	Allocated to India
Y 8	4226	Aldous	Allocated to Middle East
Y 9		Aldous	Allocated to St Athan. Disposal to Admiralty 23 August 1949
Z 1	4275	Aldous	Disposal February 1950
Z 2	4291	Aldous	Allocated to Thornaby. Disposal to Admiralty 4 March 1948
Z 3		Aldous	Allocated to Thornaby
Z 4		Aldous	Allocated to Thornaby
Z 5		Aldous	Allocated to India (ACSEA)
Z 6	4131	Aldous	Allocated to Thornaby. Dropped by 280 Sq; Disposed to Calshot Club 21 August 1946
Z 7		Aldous	Allocated to Thornaby
Z 8		Aldous	Allocated to Thornaby
Z 9	4132	Aldous	Allocated to Blackpool A/SR School. Disposed to Calshot Club 21 August 1946
AA 1		Aldous	Allocated to North West Africa
AA 2	4133	Aldous	Allocated to Thornaby. Disposal to Admiralty 17 September 1947
AA 3		Aldous	Allocated to Thornaby
AA 4	4134	Aldous	Allocated to Survival and Rescue Training Unit Calshot. Reduced to Produce 11 November 1950
AA 6		Aldous	Allocated to Thornaby. 279 Sp. drop 26 May 1945
AA 7	4047	Aldous	Allocated to Thornaby. Reduced to Produce 12 October 1950
AA 8		Aldous	Allocated to Thornaby

AA 9	4276	Aldous	Allocated to Thornaby
AB 1	4227	Aldous	Allocated to Middle East. Phoenix Boat Club RAF Fayid 12 May 1950
AB 2	4139	Aldous	Allocated to India (ACSEA). RAFSA 17 July 1950
AB 3	4030	Aldous	Now at RAF Museum, Hendon
AB 4	4228	Aldous	Allocated to MEDME
AB 5	4135	Aldous	Allocated to Flying Training Command. Reduced to Produce 12 September 1950
AB 6	4136	Aldous	Allocated to Thornaby. Disposal to Admiralty 10 September 1947
AB 7	4032	Aldous	Allocated to Thornaby. Written off 13 December 1949
AB 8		Aldous	Allocated to 278 Squadron
AB 9	4137	Aldous	At Andreas (IOM) Fighter Training Command. Disposal to Admiralty 28 July 1947
AC 1	4138	Aldous	Allocated to 278 Squadron. RAFSA 3 July 1950
AC 2	4139	Aldous	To Graveley Bomber Command. RAFSA 17 July 1950
AC 3	4140	Aldous	Allocated to Lindholme. RAFSA 3 July 1947
AC 4	4141	Aldous	Allocated to 72 Base, Bottesford. RAFSA 3 July 1950
AC 5	4142	Aldous	Allocated to 73 Base, North Luffenham
AC 6		Woodnutt	Allocated to 284 Squadron
AC 7		Woodnutt	Allocated to 284 Squadron
AC 8		Woodnutt	Allocated to 284 Squadron
AC 9	4229	Woodnutt	Allocated to MEDME
AD 1	4230	Woodnutt	Allocated to MEDME. Sold March 1949
AD 2		Woodnutt	Allocated to 293 Squadron
AD 3		Woodnutt	Thornaby to 293 Squadron
AD 4	4143	Woodnutt	Allocated to Thornaby. Disposal to Admiralty 10 September 1947
AD 5	4144	Woodnutt	Allocated to Thornaby. Disposal to Admiralty 10 September 1947
AD 8	4231	Woodnutt	Allocated to MEDME. Sold march 1949
AD 9		Woodnutt	To 351 Maintenance Unit
AE 1	4232	Woodnutt	Allocated to MEDME. Sold March 1949
AE 2	4233	Woodnutt	Allocated to MEDME
AE 2	4284	?	Allocated to Marine Craft Section Kai Tak (Hong Kong)

AE 3		Woodnutt	To 351 Maintenance Unit
AE 4	4250	Woodnutt	Allocated to India
AE 5		Woodnutt	Allocated to India
AE 7	4251	Woodnutt	Allocated to India. Written Off February 1949
AE 8		Woodnutt	Allocated to Davidstow Moor
AE 9	4145	Woodnutt	Allocated to Thornaby. Disposal to Admiralty 17 September 1947
AF 2	4055	Woodnutt	Allocated to St Eval. RAFSA 3 July 1950
AF 3	4146	Woodnutt	Allocated to Bradwell Bay and Pembury. RAFSA 3 July 1950
AF 4		Woodnutt	For Training and Experimental
AF 5		Woodnutt	Allocated to Bradwell Bay
AF 6	4147	Woodnutt	Allocated to Davidstow Moor. RAFSA 3 July 1950
AF 7		Woodnutt	Allocated to Davidstow Moor 8 April 1948. Disposal to Admiralty
AF 8	4042	Woodnutt	Allocated to Thornaby. Disposal to Admiralty 10 April 1948
AG 1	4252	Woodnutt	Allocated to India. Written Off March 1949
AG 2	4253	Woodnutt	Allocated to India
AG 3		Woodnutt	To 351 Maintenance Unit
AG 5		Woodnutt	To 351 Maintenenca Unit
AG 6	4234	Woodnutt	Allocated to MEDME. RAF Kabrit Sailing Club 12 May 1950
AG 7	4274	Woodnutt	Allocated to Middle East. RAF Sailing Club, Kabrit 12 May 1950
AG 8	4235	Woodnutt	Allocated to MEDME
AG 9		Woodnutt	Allocated to Thornaby
AH 1	4148	Woodnutt	Allocated to Thornaby and Reykjavik. RAFSA 3 July 1950
AH 2		Woodnutt	Allocated to Thornaby
AH 4	4149	Woodnutt	Allocated to Thornaby. RAFSA 3 July 1950
AH 5		Woodnutt	Allocated to Thornaby
AH 6	4236	Woodnutt	Allocated to MEDME. RAF Yacht Club Malta 12 May 1950
AH 7	4237	Woodnutt	Allocated to MEDME
AH 8	4254	Woodnutt	Allocated to India
AH 9		Woodnutt	Allocated to India
AJ 1	4255	Woodnutt	Allocated to India. RAF Sailing Club Negombo
AJ 2	4256	Woodnutt	Allocated to India. Written Off January 1949
AJ 3	4060	Woodnutt	Allocated to St Eval and St Mawgan.

			Disposal to Admiralty 4 March 1948
AJ 4	4061	Woodnutt	Allocated to Thornaby and St Eval. RAFSA 3 July 1950
AJ 5	4150	Woodnutt	Allocated to Thornaby. RAFSA 3 July 1950
AJ 6		Uffa Fox	Allocated to Thornaby
AJ 7		Uffa Fox	Used for 3 Trial Drops
AJ 8	4037	Uffa Fox	Allocated to Pembroke Dock. RAFSA 3 July 1950
AJ 9		Uffa Fox	Allocated to Davidstow Moor
AK 1	4059	Uffa Fox	Allocated to St Eval. RAFSA 3 July 1950
AK 2	4151	Uffa Fox	Disposal to Admiralty 17 September 1947
AK 3	4257	Uffa Fox	Allocated to India
AK 4	4258	Uffa Fox	Allocated to India
AK 6	4152	Uffa Fox	Allocated to Thornaby. Disposal to Admiralty 17 September 1947
AK 7	4153	Uffa Fox	Allocated to Thornaby
AK 8		Uffa Fox	Dropped by 280 Squadron 18 April 1945
AK 9	4057	Uffa Fox	Allocated to St Eval. RAFSA 3 July 1950
AL 4		Uffa Fox	Allocated to Bircham Newton
AL 8	4073	Uffa Fox	Disposal to Admiralty 17 September 1947
AL 9	4074	Uffa Fox	Disposal to Admiralty 24 February 1950
AM 1	4277	Uffa Fox	Allocated to Bircham Newton. RAFSA Jurby (IOM) 3 July 1950
AM 4	4075	Uffa Fox	Allocated to Mount Batten. Local sale at Tadcaster 13 November 1950
AM 5	4063	Uffa Fox	RAFSA 3 July 1950
AM 6	4076	Uffa Fox	Reduced to Produce 7 November 1950
AM 7	4243	Uffa Fox	Allocated to Bircham Newton. Dropped by 280 Sq. 18 April 1945
AN 2	4077	Uffa Fox	Allocated to Bircham Newton. Disposal to Admiralty 4 March 1948
AN 3		Uffa Fox	Allocated to Bircham Newton
AN 4		Uffa Fox	Allocated to The Azores
AN 5	4063	Uffa Fox	Allocated to Iceland & Thornaby. RAFSA 3 July 1950
AN 6	4064	Uffa Fox	Allocated to Iceland. Reduced to Salvage 30 December 1949
AN 9		Uffa Fox	Allocated to Bircham Newton
AO 1		Uffa Fox	Allocated to A/SR School, Blackpool
AO 2		Uffa Fox	Bircham Newton & RNAS

			Machrihanish
AO 3		Uffa Fox	Allocated to Bircham Newton
AO 4	4286	Uffa Fox	Allocated to Bircham Newton & Gibraltar. RAF Yacht Club, Gibraltar 12 May 1950
AO 5		Uffa Fox	Allocated to Bircham Newton
AO 6		Uffa Fox	Allocated to Bircham Newton
AO 7	4078	Uffa Fox	Allocated to Bircham Newton. Reduced to Produce 2 June 1951
AO 8	4259	Uffa Fox	Allocated to Bircham Newton and Iceland
AP 1		Uffa Fox	Allocated to Bircham Newton
AP 2		Uffa Fox	Allocated to The Azores
AP 3		Uffa Fox	Allocated to Bircham Newton
AP 7		Uffa Fox	Allocated to India
AP 8		Uffa Fox	Allocated to Bircham Newton
AP 9		Uffa Fox	Allocated to Bircham Newton
AQ 1		Uffa Fox	Allocated to Bircham Newton
AQ 2	4243	Uffa Fox	Allocated to Bircham Newton. Reduced to Produce 16 June 1947
AQ 4	4079	Uffa Fox	Allocated to Langham and Thorney Island. Disposal to Admiralty 11 February 1948
AQ 5	4080	Uffa Fox	Allocated to Bircham Newton and Aldergrove. RAFSA 3 July 1950
AQ 6	4279	Uffa Fox	Allocated to Middle East
AQ 7		Uffa Fox	Allocated to 294 Squadron
AQ 8		Sycamore	Allocated to India
AR 2	4260	Sycamore	Allocated to ACSEA
AR 3		Sycamore	To 351 Maintenance Unit
AR 5		Sycamore	Allocated to Llandwrog. Reduced to Produce
AR 6		Sycamore	Allocated to Thornaby
AR 9	4036	Sycamore	Allocated to Pembroke Dock. Reduced to Salvage 27 February 1950
AS 1	4238	Sycamore	Allocated to MEDME. RAF Yacht Club, Malta 12 May 1950
AS 2	4154	Sycamore	Allocated to Thornaby. RAFSA 3 July 1950
AS 3	4155	Sycamore	Allocated to North West Africa; Damaged in Transit. RAFSA 3 July 1950
AS 4		Sycamore	Allocated to Titchfield. No Trace of Receipt
AS 5	4155	Sycamore	Damaged in Transit. Written Off?
AS 6		Sycamore	Allocated to Thornaby
AS 8		Sycamore	Allocated to Thornaby
AS 9	4053	Sycamore	Allocated to Thornaby and Kinloss.

			RAFSA 3 July 1950
AT 1	4156	Sycamore	Allocated to Survival and Rescue Training Unit, Calshot. RAFSA 3 July 1950
AT 2		Sycamore	Allocated to Thornaby
AT 3		Sycamore	Allocated to Thornaby; Survival and Rescue Unit, Calshot. Reduced to Produce 27 November 1946
AT 4	4239	Sycamore	Allocated to North West Africa & MEDME
AT 5	4157	Sycamore	Allocated to Thornaby and Kinloss. Reduced to Salvage 12 September 1949
AT 6		Sycamore	Allocated to Titchfield. No Trace of Receipt
AT 7		Sycamore	Allocated to Titchfield. No Trace of Receipt
AT 8		Sycamore	Allocated to Marston Moor
AT 9	4158	Sycamore	RAFSA 3 July 1950
AU 1	4058	Brooke	Allocated to St Eval. RAFSA 3 July 1950
AU 2		Woodrow	Allocated to Rochford. Disposal to Admiralty 28 July 1949
AU 3	4159	Woodrow	Allocated to Thornaby. Disposal to Admiralty 4 March 1949
AU 4	4160	Woodrow	Reduced to Salvage. RAFSA 3 July 1950
AU 5		Woodrow	Allocated to Portreath
AU 6	4161	Woodrow	Reduced to Produce 12 September 1950
AU 7		Woodrow	Allocated to Portreath
AU 9		Woodrow	Allocated to Davidstow Moor
AV 1	4162	Woodrow	Allocated to RNAS, Crimond and Davidstow Moor. RAFSA 3 July 1950
AV 2	4039	Woodrow	Allocated to Thornaby, Thorney Island, Castle Archdale and Pembroke Dock. RAFSA 3 July 1950
AV 3	4163	Woodrow	Allocated to Thornaby. Deleted from Records 15 December 1947
AV 4	4164	Woodrow	Allocated to Thornaby. RAFSA 3 July 1950
AV 5	4165	Woodrow	RAFSA 3 July 1950
AV 7		Woodrow	Allocated to Thornaby
AV 8		Woodrow	Allocated to Thornaby
AV 9	4166	Woodrow	Allocated to Bradwell Bay. RAFSA 27 July 1950
AW 1	4167	Woodrow	Allocated to Bradwell Bay. Disposal to Admiralty 17 September 1947

AW 2	4168	Woodrow	Allocated to Thornaby. RAFSA 3 July 1950
AW 4	4040	Woodrow	Allocated to Thorney Island and Binbrook. RAFSA 3 July 1950
AW 6	4169	Woodrow	Allocated to Thornaby. Reduced to Salvage 19 December 1949
AW 7	4044	Woodrow	Allocated to Alness and Mount Batten. Reduced to Salvage 7 February 1950
AW 8		Woodrow	Allocated to Thornaby
AW 9	4170	Woodrow	Allocated to Thornaby and Kinloss. Reduced to Salvage 27 February 1950
AX 1	4171	Woodrow	Allocated to Thornaby. Disposal to Admiralty 10 September 1947
AX 2	4031	Woodrow	Written off 13 December 1949
AX 3		Woodrow	Allocated to The Azores
AX 4	4172	Woodrow	Allocated to Thornaby. RAFSA 3 July 1950
AX 5	4173	Woodrow	Allocated to Thornaby. Disposal to Admiralty 10 September 1947
AX 7		Sadd	Allocated to Bradwell Bay
AX 8	4174	Sadd	Allocated to Davidstow Moor and St Eval. Disposed to Salvage in Düsseldorf
AX 3?	4287	Sadd	Dinghy Sailing Training
AX 9	4175	Sadd	Allocated to Thornaby. RAFSA 3 July 1950
AY 1	4046	Sadd	Allocated to Leuchars. RAFSA 3 July 1950
AY 2	4055	Sadd	Eastleigh School of Safety Equipment. RAFSA 3 July 1950
AY 3		Sadd	Allocated to India (ACSEA)
AY 4		Sadd	Allocated to Thornaby
AY 5		Sadd	Allocated to North West Africa (MEDME)
AY 6		Sadd	Allocated to Thornaby
AY 8	4287	Sadd	Allocated to Thornaby. RAFSA for Abingdon 3 July 1950
AY 9	4049	Sadd	Allocated to Kinloss. RAFSA 3 July 1950
AZ 1	4176	Sadd	Allocated to Thornaby. RAFSA 3 July 1950
AZ 2	4177	Sadd	Allocated to Thornaby. RAFSA 3 July 1950
AZ 3	4048	Sadd	Allocated to Kinloss. RAFSA 3 July 1950
AZ 4		Sadd	Allocated to Titchfield. No Trace of Receipt

AZ 5		Sadd	Allocated to Titchfield. No Trace of Receipt
AZ 6	4178	Sadd	Allocated to Finningley. RAFSA 3 July 1950
AZ 7		Sadd	Allocated to RNAS Lee on Solent
AZ 8		Sadd	Allocated to Lagens (Azores)
AZ 9		Sadd	Allocated to Lagens (Azores)
BA 1	4276	Sadd	Disposal to Admiralty 21 March 1949
BA 2	4179	Sadd	Allocated to Thornaby. Disposal to Admiralty 10 September 1947
BA 3		Sadd	Allocated to St Eval
BA 4	4288	Sadd	Allocated to Thornaby. RAF Yacht Club, Gibraltar 6 July 1950
BA 5		Sadd	To Aircraft Exhibition
BA 6	4033	Sadd	RAFSA 3 July 1950
BA 7	4289	Sadd	Allocated to Gibraltar. RAF Yacht Club, Gibraltar 6 July 1950
BA 8	4290	Sadd	Allocated to Gibraltar. RAF Yacht Club, Gibraltar 6 July 1950
BA 9		Brooke	Allocated to Davidstow Moor. RNAS Inskip 20 August 1945
BB 1	4043	Brooke	Allocated to Gibraltar. RAF Yacht Club, Gibraltar 6 July 1950
BB 3	4261	Brooke	Allocated to India
BB 4		Brooke	Allocated to India (ACSEA)
BB 5		Brooke	Allocated to North West Africa, 351 Maintenance Unit
BB 6	4240	Brooke	Allocated to North West Africa and MEDME. RAF Yacht Club, Malta 12 May 1950
BB 7	4065	Brooke	Allocated to Thornaby. Disposal to Admiralty 6 September 1949
BB 8	4241	Brooke	Allocated to North West Africa and MEDME. RAF Yacht Club, Malta 12 May 1950
BC 1		Brooke	Allocated to North West Africa (MEDME)
BC 2	4262	Brooke	Allocated to India. RAF Sailing Club, Seletar
BC 4	4242	Brooke	Allocated to North West Africa and MEDME
BC 5		Brooke	Allocated to Thornaby
BC 6	4180	Brooke	260 Maintenance Unit, Errol
CD 1		Vosper	(Prototype) Dinghy Sailing Training
CD 2		Uffa Fox	Prototype
CD 3		Uffa Fox	Prototype
CD 4		Uffa Fox	Allocated to Farnborough for

			experimental purposes, later at MAEE Felixstowe
CD 5		Uffa Fox	Allocated to Thornaby. Disposal to Admiralty 6 February 1948
CD 7	4331	Uffa Fox	Allocated to Thornaby. Disposal to Admiralty 13 October 1948
CD 8		Uffa Fox	Allocated to Thornaby. Disposal to Admiralty 6 February 1948
CD 9		Uffa Fox	Allocated to Thornaby; then Mount Batten. Disposal to Admiralty 15 October 1947
CE 1	4358	Uffa Fox	Allocated to Kingston Bagpuize. Written Off 9 February 1951
CE 2	4359	Uffa Fox	Allocated to Kingston Bagpuize. Disposal to Admiralty 6 December 1948
CE 3	4360	Uffa Fox	Allocated to Kingston Bagpuize. Reduced to Produce 7 November 1950
CE 4	4361	Uffa Fox	Allocated to Kingston Bagpuize. Disposal to Admiralty 9 November 1951
CE 5		Uffa Fox	Allocated to St Eval. Completely wrecked 12 December 1946
Ce 6		Uffa Fox	Allocated to Pershore then Leuchars. Disposal to Admiralty 13 April 1948
CE 7	4363	Uffa Fox	Allocated to Kingston Bagpuize
CE 8	4332	Uffa Fox	Allocated to Titchfield
CE 9		Uffa Fox	To Uffa Fox for MAP Trials, then to H. Woods for Modifications and MAEE Felixstowe
CF 3	4366	Uffa Fox	Allocated to Titchfield and Thornaby
CF 4	4367	Uffa Fox	Allocated to Titchfield and Thornaby. Disposal to Admiralty 20 May 1949
CF 5		Uffa Fox	Allocated to Thornaby, then St Eval. Disposal to Admiralty 27 April 1948
CF 6		Uffa Fox	Allocated to Titchfield, the Leuchars. Disposal to Admiralty 3 December 1947
CF 7	4333	Uffa Fox	Allocated to Titchfield. Disposal to Admiralty
CF 8	4334	Uffa Fox	Allocated to Titchfield. Disposal to Admiralty 13 October 1948
CF 9		Uffa Fox	To MAEE Helenburgh, then H. Woods and MAEE Felixstowe
CG 2	4336	Uffa Fox	Allocated to Titchfield. Disposal to Admiralty 7 March 1955
CG 3	4337	Uffa Fox	Allocated to Titchfield. Disposal to Admiralty 7 March 1955
CG 4		Uffa Fox	Allocated to Titchfield, then Thornaby.

			Disposal to Admiralty 6 February 1948
CG 7	4370	Uffa Fox	Allocated to Titchfield
CG 8	4371	Uffa Fox	Allocated to Titchfield
CG 9	4372	Uffa Fox	Allocated to Titchfield. To RAAF 11 April 1949
CH 1	4372	Uffa Fox	Allocated to Titchfield. Disposal to Admiralty 6 December 1948
CH 2	4374	Uffa Fox	Allocated to Titchfield. Disposal to Admiralty 6 December 1948
CH 3	4338	Uffa Fox	Allocated to Beccles. Disposal to Admiralty 25 March 1949
CH 4		Uffa Fox	Allocated to Beccles. Disposal to Admiralty 6 February 1948
CH 5	4339	Uffa Fox	Allocated to Beccles
CH 6	4375	Uffa Fox	Allocated to Kingston Bagpuize. Disposal to Admiralty 9 February 1949
CH 7	4376	Uffa Fox	Allocated to Kingston Bagpuize. Disposal to Admiralty 1 October 1949
CH 8	4377	Uffa Fox	Allocated to Kingston Bagpuize. Disposal to Admiralty 12 December 1950
CJ 1		Uffa Fox	Allocated to Titchfield, then Blackpool Exhibition. Disposal to Admiralty 28 July 1949
CJ 2	4379	Uffa Fox	Issued to 279 Squadron at Thornaby and MEDME
CJ 3	4380	Uffa Fox	Allocated to Thornaby and Malta. Written Off November 1949
CJ 5	4382	Uffa Fox	Allocated to Titchfield and MEDME
CJ 7	4384	Uffa Fox	Allocated to Titchfield and MEDME
CJ 9	4386	Sycamore	Allocated to Titchfield. Sold to French Naval Air Arm 13 February 1952
CK 1	4387	Sycamore	Allocated to Titchfield, Aldergrove and Ballykelly
CK 2	4388	Sycamore	Allocated to Titchfield, Thornaby and MEDME
CK 3	4389	Sycamore	Allocated to Titchfield and MEDME (Malta). Struck Off Records 1949
CK 4	4340	Uffa Fox	Allocated to Titchfield. Disposal to Admiralty 7 March 1955
CK 5	4341	Sycamore	Allocated to Titchfield. Disposal to Admiralty 7 March 1955
CK 7	4391	Sycamore	Allocated to Titchfield and MEDME
CK 8	4392	Sycamore	Allocated to Titchfield and 279 Squadron and MEDME
CK 9	4393	Sycamore	Allocated to Titchfield. Disposal to Admiralty 4 June 1951
CM 2	4394	Woodrow	Allocated to Titchfield. Sold to French

			Naval Air Arm 13 February 1952
CM 5	4397	Woodrow	Allocated to Titchfield and Thornaby
CM 7	4399	Woodrow	Allocated to Titchfield and Port Said
CM 8	4400	Woodrow	Allocated to Titchfield. Sold to French Naval Air Arm 13 February 1952
CM 9	4401	Woodrow	Allocated to Titchfield and Malta
CN 1	4402	Woodrow	Allocated to Titchfield and MEDME
CN 3	4404	Woodrow	Allocated to Titchfield and MEDME
CN 4	4342	Woodrow	Allocated to Titchfield. Disposal to Admiralty 5 September 1949
CN 5	4343	Woodrow	Allocated to Titchfield. Disposal to Admiralty 2 January 1951
CN 7	4406	Woodrow	Allocated to Titchfield, Thornaby and MEDME. Sunk in Operations 27 January 1948
CO 1	4409	Woodrow	Allocated to Titchfield. Disposal to Admiralty 19 December 1950
CO 4	4344	Woodnutt	Allocated to Titchfield. Disposal to Admiralty 7 March 1955
CO 5	4345	Woodnutt	Allocated to Titchfield. Disposal to Admiralty 25 March 1949
CO 7	4413	Woodnutt	Allocated to Titchfield, Thornaby and Malta
CP 1		Woodnutt	Allocated to Titchfield, then Mount Batten. MAEE Felixstowe
CP 3	4346	Woodnutt	Allocated to Titchfield. Disposal to Admiralty 3 September 1949
CP 4	4347	Woodnutt	Allocated to Titchfield. Disposal to Admiralty 9 February 1948
CP 5	4348	H. Woods	Allocated to Thornaby. Disposed through Admiralty 7 March 1955
CP 6		H. Woods	Disposal to Admiralty 6 February 1948
CP 8		H. Woods	Disposal to Admiralty 6 February 1948
CQ 1	4418	H. Woods	Allocated to Kingston Bagpuize. Sold to French Naval Air Arm 29 February 1952
CQ 3	4419	H. Woods	Allocated to Kingston Bagpuize and MEDME. Struck Off Records September 1950
CQ 4	4420	H. Woods	Allocated to Kingston Bagpuize. Disposal to Admiralty 13 October 1948
CQ 6	4422	H. Woods	Allocated to Kingston Bagpuize and MEDME. Dropped on Exercise at Malta 10 December 1947
CQ 7	4423	H. Woods	Allocated to Kingston Bagpuize. Disposal to Admiralty 11 April 1949
CR 1	4426	H. Woods	Allocated to Titchfield. In Displays at

			Farnborough and Andover
CR 2	4349	H. Woods	Allocated to Titchfield. Disposal to Admiralty 23 December 1949
CR 3	4350	H. Woods	Allocated to Titchfield. Disposal to Admiralty 7 March 1955
CR 6	4429	H. Woods	Allocated to Titchfield and MEDME
CR 9	4351	H. Woods	Allocated to A/SR School Calshot. Disposal to Admiralty 25 March 1949
CS 1	4432	H. Woods	Allocated to Titchfield. Sold to French Air Arm 13 February 1952
CS 2		H. Woods	Disposal to Admiralty 6 February 1948
CS 3	4433	H. Woods	Allocated to Titchfield. Sold to French Air Arm 29 February 1952
CS 7	4353	H. Woods	Allocated to Titchfield. Disposal to Admiralty 1 October 1949
CS 8	4436	H. Woods	Allocated to Titchfield
CT 1	4438	H. Woods	Allocated to Titchfield; Practice Drops Thorney Island. Disposal to Admiralty 6 December 1948
CT 4	4441	H. Woods	Allocated to Titchfield and MEDME. Craft sabotaged and handed over to Italian salvors
CT 6	4443	H. Woods	Allocated to Titchfield
CT 7	4444	H. Woods	Allocated to Titchfield. Disposal to Admiralty 2 January 1951
CT 9	4354	H. Woods	Allocated to Titchfield. Disposed through Admiralty 7 March 1955
CU 1	4446	H. Woods	Allocated to Titchfield. Disposed to Admiralty 9 November 1951
CU 2		H. Woods	Disposal to Admiralty 31 December 1947
CU 3		H. Woods	Disposal to Admiralty 31 December 1947
CU 4	4447	H. Woods	Allocated to Titchfield and 279 Squadron. Disposal to Admiralty 7 September 1948
CU 5	4355	H. Woods	Allocated to Titchfield. Disposed through Admiralty 7 March 1955
CU 8	4356	H. Woods	Allocated to Titchfield. Disposal to Admiralty 6 December 1948
CU 9	4357	H. Woods	Allocated to Titchfield. Disposal to Admiralty 6 December 1948
	4099	?	Disposal to Admiralty 19 December 1947
	4181	?	Allocated to Barrow. Reduced to Salvage 30 December 1949
	4182	?	Allocated to Driffield. RAFSA

		Bridlington 1950
4183	?	Allocated to Swanton Morley. RAFSA Hendon 1950
4184	?	Allocated to Fighter Training Command Manby. RAFSA Cranwell 1950
4185	?	Calshot Club 1946
4186	?	Calshot Club 1946
4187	?	Calshot Club 1946
4188	?	Calshot Club 1946
4189	?	Calshot Club 1946
4190	?	Calshot Club 1946
4191	?	Calshot Club 1946
4192	?	Calshot Club 1946
4193	?	Calshot Club 1946
4194	?	Calshot Club 1946
4195	?	Calshot Club 1946
4263	?	390 Maintenance Unit. Struck Off Records 1949
4264	?	Seletar Yacht Club
4265	?	Seletar Yacht Club
4266	?	Seletar Yacht Club
4267	?	Seletar Yacht Club
4268	?	Seletar Yacht Club
4269	?	Seletar Yacht Club
4278	?	238 Maintenance Unit. Disposal to Admiralty 1948
4282	?	MCS Butterworth. Struck Off Charge 1949
4283	?	389 Maintenance Unit. Struck Off Charge 1948
4284	?	MCS Kai Tak (Hong Kong). Struck Off Charge 1947
4285	?	389 Maintenance Unit. RAFSA Seletar
4286	Uffa Fox	Bircham Newton and Gibraltar. RAF Yacht Club, Gibraltar
4287	Sadd	Thornaby.. RAFSA Ablingdon 1950
4288	Sadd	Thornaby and Gibraltar. RAF Yacht Club, Gibraltar 1950
4289	Sadd	Gibraltar. RAF Yacht Club, Gibraltar 1950
4290	Sadd	Gibraltar. RAF Yacht Club, Gibraltar 1950
4291	Aldous	Thornaby. Disposal to Admiralty 1948
4292	?	RAF Benson CC and Gibraltar. Sold to RAF Yacht Club, Gibraltar
4294	?	Driffield Flying Training Command.

RAFSA 1950

4331	Uffa Fox	Thornaby. Disposal to Admiralty 1948
4332	Uffa Fox	Titchfield. To Admiralty for Disposal 1954

Mark III. All built by Saunders Roe (total 34)

803	St Eval for Trials. Loan to MAEE Felixstowe
804	Pembroke Dock for Trials; St Eval
805	Kinloss for Trials; St Eval
806	Calshot for Trials; St Eval
807	Ballykelly
808	Ballykelly
809	Gibraltar
810	Gibraltar
811	Luqa (Malta)
812	Malta
813	Kinloss
814	St Eval
815	No 47 Maintenance Unit
816	Ballykelly
817	Ballykelly
818	Kinloss
819	Malta
820	Luqa (Malta)
821	Luqa
822	Luqa
823	Luqa
824	Kinloss
825	238 Maintenance Unit
826	238 Maintenance Unit
827	238 Maintenance Unit
828	47 Maintenance Unit
829	Maintenance Units
830	Maintenance Units
831–6	47 Maintenance Unit

Glossary

AOC	Air Officer Commanding
A/SR	Air/Sea Rescue
ASR	Anti Submarine Radar
ASV	Air to Surface Vessel (Radar)
Bandits	Enemy Fighter aircraft
Bermuda rig	A fore and aft rig with triangular mainsail, having no upper spar
Bungee cord	An elastic rope
B 17	'Flying Fortress' aircraft
B 24	'Liberator' aircraft
B 29	'Super Fortress' aircraft
Canso	Catalina (PBY5) in Canadian service
CCHQ	Coastal Command Headquarters
Centreboard	A portable fin-shaped keel
Clew	The lower aftermost corner of a sail
Clencher, Clinker	Method of boatbuilding where planks overlap
DDASR	Deputy Director Air Sea Rescue
Dodderman	A snail (Norfolk dialect)
Dolly	A piece of iron or steel for 'holding on'
Drogue	A sea anchor
Dumbo	Code name for any USAAF rescue aircraft (commonly a B 17: B 29 was Super Dumbo)
ERS	Emergency Rescue Squadron (USAAF)
ETA	Estimated Time of Arrival
ETOUSA	European Theatre of Operations (United States of America)
FAA	Fleet Air Arm
F/E	Flight Engineer
F/L	Flight Lieutenant
Flak	Corruption of German term for anti-aircraft fire
F/O	Flying Officer
FOIC	Flag Officer in Charge
Forestay	Rigging rope or wire from masthead to bows

F/S	Flight Sergeant
FW	Focke Wulf aircraft
Garboard strake	Plank adjacent to the keel
Gee	Medium range radio aid to navigation
Gp. Capt.	Group Captain
Gremlin	Invisible mischievous imp peculiar to aircraft
Gunter rig	A fore and aft sail in which the upper spar is vertical
Head (of a sail)	The upper edge or corner.
HSL	High Speed Launch (RAF)
Jury (rig etc.)	A temporary or makeshift arrangement
LAC	Leading Aircraftman
Larboard	Original name for 'left hand' side of a vessel often still used when marking
Lt.	Lieutenant
M	Following a course to steer indicates a 'magnetic pole' bearing as opposed to 'true'.
MAP	Ministry of Aircraft Production
MGB	Motor Gunboat
MTB	Motor Torpedo Boat
OTU	Operational Training Unit
P 38	Lightning aircraft
P 40	Tomahawk aircraft
P 47	Thunderbolt aircraft
P 51	Mustang aircraft
PBY5	USA designation for Catalina flying boats.
PLE	Permitted Limit of Endurance
P/O	Pilot Officer
PRO	Public Record Office (Kew)
RAAF	Royal Australian Air Force
RCAF	Royal Canadian Air Force
RDS3	Research & Development Survival Dept. 3 (RAF)
RML	Rescue Motor Launch (Royal Navy)
RNAS	Royal Naval Air Service
RNR	Royal Naval Reserve
RNVR	Royal Naval Volunteer Reserve
SAAF	South African Air Force
Seagull	Open radio code name for HSLs and RMLs
Shagbat	Nickname for Walrus flying boat

Sheet	The rope which controls the set of a sail
Shrouds	Supporting ropes or wires for the mast
Sq. Ldr.	Squadron Leader
SWG	Standard Wire Gauge
T	When following a course to steer indicates a 'true' bearing as opposed to magnetic
Tack	The leading lower corner of a sail
Tack	Diagonal progression when sailing a craft into the wind
Teamwork	Open radio code name for ERS Thunderbolts, Catalinas (PBY5As) and Flying Fortresses
Tiller	The handle by which the rudder is controlled
U/S	Unserviceable
USAAF	United States Army Air Force
W/Cdr.	Wing Commander
Wear	To turn a sailing craft before the wind
W/O	Warrant Officer
WO/AG	Wireless Operator – Air Gunner
W/Op	Wireless Operator

George Lindsay – Flt/Lt
A tribute

I first met George during the early summer of 1943. As a new commissioned RAF Air/Sea Rescue Officer I had just been appointed to my first command. George, even then, was a veteran with over two years' service as a Skipper and many 'pick-ups' to his credit.

Physically he was a man of forty-three. Average height, sandy hair, blue eyes, a fresh complexion and wiry frame made him look rather less. In vigour, vitality and endurance he was the equal of most men ten years his junior. Mentally and spiritually he was still a boy.

I learned a lot from George, a debt I can never repay. When I joined the Unit and took command of my first High Speed Launch I knew that my technical qualification were equal to the task ahead. Technical qualifications, however, are not enough to enable a man to take a small fast craft to sea under all and any conditions. Technical qualifications alone are not enough to enable him to carry the responsibility of his craft, the responsibility of the lives of his twelve crew, the responsibility of the lives of the men he has been sent out to save. At those times self-confidence is as important as knowledge; and George, by his own quiet assurance and his unspoken but none the less real acceptance of me as a colleague helped to build that all important confidence during those early months. George, without ever appearing obviously to teach, helped me, and many before and some after me, to realise the difference between the theory of the schoolroom and the reality of the sea under operational conditions.

The winter of 1943/44 brought greatly increased work. More boats were posted to us, and the spring of 1944, which saw the start of the American mass daylight raids, found us at sea most days – and nights – in whatever weather the North Sea chose to offer.

Fierce, but ever friendly, inter-boat rivalry was symptomatic of the keenness which permeated the whole Base. No man was keener than George. Whatever the weather, however long, ardous, or hazardous the proposed trip, George never grumbled – never hesitated. if our controlling authority said that adverse weather, or the proximity of our objective to the enemy coast, made a trip impossible, George always pleaded and argued for a chance to try.

His crew almost worshipped him. They worked miracles to keep serviceable his greatly over-worked and frequently over-driven boat. In a heavy sea, when physical endurance and the sheer will to 'take it' are all important, few of us could equal George – none could excel him. The performance of a small ship in bad weather is largely a reflection of the personality of the Master. George's boat was unbeatable. Several times he brought back survivors in a craft damaged by hard driving in bad weather, but regularly, and consistently, despite wind and rain and cold and fog he got there, made his pick-up and got back to harbour. His record of 'pick-ups' was unequalled in the entire service.

Ashore George was a family man. he lived near the harbour with a charming wife and two grand kids. His house was always open to us all. Always we were welcome to a chair by their fireside – to a share of their simple supper. One or other of us was always ready and willing to play 'nursemaid' and sit with the youngsters enabling George to take his wife to an infrequent 'flic'.

One evening remains vividly in my mind. There had been no flying and we were all ashore. The early evening found us sitting in the 'local'. It was rare for us all to be ashore together – we felt like having a party and we wanted George to join us. We wrote a note to his wife:

"Dear Con:
    Please may we borrow George for the evening. We promise to return him in a satisfactory condition.
    With love,
        The Skippers.
    P.S. Please put some money in his pocket before sending him out.

A small boy on a bicycle delivered the note to his house, and, of course, George came. We returned him in the small hours of the morning in some trepidation as to our reception. We need not have worried. His wife, who had long since gone to bed, got up, donned a house-coat, dragged us all in, and made coffee and sandwiches. A grand couple!

George was killed during the summer of 1944. He had taken his launch to within three miles of the Dutch coast, in broad daylight, to rescue the crew of a ditched Fortress 390 B.G. Pilot Edgar Moody 1st mission (replacement crew). The coastal defences of Ijmuiden were clearly visible as he went in, found the dinghy, made his 'pick-up' and headed for home. He had been running west, flat out, for about forty-five minutes when the JU 88's appeared. There were two of them. One peeled off and came in to the attack. The first burst killed two of the American survivors and two of the crew. The second burst set the little ship ablaze from end to end. Abandon ship was the only possible order, and George gave it. Over the side they went, taking with them as much flotation gear as had escaped damage by the bullets. One of the engine room staff was badly wounded. Five men, including George, held him on to a damaged rubber dinghy.

An hour and a half passed before another launch reached the scene. The survivors were picked up; george was found, floating nearby in his Mae West, dead. We learned afterwards that he had set out to swim to fetch another dinghy, the better to support his wounded fitter. he never reached that other dinghy. The doctors said he died of exhaustion.

George was buried at sea a few days later. It was a solemn and moving occasion. The weather was kind to us; a brilliant sun was accompanied by a crisp wind strong enough to give the sea life without roughness. My launch was chosen for the task. George, sewn up in weighted canvas in the traditional manner of the sea, was laid on a specially constructed slide and covered with an ensign. The narrow deck around was ablaze with wreaths; at each corner stood a Naval rating with reversed arms. Aboard, in addition to my crew, white sweatered and seabooted were the other Skippers of the Base, representatives from the Royal Navy, representatives from 16 Group and Coastal Command, a senior American Officer representing the USAAF and a Naval Padre.

At 10.30 hours engines were started, and with ensign fluttering at half mast, we slipped our moorings. The RN Minesweeping base across the river called out a guard of Honour and presented arms in salute as we dropped downstream. For escort we had two RN Air/Sea Rescue craft and the other launches of our own Base. As we cleared the harbour throttles were opened, twenty-four unrestrained aero engines, three per boat, roared their full-throated tribute and we raced out to sea as George had so often raced before.

No words of mine can adequately describe my feelings during that short trip. I can make no attempt to interpret the thoughts of my companions. We had lost a friend, a well loved Friend. We had lost the finest Air/Sea Rescue Skipper on the East coast, perhaps on any coast. We had lost physical contact with a man who had been a continual source of help and inspiration. And yet in his dying, in the very manner of his death he had given us a great a more lasting inspiration.

Such thoughts mingled in my mind with more mundane and practical ones. Humbly proud to be taking George for this, his last trip, in an Air/Sea Rescue Launch, I was extremely anxious that my own seamanship and that of my crew should be above reproach. Rivalry between Skippers had always been keen and I could just visualize the smile on George's face if he were looking on and could see a fender hanging overside or an irish pennant in the rigging. Was I holding exactly the pre-arranged speed? Was my coxswain holding a perfect course? Were all those little things, which together make up a seamanlike vessel just right? I think they were.

We were about half an hour running out to the spot we had chosen. We hove to. Our escorts formed themsleves into a circle around us, engines were silenced and over the Tannoy loudhailer came the voice of the Padre reading the service which committed to the deep he loved and understood, the mortal remains of one I believe to have been a great man, a great simple man.

Our wreaths followed George. They floated out into the circle formed by the boats as we slowly orbited the spot. Then came the planes. three Fortresses representing the 8th USAAF flew over, dipped in salute and dropped a wreath. They were followed by three Thunderbolts representing the American Air/Sea Rescue organisation and by three Warwicks of the Royal Air Force ASR Squadron.

We didn't talk much during the run back to harbour. The occasion, its setting and the reason for it had affected the most cyncial of us. We were quietly glad we had done at least our best to pay a fitting last tribute.

In the pub before lunch we drank a toast. We drank it without formality. We drank it in the free and easy manner which George himself so often used to cloak a deep sincerity. We drank to — George, a good type.

Index

HSL 2696 56
HSL 2697 96
HSL 2706 56 (lost in action)
HSL 2707 56
HSL 2723 49
HSL 2732 88
1241 Pinnace 25
1679 Pinnace 53
1506 Seaplane Tender 48
1515 Seaplane Tender 48

ASR UNITS

22 ASRU Grimsby 24
23 ASRU Wells on Sea 25
24 ASRU Gorleston (Gt. Yarmouth) 28, 30,
31, 34, 39, 41, 43, 46, 49, 52, 53, 54, 55, 56, 93,
95, 96, 99, 100, 107
25 ASRU Lowestoft 56
26 ASRU Felixstowe 53, 80
28 ASRU Newhaven 26

RESCUE MOTOR LAUNCHES (RML's) & NAVAL VESSELS

– unidentified 24, 32, 40, 49, 80, 88, 91, 93, 99,
100, 107
RML 498 55, 107
RML 499 55
RML 514 107
RML 515 99
RML 526 40
RML 534 40
RML 547 79
RML 550 36, 93
MGBs 49, 57, 63
MTBs 41, 49, 57, 63, 110
Fairmile 99
60th Flotilla 99
HMS Midge 55, 99, 107 (Stone Frigate)
HMS Miranda 55 (Stone Frigate)
HMS Watchful 55 (Stone Frigate)
HM Corvette L65 92
HM Destroyers 90, 91
HMS Leander 140
HMS Virago 140

UNITED STATES VESSELS

PT Boats 134, 138
Submarines 133, 135, 174
US Minesweeper 'Munsey' 143

UNITED STATES ARMY AIR FORCE UNITS

28 Bombardment Sq 141
78 Bombardment Sq 47
92 Bombardment Sq 94
94 Bombardment Sq 28, 29, 30
95 Bombardment Sq 34
96 Bombardment Sq 34
100 Bombardment Sq 46
303 Bombardment Sq 34
305 Bombardment Sq 103
357 Bombardment Sq 48, 104

381 Bombardment Sq 47, 80
388 Bombardment Sq 28
390 Bombardment Sq 53, 54
398 Bombardment Sq 99
445 Bombardment Sq 49
447 Bombardment Sq 41, 46
448 Bombardment Sq 41, 88
453 Bombardment Sq 90
457 Bombardment Sq 80, 95
458 Bombardment Sq 88
467 Bombardment Sq 103
479 Bombardment Sq 94
487 Bombardment Sq 94
489 Bombardment Sq 88
492 Bombardment Sq 78
493 Bombardment Sq 80
65th Control Wing 53
514 Weather Reconn 141
5th Air Force 140
Emergency Rescue Sqs 46, 100, 105, 108, 109,
110, 114, 116, 133, 134, 135, 138, 139, 140, 141,
165, 206

AIRCRAFT (Various Nationalities)

Anson 44, 87, 139
Baltimore (A.30) 103
Barracuda 157
Beaufighter 31, 32, 34, 36, 40, 44, 52, 95, 97,
100, 101, 107, 114
Boston (USA Havoc-A20) 103
Catalina (Canso-PBY5) 25, 37, 48, 49, 50, 51,
52, 91, 92, 103, 104, 106, 108, 109, 110, 113,
114, 116, 117, 135, 156, 168
Commando (C 46) 138, 141
Dakota (C 47) 139, 140
Dornier 36, 96
Flying Fortress (B 17) 25, 28, 30, 32, 34, 36, 41,
46, 47, 53, 54, 55, 78, 79, 80, 81, 82, 83, 84, 86,
91, 94, 99, 101, 103, 105, 107, 116, 133, 134,
135, 136, 138, 140, 141, 143, 157, 165, 166, 235
Focke Wulf 26, 29, 30, 101
Grumman P.50 140
Halifax 23, 24, 29, 30, 32, 44, 116, 135, 136
Hampden 155
Heinkel 93
Hudson 11, 12, 14, 15, 22, 23, 24, 25, 29, 30, 31,
32, 38, 41, 82, 84, 89, 90, 92, 93, 119, 145, 164,
178
Hurricane 44
Junkers (JU) 39, 53, 54, 81, 89, 94, 101, 234
Lancaster 6, 22, 29, 36, 37, 39, 40, 47, 49, 79,
82, 88, 89, 90, 92, 93, 94, 95, 101, 136, 140, 143,
157, 160, 164, 169, 178
Liberator (B 24) 40, 41, 48, 49, 51, 78, 79, 80,
81, 87, 88, 89, 90, 92, 94, 103, 133, 135
Lightning (P 38) 45, 79, 81, 87
Lincoln 160, 169, 172
Lysander 3, 5, 6, 97
Messerschmitt (Me) 36, 53, 54, 96, 104, 109
Mitchell (B.25) 30, 32, 34
Mosquito 39, 40, 43, 48, 63, 79, 93, 96, 98, 100,
103, 113
Mustang (P 51) 37, 48, 91, 94, 95, 98, 99, 100,
104, 109, 116, 134, 140, 150
PBY 5 (Catalina, Canso) 25, 37, 48, 49, 50, 51,
52, 91, 92, 104, 106, 108, 109, 110, 113, 114,
116, 117, 156, 168

Shackleton 118, 119, 153, 174, 179
Skymaster (C 52) 54, 87
Spitfire 6, 26, 41, 47, 80, 81, 89, 104, 110, 113, 139
Stirling 25, 26
Sunderland 43, 48, 51, 156
Super Fortress (B 29) 141, 169
Tempest 139
Thunderbolts (P47) 46, 52, 55, 79, 80, 92, 93, 99, 101, 113, 235
Typhoon 26
Walrus 6, 26, 30, 43, 44, 53, 81, 87, 91, 103, 104, 109, 114, 133, 156, 199, 203
Warwick 22, 37, 40, 41, 43, 44, 45, 46, 47, 48, 49, 51, 52, 53, 55, 78, 79, 80, 81, 82, 87, 89, 90, 92, 93, 94, 95, 96, 99, 101, 103, 105, 107, 108, 109, 110, 113, 116, 117, 119, 135, 136, 139, 163, 164, 178, 235
Wellington 25, 26, 27, 37, 38

ALPHABETICAL INDEX

Wachinobe 140
Waddington 93
Walcheren 45, 91
Walmer Manufacturing Co. 195
Waring, Gp Capt 5, 8, 9, 11, 12, 13, 22, 74, 155
Wash, The 5
Watchful 55
Wates 160, 161
Watson-Watt, Sir Robert 196
Wells 25
Western Plastics 165, 166
West Indies 143
West Voe 97
Whaleback 54
Wick 44, 49, 50, 78, 94, 98
Wilhelmshaven 93
Wills & Roberts Plastics 166
Wisconsin Motor Corp 167
Woodnutt 194, 211, 212, 217, 218, 219, 226
Woodrow (Taylor) 194, 221, 222, 225, 226
Woods, Herbert 19, 61, 62, 194, 214, 216, 224,
226, 227
Wright Field 11, 12, 14

Yugoslavia 89, 91

Printed in the United Kingdom for HMSO

Dd 296696   C 15   6/94   (20249)